ANATOMY OF THE MONOCOTYLEDONS

VI

DIOSCOREALES

ANATOMY OF THE MONOCOTYLEDONS

EDITED BY C. R. METCALFE
Formerly Keeper of the Jodrell Laboratory
Royal Botanic Gardens, Kew

VI. DIOSCOREALES

BY

E. S. AYENSU

Chairman, Department of Botany
National Museum of Natural History
Smithsonian Institution
Washington, D.C., U.S.A.

OXFORD
AT THE CLARENDON PRESS
1972

Oxford University Press, Ely House, London W. 1

GLASGOW NEW YORK TORONTO MELBOURNE WELLINGTON
CAPE TOWN IBADAN NAIROBI DAR ES SALAAM LUSAKA ADDIS ABABA
DELHI BOMBAY CALCUTTA MADRAS KARACHI LAHORE DACCA
KUALA LUMPUR SINGAPORE HONG KONG TOKYO

PRINTED IN GREAT BRITAIN
AT THE UNIVERSITY PRESS, OXFORD
BY VIVIAN RIDLER
PRINTER TO THE UNIVERSITY

Fifty-eight years have passed since by accident it fell to me to study Dioscorea in life. The material wanted has often come to hand very slowly; and there is much that I have tried in vain to get. In publishing what I now know, I am moved much more by the hope of interesting others than by anything else.

I. H. BURKILL, 1960

EDITOR'S PREFACE

THE late Mr. I. H. Burkill's classical work on the morphology and taxonomy of the Dioscoreaceae is well known. Towards the end of his life Mr. Burkill, who was a frequent visitor to the old Jodrell Laboratory, drew my attention to the great need for further work on the histology of the family which he himself would never have an opportunity to accomplish. My own investigations on other families of monocotyledons prevented me from undertaking these further studies on the Dioscoreaceae that Mr. Burkill realized were so desirable. The gap has now been very ably filled by Dr. E. S. Ayensu, the author of this present volume, the publication of which would, I feel sure, have given great pleasure to Mr. Burkill.

I first met Dr. Ayensu, who is a native of Ghana, at the Smithsonian Institution at Washington D.C., U.S.A., when he was a postgraduate student working under the supervision of Professor William L. Stern, now of the University of Maryland, but who was then Curator of Woods at the Smithsonian Institution. Dr. (then Mr.) Ayensu was, at the time, studying the stem anatomy of the Passifloraceae. Following the successful conclusion of these early investigations in 1963 Professor Stern asked me if it would be possible for Dr. Ayensu to broaden his experience of systematic anatomy while studying for a Ph.D. at the University of London. Thanks to the ready collaboration of the authorities at Queen Elizabeth College it was arranged for Dr. Ayensu to work under the supervision of Dr. J. G. Vaughan, with an understanding that there would be frequent discussions at the herbarium and Jodrell Laboratory at Kew.

I immediately realized that this situation provided a wonderful opportunity for undertaking the anatomical work on the Dioscoreaceae for which Mr. Burkill had seen the need. Dr. Ayensu was exceptionally well qualified for the task. He was already familiar with the yams, the tubers of which constitute an important food stuff not only in his native Ghana but also in many other tropical countries. Furthermore, his studies on the twining stems of Passifloraceae provided a good training for these more extensive studies on the Dioscoreaceae. Dr. Ayensu applied himself to his task with great enthusiasm and ever-increasing skill, with the result that, besides being awarded a Ph.D. in 1966, he has continued the investigations since then at the Smithsonian Institution with the consequence that we have before us another volume in the series being published under the title of *Anatomy of the monocotyledons*.

In this volume Dr. Ayensu discusses the various attempts that have been made to classify the plants that constitute the Dioscoreaceae, and also the plants belonging to certain smaller families, of which some are generally accepted as being related to the Dioscoreaceae, while of others the precise taxonomic position is more controversial. The interrelationships of all of these genera are discussed in the light of anatomical evidence and in doing this Dr. Ayensu has made an entirely new contribution to the taxonomy of the group.

There are several curious features about the anatomy of the Dioscoreaceae that have been scarcely appreciated until now. One of these is the structure of the nodes, in which, in many members of the family, there are complex entanglements of distorted xylem and phloem elements known as glomeruli. Another important character is the very unusual manner in which the xylem and phloem are interwoven in the vascular bundles of the stems. This gives the vascular bundles a highly distinctive appearance in transverse sections, and it is indeed curious that such unusual vascular bundles have not previously received much attention. Thirdly, we may note the exceptionally wide diameter of some of the sieve elements in the phloem of the stem bundles. Indeed the elements are so wide that they could easily be mistaken for xylem vessel elements unless critically examined. The peculiar structure and mode of development of the vascular system of the Dioscoreaceae should be of great interest to physiologists who are concerned with the translocation of foodstuffs within the plant body. We may well ask ourselves why these vascular peculiarities should have been evolved, so far as we are aware, only in the Dioscoreaceae and not in members of other families with a similar twining habit.

This volume is shorter than some of the others in this series. The Dioscoreales, however, form a self-contained order that is very distinctive in structure. This distinctiveness, as well as the economic importance of some members of the group, provide ample justification for giving Dr. Ayensu's work separate treatment. The volume provides essential reading for those who are concerned with the classification of the Dioscoreales or with the cultivation and physiology of yams.

C. R. METCALFE

Royal Botanic Gardens, Kew   *Lately Keeper of the*
December 1969   *Jodrell Laboratory*

AUTHOR'S PREFACE

THIS volume owes its existence to the need for a comprehensive anatomical presentation of the order Dioscoreales, including the yam family which is one of the most important economic food stuffs in the diet of most tropical peoples. The Dioscoreales—Dioscoreaceae, Stenomeridaceae, Trichopodaceae, and Stemonaceae—have been neglected by anatomists throughout the years, partly because it is often assumed that we already know everything that we need to know about the plants of economic importance and partly because most of the materials needed for this study are rare in areas where botanical collecting has been concentrated. Even Solereder and Meyer's *Systematische Anatomie der Monokotyledonen* (1928–33) makes no reference to the Dioscoreales, but this was because their work had to be abandoned before it was finished.

Following the procedures adopted in previous volumes of *Anatomy of the monocotyledons*, I have described representative materials from both the Old World and the New World tropics as well as specimens from the temperate regions.

The information in this volume is by no means the final word on the group. It is intended rather as a starting-point for more intensive studies on individual taxa within the assemblage. It is also hoped that this book will help in the identification and classification of the most important species of the group. The descriptions, and especially the photomicrographic illustrations of the simple hand sections of the stems, are expected to be especially useful to taxonomists.

Part I is devoted to introductory remarks about, and general descriptions of, the vegetative organs of the order, followed by general systematic conclusions based on anatomical evidence. In Part II there are anatomical descriptions of the individual organs with the sections of the genera and subgenera of the order. For the sake of brevity, descriptions of individual species have been avoided. However, some comments about certain significant differences within species have been included. The appendices at the end embody the keys to the Dioscoreaceae proposed by Knuth, Burkill, and Matuda respectively and on which my analysis of the genera of the Dioscoreaceae is based. A list of some of the important diagnostic features observed in the genera of the Dioscoreales is also included.

This volume was prepared at the invitation of Dr. C. R. Metcalfe. I am most grateful to him for his inspiration and help throughout the preparation of this work. Without his guidance and advice this work could not have been completed.

It is with pleasure that I thank the authorities at the Sir John Atkins Laboratories, Queen Elizabeth College, University of London, where a large part of this work was carried out, and Dr. John G. Vaughan, for his assistance, particularly in procuring material from his many botanical friends in the Old World tropics. I am also very grateful to Dr. William

L. Stern, University of Maryland, College Park, who likewise helped me
to obtain a large collection of New World material used in this study. My
sincere thanks are extended to Dr. Franklin W. Martin, Federal Experi-
mental Station, U.S.D.A., Mayagüez, Puerto Rico, for making available to
me most of the species of *Dioscorea* that produce sapogenin. Mr. A. W. Waitt,
Senior Specialist Officer, Agricultural Research Station, Umudike, Umuahia-
Ibeku, Eastern Nigeria, was most kind in sending me pickled material of some
twenty-nine specimens of *Dioscorea*. The Chief, Botanical Research Institute,
Department of Agricultural Technical Services, Pretoria, furnished me with
some critical South African *Dioscorea* species for which I am most grateful.

Because of the difficulty of obtaining fresh material of many species,
I relied mostly on vouchered herbarium specimens from the Royal Botanic
Gardens, Kew, England, and the United States National Herbarium, Smithsonian Institution, Washington, D.C. For these and other courtesies I am
grateful to the Directors of these institutions.

During the preparation of this volume, portions of the manuscript were
read by Mr. H. K. Airy Shaw, Royal Botanic Gardens, Kew, England; Dr.
H. Robinson, Smithsonian Institution, Washington, D.C.; and Dr. B. G.
Schubert, Arnold Arboretum, Harvard University, Cambridge, Massa-
chusetts. I gratefully appreciate their kind and constructive criticism freely
offered in the course of this study. I, however, assume full responsibility for
any errors and omissions that may occur in this survey.

I am especially thankful to Miss Mary Gregory, bibliographer at the Jodrell
Laboratory, Kew, for the painstaking and meticulous proof-reading of the
manuscript, for help in compiling the literature citations, and the preparation
of the index. My sincere thanks are extended to Mrs. Gesina B. Threlkeld
for her help in preparing many of the line drawings.

I am indebted to the Council of the Linnean Society for permission to
reproduce illustrations rearranged as Figs. 1, 2, 9, and 31 from the *Journal
of the Linnean Society* (Botany), volumes 56 (1960) and 59 (1966). Likewise,
I wish to thank the editors of the *Journal of the Arnold Arboretum* for permission to reproduce Figs. 32–4 and Plates II and III from volumes 49 (1968)
and 50 (1969) respectively.

Finally, I wish to thank all those who have helped me in various ways to
gain a better understanding and appreciation of the families treated in this
volume.

                                                    E. S. AYENSU

Smithsonian Institution
Washington, D.C., U.S.A.
28 August 1969

CONTENTS

PART I
GENERAL MORPHOLOGY AND ANATOMY

PART I
GENERAL MORPHOLOGY AND ANATOMY

1. INTRODUCTION

ANATOMICAL and histological methods, especially when used in comparative studies of plant vegetative organs, are playing an ever-increasing role in the attempt to arrive at a more natural system of monocotyledon classification. The publication of the earlier volumes of this series has indicated the urgency for further anatomical work on the monocotyledons. The Dioscoreales present some major difficulties because *Dioscorea*, the largest genus of the order, is made up almost entirely of dioecious plants. Because of the lianoid habit that characterizes the group, the collection of plants of both sexes of the same species has often been difficult. Consequently there have, in the past, been occasions when the male and female plants of a single species have been described as two distinct taxa.

The Dioscoreaceae are due for revision, seeing that the last monograph of the family was published in 1924 by Knuth. It is hoped that detailed studies such as that of Schubert (1966) will lead to a more comprehensive taxonomic treatment of the group in future.

Information on the vegetative anatomy of the Dioscoreales that has hitherto been available does not constitute a comprehensive volume of knowledge. However, there are some outstanding studies that are worthy of special mention. Falkenberg (1876) is credited with being the first serious investigator of the anatomy of the Dioscoreaceae. His work on *Dioscorea villosa* was concentrated on the petiole, especially in the region where the leaf is attached to the stem. Jungner (1888) studied the leaf anatomy of various species, including *D. japonica*. He pointed out the presence of three, two, and one phloem units within the vascular bundles of the median, secondary, and tertiary veins respectively. Bucherer (1889) described further the venation of the leaf of the Dioscoreaceae, especially with reference to the course of vascular bundles in the petiole of *Tamus*. This study was preceded by the work of Correns (1888) in which the development and structure of the extra-floral glands that occur in some species of *Dioscorea* was described.

The aerial stem of the Dioscoreaceae received greater attention from von Mohl (1845) and Nägeli (1858). These investigators pointed out that the phloem in each vascular bundle is made up of distinct units. Von Mohl (1845) was the first to study in some detail the vascular bundle of the stem, and his observations included comparative studies with palms. He described the structure of the vascular bundles and concluded that each bundle is an anastomosis into which enter three simple bundles, one of which is larger

B

than the two others. In 1858 Nägeli made an extensive study of vascular bundles of stem and root of *Dioscorea batatas* and *Tamus communis*. During his studies of the vegetative structures of monocotyledons Falkenberg (1876) described the course of the vascular bundles in stems of *D. villosa*. Beauvisage (1888) re-examined the course of bundles in the stem of *D. batatas*. These studies were, however, incidental references given in works on the anatomy of the monocotyledons as a whole. A more important study of the Dioscoreaceae was made by Jungner (1888) who worked on the differentiation of the tissues of the stem and leaf in *D. punctata* and *D. retusa*. He noted that the vascular bundle of the stem is derived from meristematic cells and this led him to conclude that the bundles are simple. He stated that structural differences could be observed in various bundles of a single plant or even in various internodes of the same plant. He further pointed out that the bundles descending from a leaf into the stem behave uniformly in different individuals of the same species and in all the species of the Dioscoreaceae.

In evaluating these studies it seems clear that two divergent opinions existed. Von Mohl (1845) and Bucherer (1889) considered the vascular bundles of the stem to be compound in origin, while Falkenberg (1876) and Jungner (1888) regarded them as simple structures.

Apart from these studies the most intensive work on the Dioscoreaceae was that of Queva (1893a, b; 1894a, b, c) on *Dioscorea batatas, D. elephantipes, D. sinuata, Tamus communis*, and many other species. Perhaps the most comprehensive study of the Dioscoreaceae, including many points of anatomical interest, is Burkill's (1960) publication on *The organography and the evolution of Dioscoreaceae, the family of the yams*. A more recent publication on *Yams* (Coursey 1967), while covering almost all aspects of the yam, does not include any information on the anatomy and histology of its tissues.

Of the Trichopodaceae, Watson (1936) made a detailed study of the vegetative organs of *Trichopus* and, like Burkill (1960), concluded that this genus should be included in the Dioscoreaceae—a view that the author does not share (cf. Ayensu 1966). The Stemonaceae (Roxburghiaceae) have been studied in some detail by Ayensu (1968a) and Tomlinson and Ayensu (1968).

Useful but isolated anatomical studies of individual organs have been made by a number of investigators, but these lack the broad perspective needed for a total understanding of the order as a whole. The present investigation has therefore been undertaken with two main objectives in mind: (1) to furnish descriptions of the vegetative organs of a large number of species, most of which are not mentioned in the anatomical literature, with the hope that this information will provide a better understanding of the structural range in the order; (2) to provide a contribution towards resolving the existing lack of agreement concerning the classification and phylogeny of the Dioscoreales and their allies by combining anatomical data with information derived from other disciplines.

GEOGRAPHIC DISTRIBUTION

The distribution of the genera in the Dioscoreales falls into many categories. The largest genus of the order—*Dioscorea*—is pan-tropical in its distribution. There is good evidence that the centre of distribution for this genus is eastern

(Vavilov 1951, Burkill 1960). Important secondary centres of distribution include India, Burma, Malaya, and various parts of south-east Asia such as Java, Borneo, Sumatra, and the Philippines. Species of *Dioscorea* also occur not only in the Americas, Africa, the Malagasy Republic (Madagascar), and Asia but a few species are encountered in Australasia and even in some wholly temperate parts of the world. Individual species of *Dioscorea* often require precise edaphic conditions, and this accounts for their occurrence in such diverse habitats as rain forests, savannah woodlands, and coastal plains, as well as at high altitudes.

Of the other genera in the Dioscoreaceae, *Tamus* is confined to the Old World and grows in the Canary Islands, the Mediterranean region, and temperate Asia, extending into Western Europe and actually reaching the British Isles where *T. communis* is quite abundant. *Rajania* is the only genus of the Dioscoreaceae that is confined to the New World, being especially common in the West Indies.

The family Stenomeridaceae with its monotypic genus *Stenomeris* is endemic to Malaysia. The 2 species of the genus are restricted to the regions of the Malay Peninsula, Borneo, and the Philippine Islands, growing between the equator and latitude 20° N.

The genera of the Trichopodaceae, *Avetra* and *Trichopus*, are confined to the Old World. *Avetra* is a monotypic genus that occurs in Tamatave, Malagasy Republic, where there are numerous endemics and there is an annual rainfall of 115 inches. *Trichopus* also has one species and this grows in Ceylon, Madras, and the Malay Peninsula. The species *T. zeylanicus* grows very well in Ceylon's south-west monsoon regions.

The Stemonaceae (Roxburghiaceae) fall under the category of Discontinuous Families in the tropics (cf. Good 1964). Of the three genera in this family, *Croomia* is confined to the south-eastern United States while *Stemona* and *Stichoneuron* are found predominantly in Eurasia.

ORIGIN OF THE YAM

The origin of the cultivated yam is unknown. Ting and Chi (1948) reported that *Dioscorea esculenta* (Lour.) Burk. was known to the Chinese before the third century A.D. It is also reported by Sampson (1936) that *D. alata* L. originated in south-east Asia and was widely distributed in prehistoric times throughout tropical Asia and the Pacific. The yam was taken to the Malagasy Republic by the Malays in about the tenth century and by the Arabs to Zanzibar (Tanzania) in about the eleventh century. It was probably carried round the Cape of Good Hope to West Africa in about the fifteenth century. By the end of the fifteenth century the yam was among the limited indigenous food-stuffs of the Congo basin (Johnston 1908). While working on the ethnobotany of certain African food-stuffs, Goodwin (1939) remarked that the word 'yam' appeared to have had an African origin from 'igname' or 'inhame' which means 'to eat'. He also stated that the edible *Dioscorea* may have been first cultivated in south-eastern Asia, as was suggested by Sampson (1936). This hypothesis was based on the evidence that Indonesians from the southern part of the Malay Peninsula and from southern Sumatra colonized the Malagasy Republic from the second to the tenth centuries in two distinct migrations. Hornell (1934) has made a comprehensive summary of the evidence in favour of this hypothesis, based on the physical characteristics, linguistics, and cultural elements of the people concerned. It is also known that certain cultural groups in West Africa show a strong superficial resemblance to elements found in Indonesia. From the Malagasy Republic to West Africa the tropical Zambesi valley provided an almost ideal route for the penetration of elements of culture, including plants (Ankermann 1905).

ECONOMIC IMPORTANCE

By far the most economically important Dioscoreas belong to the section Enantiophyllum. Included in this section are the three main cultigens, namely *Dioscorea alata* L., which Vavilov (1951) has suggested is derived from the Indian centre of origin, and *D. rotundata* Poir. and *D. cayenensis* Lamk. which are produced in West Africa, the most important yam-producing area in the world. Other species that have been grown for food are *D. esculenta* (Lour.) Burk., *D. dumetorum* Pax, *D. bulbifera* L., and *D. trifida* L. Apart from food, the tubers of *D. cirrhosa* Lour., for example, contain tannins that are used by the Chinese to tan sails, fishing nets, and lines. *D. piscatorum* Prain and Burk. is a species that occurs wild in Malaya and the tuber is used as fish poison. The poisonous principle found in the tuber is saponin in the form of a sapotoxin. In Burkill's (1935) *A dictionary of economic products of the Malay Peninsula*, most of the species known to be important up to the time of its publication are recorded. The publication by Coursey (1967) contains very useful additions to the list.

Soon after the Second World War investigators began to search for possible sources of vital drugs, such as cortisone, of vegetable origin. Cortisone was originally isolated from the adrenal cortex of cattle. Its commercial development was based on synthesis from bile acids. Although recent improvement of extraction methods has resulted in a much greater production of cortisone from this source than that originally obtained, the supply of these acids is naturally limited by the number of cattle slaughtered (Correll *et al.* 1955). It has therefore become desirable for a cheaper and potentially unlimited vegetable source of cortisone to be sought. As pointed out by Correll *et al.*, the first of these efforts to find possible plant sources of the drug cortisone was initiated by a United States presidential decree in 1950. The two governmental agencies charged with this duty were the Department of Agriculture and the National Institute of Health.

The importance of *Dioscorea* tubers as the chief plant source of sapogenic precursors of cortisone and steroidal hormones is reflected by the researches on the following species: *D. belizensis* (Blunden, Hardman, and Trease 1963, 1966), *D. composita* (Cruzado, Delpin, and Roark 1965), *D. deltoidea* (Barua, Chakravarti, and Chakravarti 1956), *D. floribunda* (Cruzado *et al.* 1965), *D. friedrichsthalii* (Martin, Delfel, and Cruzado 1963), *D. hispida* (Anzaldo, Marañon, and Ancheta 1956), *D. lecardii* (Peal 1961), *D. mexicana* (Barua *et al.* 1956), *D. multiflora* (Labat 1959), *D. prazeri* (Barua *et al.* 1954), *D. spiculiflora* (Martin and Delpin 1965), *D. sylvatica* (Blunden and Hardman

1963) and *D. villosa* (Wall *et al.* 1954*a*). Researches by the following authors have also shed more light on the chemical analyses of yams: Akahori (1965); Maker and Applezweig (1949); Maker *et al.* (1947); Martin, Cabanillas, and Gaskins (1966); Wall *et al.* (1954*a*, *b*; 1955*a*, *b*), and Willaman, Fenske, and Correll (1953).

A comprehensive review of saponins and sapogenins has been made by A. J. Feuell, Tropical Products Institute, London, in Coursey's (1967) book on yams. Likewise, Coursey's book contains other interesting topics on *Dioscorea* which will complement this volume.

2. TAXONOMIC REVIEW

THE taxon DIOSCOREAE proposed by Brown (1810) is now generally accepted by botanists as a distinct family, although there have been disagreements about the genera to be included in it. In an effort to obtain a clearer picture of the taxonomic status of the group, the literature referring to it has been searched as thoroughly as possible. This has revealed that a comprehensive taxonomic revision is needed. Burkill's (1960) attempt to improve the classification was only partially successful because he was able to treat in detail only the Old World species. The following is a review of the family as revealed in the literature.

In his *Genera Plantarum*, Linnaeus (1737) placed under the order VI Hexandria the following genera whose male plants have flowers with six stamens: *Smilax, Tamus, Rajania,* and *Dioscorea.* With the publication of his *Species Plantarum* (1753) he added another genus to the order VI Hexandria and described 2 species for *Tamus,* 13 species for *Smilax,* 3 species for the new genus *Cissampelos,* 3 species for *Rajania,* and 8 species for *Dioscorea.* In both publications Linnaeus presented a conspectus for his genera. Presumably he separated his genera on their fruit characters, since the morphology of the leaves of the above genera are quite similar.

In De Jussieu's *Genera Plantarum* (1789), we find placed under the order II Asparagi the following:

Section I.   Flowers bisexual: *Dracaena, Dianella, Flagellaria, Asparagus, Callixene, Medeola, Trillium, Paris,* and *Convallaria.*
Section II. Flowers dioecious; ovary superior: *Ruscus, Smilax,* and *Dioscorea.*
Section III. Flowers dioecious; ovary inferior: *Tamus* and *Rajania.*

In 1810 Brown grouped *Dioscorea, Rajania,* and *Tamus* under the family Dioscoreae (Dioscoreaceae). This new family concept meant the rearrangement of de Jussieu's order Asparagi. Brown achieved this by putting sections II and III together but excluding *Ruscus* and *Smilax* from section II. He then gave a complete description of his family based on the following characters: Flowers dioecious. Calyx and corolla irregular, superior. Stamens 6, inserted into the base of the sepals and petals. Ovary 3-celled, with 1–2-seeded cells; style deeply trifid; stigma undivided. Fruit leaf-like, compressed, with 2 of its cells sometimes abortive. Seeds flat, compressed; embryo small, near the hilum, lying in a large cavity of cartilaginous albumen. Twining shrubs. Leaves alternate, occasionally opposite, usually with reticulated veins. Flowers small, in spikes, with 1 to 3 bracts each.

Brown observed that the Dioscoreae showed the nearest approach among the monocotyledons to the dicotyledons. The leaves resembled those of dicotyledons but the stems, flowers, and seeds were those of monocotyledons. It is suspected that Brown may have realized that there was no cambial activity in the stems of his Dioscoreae. Discussing the relationships of the

Dioscoreae, he pointed out that the Smilaceae were close to the Dioscoreae in structure and habit, but the latter could be separated from the former by the threefold character of the inferior ovary, the capsular fruit, and the large cavity of the albumen. He suggested that *Tamus* was a link between the two taxa, because its bracts agreed with those of the Smilaceae although the inferior ovary of *Tamus* agreed with that of the rest of the Dioscoreae.

Brown did not present a key to the generic characters of his Dioscoreae except for *Dioscorea*, which he stated had a capsular fruit. This meant that he realized the importance of the various types of fruit within the family— *Dioscorea* (capsule), *Rajania* (samara), and *Tamus* (berry).

Lindley (1853) was likewise aware of the peculiar nature of *Dioscorea* when he said 'There is among the plants referred by Jussieu to his Mono-cotyledons, and consequently by later Botanists to Endogens, a small number of species whose foliage and habit of growth are so very peculiar, that the reference of them to Endogens is wholly dependent upon their conformity in the structure of the Embryo. They have a broad net-veined foliage, which usually disarticulates with the stem and in some cases the small green flowers are very nearly the same as those of such plants as *Menispermum*, among Exogens.' Lindley was very impressed with the unusual anatomy and mor-phology of the Dioscoreaceae, and considered it to be of sufficient significance to warrant the creation of a transition group, dictyogens, co-ordinate with endogens and exogens.

Earlier, Gaertner (1788) had described the genus *Trichopus*, with the single species *T. zeylanicus*, from a dried specimen of a plant received from Ceylon. This genus exhibited the following characters: superior ovary, membranous capsule, 3-winged, very long peduncle; seeds with entire margins. He was unable to assign it to any known family but, in 1832, Lindley put *Trichopus* with *Aristolochia* and *Asarum*. He, however, did not give any specific reasons for including *Trichopus* in the Aristolochiaceae, but gave the following description to cover the three genera: Flowers hermaphrodite. Calyx superior, tubular, with 3 segments valvate in aestivation, sometimes regular or un-equal. Stamens 6 to 10, epigynous, distinct or adhering to the style and stigmas. Ovary inferior, 3- or 6-celled; ovules numerous, horizontally attached to the axis; style simple, stigmas radiating, as numerous as the cells of the ovary. Fruit dry or succulent, 3- or 6-celled, many seeds. Seeds with a very minute embryo placed in the base of fleshy albumen. Herbaceous plants or shrubs, the latter often climbing. Leaves alternate, simple, stalked, often with leafy stipules. Flowers axillary, solitary, brown or some dull colour.

Klotzsch (1859) disagreed with Lindley's (1832) inclusion of *Trichopus* in the Aristolochiaceae and consequently removed it to the Dioscoreaceae. With such an assignment, the boundary of the Dioscoreaceae, as understood by Brown (1810), was extended to include bisexual flowers and non-climbers.

In 1790 Loureiro described the genus *Oncus* and placed it with the order VI Hexandria in Linnaeus's classification. Lindley (1832), recognizing the new genus, included it in the Dioscoreae without giving any reasons but, in 1866, Salisbury suggested that *Oncus* was close to *Tamus* because of the succulent fruit, differing from the latter genus in its hermaphrodite flowers.

During his travels in the interior of southern Africa, Burchell (1824) found 'extraordinary' plants called Hottentots Brood (Hottentot's Bread) growing wild on the Cape of Good Hope. From this plant Salisbury created the genus *Testudinaria* and so named it because the tuber resembled a hibernating tortoise. Salisbury (1866) stated that the first species was referred to *Tamus* by L'Héritier merely because of the superficial resemblance of their male flowers, although L'Héritier had never seen the capsules of *Testudinaria* which were precisely those of *Dioscorea*. Salisbury described his new genus as having hard and tough although herbaceous stems, dying down to the tuber annually; styles united; stigmata short and obtuse; seeds only winged at the apex. These characters, combined with the long floral envelope, suggested its closeness to *Dioscorea*.

In 1852 Planchon described a new genus *Stenomeris* from a Philippine plant and named it *S. dioscoreifolia*. This genus was put in the Burmanniaceae because the flowers looked like those of *Thismia*, but in 1870 Beccari brought it into the Dioscoreaceae. He suggested that although *Stenomeris* had many seeds in a loculus it was closer to the Dioscoreaceae than the Aristolochiaceae. Discussing the affinities of *Trichopus*, he consented to Klotzsch's (1859) transfer of *Trichopus* to the Dioscoreaceae. He noted that the flowers, and especially the anthers and stigma, resembled those of the Dioscoreaceae. The position and structure of the seed resembled *Thottea* and *Bragantia* of the Aristolochiaceae and *Dioscorea*. He supported Klotzsch's suggestion by pointing out that the embryo of *Trichopus* resembled that of *Tamus communis*. Solereder (1888–9) also concurred on the basis of leaf anatomy.

In 1860 von Mueller described for the first time the Australian genus *Petermannia* and assigned it to the Dioscoreaceae on the basis of the following characters: stamens 6, inserted at the base of the perianth; filament erect; anthers dorsifixed, long, 2-locular, dehiscing longitudinally; style filiform; ovary inferior, 3-locular; fruit a berry, unilocular with numerous seeds; climber. Von Mueller included *Petermannia* in the Dioscoreaceae because of the floral morphology, especially the inferior ovary, but later Bentham, when preparing his and Hooker's *Genera Plantarum*, suggested that *Petermannia* was best placed in the Liliaceae. In their work (1883) they stated that 'A genus (*Petermannia*) with a habit, perianth and stamens rather of Liliaceae (Smilacaceae) than of Dioscoreaceae, but the ovary distinctly inferior, and remarkable in either family in having parietal multiovulate placentas'. Hutchinson (1934), following Bentham and Hooker (1883), created the family Petermanniaceae and placed it under the order Alstroemeriales.

Philippi's genus *Epipetrum* was originally recorded in the Annals of the University of Chile in 1862. The plant was first collected in Chile by Pavon in 1788, but it was not associated with *Dioscorea* until 1836 when Colla named it *D. humilis*, while in 1844 Hooker renamed the same species *D. pusilla*, overlooking Colla's work. In 1862 Philippi removed it from *Dioscorea*, because the seeds were wingless, and described for it the genus *Epipetrum*.

Following Philippi, Miégeville (1866) published an account of a new genus *Borderea* from a plant collected in the Pyrenees. He found the seeds to be flattened and wingless. In this feature it differed from *Epipetrum* in which the seeds were scarcely compressed but, as Philippi indicated for *Epipetrum*, *Borderea* also showed a close resemblance to *Dioscorea*.

In his posthumously published *Genera Plantarum* (which appeared in the same year as Miégeville's *Borderea*) Salisbury (1866) placed under Tribe I (Liriogamae) Class I (Spadiciferae) order 10 (Dioscorideae) three sections as follows:

Section I.   Fleshy pericarp, indehiscent: *Oncus* Lour., *Tamus* L.
Section II.   Membranous pericarp; small, 2-lobed, abortive capsule: *Rajania* L.
Section III. Membranous pericarp; large, fertile lobes: *Hamatris* Salisb., *Dioscorea* L., *Polynome* Salisb., *Merione* Salisb., *Strophis* Salisb., *Elephantodon* Salisb., *Testudinaria* Salisb.

As stated earlier, *Oncus* with succulent fruit was placed in section I with *Tamus communis*, which has stipules that are reflexed like rudimentary tendrils. A plant discovered in the Canary Islands was considered as possibly belonging to the same genus. The only species of Canary Island origin is *T. edulis* Lowe.

Salisbury placed only *Rajania* in his section II because, when in fruit, it is easily identified by the two small abortive lobes of its capsule, but the fruit when fertile is winged like a samara.

In his section III Salisbury concluded that all the genera had similar 3-lobed capsules, but they differed widely in other parts. *Hamatris* was characterized by the minute 3 outer divisions of its floral envelope and the 3 inner ones which are valvate in aestivation; its 3 stigmata are each deeply cleft as if 6; its seeds are winged only at the top; the leaves are ternate with prickly ribs and the flowers are sessile.

Salisbury described his genus *Merione* as having equal petals, spreading out widely; the filaments are deeply bifurcate so that the lobes of the anthers are separated as in some Ericaceae; seeds are winged all round; the root divided into many small branches; the leaves in whorls at the bottom of the stem but soon becoming opposite.

Salisbury described the genus *Polynome* from some varieties of *Dioscorea alata* because of the large quantity of their tubers. His genus *Strophis* was based on its tendril-climbing stems, opposite leaves, hermaphrodite flowers, and the 3 sessile anthers. *Elephantodon* is also a hermaphrodite genus but without tendrils, with broader inner petioles, and with 6 stamens; its tubers resemble the tusks of an elephant, hence the generic name.

In Bentham and Hooker's *Genera Plantarum* (1883), the Dioscoreaceae were included in the second series Epigynae, along with Scitamineae, Bromeliaceae, Haemodoraceae, Iridaceae, Amaryllidaceae, and Taccaceae. Under the Dioscoreaceae they gave the following conspectus based on the concept of normal and abnormal genera.

Normal Genera

Capsule laterally 3-lobed, almost inflated or nearly winged;
    seeds flattened, winged or nearly wingless. Tropics   1. *Dioscorea*
Capsule as in *Dioscorea*; seeds winged, samara-like;
    rhizome very large, lignified. South Africa   2. *Testudinaria*

Capsule monocarpic, flattened, winged upwards, samara-
like. West Indies   3. *Rajania*
Berry nearly spherical, indehiscent; seeds nearly spherical,
wingless; embryo small. Europe, temperate Asia, N.
Africa, and Canaries   4. *Tamus*

ABNORMAL GENERA

Stem twining; panicle axillary, short and loose; perianth
lobes bristly–acuminate; ovary 3-locular, multiovulate.
Philippines   5. *Stenomeris*
Stem short, simple; apex of leaf pointed and pedicels
nearly fasciculate; ovary 3-locular, 2-ovulate; capsule
indehiscent. E. India   6. *Trichopus*
Stem sometimes scandent; spike long, loosely subterminal;
berry oblong, 3-celled, many-seeded. China   7. *Oncus*
Stem sometimes scandent; racemes and small axillary
cymes, few flowers; ovary 1-locular, placentas 3,
parietal and multiovulate. Australia   8. *Petermannia*

Bentham and Hooker included the genera *Hamatris*, *Merione*, *Polynome*,
Strophis, and *Elephantodon* of Salisbury (1866) as part of *Dioscorea*. Burkill
(1960) later suggested that the above genera of Salisbury should cover *Dioscorea pentaphylla*, *D. villosa*, *D. bulbifera*, and varieties of *D. alata*, *D.
cirrhosa*, and a clone of *D. alata* respectively.

In 1899 the genus *Higinbothamia* was described by Uline when studying
collections of Yucatan and West Indian Dioscoreaceae. He observed the
presence of 3 and sometimes 4 fully ripe seeds in each capsule of his material,
and, comparing it with collections from many European and American
herbaria, found that not a single specimen had hitherto presented such a
character. The staminate flowers were easily distinguished from all Mexican
Dioscorea by the staminal column. Members of his section Monadelpha of
the genus *Dioscorea*, occurring in southern Brazil, Paraguay, Argentina, and
Bolivia, showed various tendencies towards the possession of coalescent
filaments, but their seeds were of the Helmia type, i.e. winged only in one
direction instead of all round. Following his analysis he suggested that,
although the coalescence in the section Monadelpha was characteristically
different from that of his new specimen, it did not follow that the character
of the filament coalescence in his plant might be interpreted as a generic
character. Uline was aware that, throughout the genus *Dioscorea*, species
showing the closest relationship in the character of the female flowers are
often found to differ widely in their staminate flowers, hence he thought that
it was possible for a second species displaying 12 ovules in a capsule to form
part of his new genus. Nevertheless, he felt compelled to propose the genus
Higinbothamia because of the 4-ovulate feature, which was admittedly the
only positive generic character.

Morton (1936) and again Burkill (1960), however, suggested that this new
genus must be abandoned or down-graded, since it was then known that the
male plant of *Higinbothamia synandra* was identical with *Dioscorea gaumeri*

Knuth and it seemed safe to assume that the female plant that Uline had should be referred to *D. gaumeri*.

In 1924 Perrier de la Bathie described the genus *Avetra* from a plant collected in Madagascar which he named *A. sempervirens*. He placed it in the Dioscoreaceae near *Trichopus* because the seeds immediately suggested *Trichopus*. He also suggested that his genus was close to *Rajania* because of the seed condition. Perrier's placement of *Avetra* in the Dioscoreaceae was within the boundary of the family as extended by Beccari (1870*a*).

Earlier in the same year in which Perrier described *Avetra*, the Dioscoreaceae were placed under the order Liliiflorae by Knuth in Engler's *Das Pflanzenreich* (1924), together with Juncaceae, Stemonaceae (Roxburghiaceae), Liliaceae, Haemodoraceae, Amaryllidaceae, Velloziaceae, and Taccaceae. Under the order Liliiflorae, Knuth followed Bentham and Hooker's suggestion and enlarged the group with the inclusion of 3 other families. Later, in Engler and Prantl's *Die natürlichen Pflanzenfamilien* (1930), Knuth divided the order Liliiflorae into two suborders, Juncineae and Liliineae; the Juncaceae were included under the Juncineae; the Stemonaceae, Liliaceae, Haemodoraceae, Amaryllidaceae, Velloziaceae, Taccaceae, and Dioscoreaceae under the Liliineae. Under the Dioscoreaceae he divided the genera into two tribes and presented the following key.

A. Flowers dioecious   Tribe I. Dioscoreae
  a. Capsule:
    Capsule 3-angled or 3-winged:
     I. Seeds winged, mostly flattened:
       1. Seeds in each loculus 2   1. *Dioscorea* L.
       2. Seeds in each loculus 3–4   2. *Higinbothamia* Uline
     II. Seeds not winged:
       1. Seeds flattened. Style rudiment very
          small   3. *Borderea* Miegev.
       2. Seeds scarcely compressed. Style
          rudiment very large   4. *Epipetrum* Phil.
    Capsule winged
    Seeds not winged   5. *Rajania* L.
  b. Berry spherical. Seeds spherical, not winged   6. *Tamus* L.

B. Flowers bisexual. Two or more seeds in every loculus
                                  Tribe II. Stenomerideae
  a. Ovary 3-locular:
    Seeds many per loculus:
    Axillary panicles short, but loose. Stem
      climbing highly   7. *Stenomeris* Planch.
    Seeds only 2 per loculus:
    Capsule indehiscent:
      1. Stem short, bearing 1 leaf and several
          flowers   8. *Trichopus* Gaertn.
      2. Stem twining, leaves alternate   9. *Avetra* Perrier
  b. Ovary 1-locular. Seeds many. Fruit a berry.
    Stem climbing highly   10. *Petermannia* F. Muell.

Knuth's (1924, 1930) classifications were an extension and a revision of the family since Bentham and Hooker's (1883) publication. Of the 10 genera in his family, Knuth noted that the genus *Higinbothamia* could be referred to *Dioscorea* but for the 4 ovules in each loculus of the former, which later yielded 3–4 ripe seeds. A similar observation had been made by Uline (1899) who described the genus. Knuth also discovered that *Borderea* differed from *Dioscorea* only by its wingless seeds. He considered the relationship of *Petermannia* to the Dioscoreaceae as being very doubtful, but he did not remove it from the family. Similarly, he was aware of the closeness of *Higinbothamia* and *Borderea* to *Dioscorea*, but he did not find it necessary to reduce or discard them. The genus *Oncus* was reduced to species level and considered as *D. esculenta* of the section Combilium.

In an attempt to arrange the families according to their phylogenetic relations, Hutchinson (1959) included Stenomeridaceae, Trichopodaceae, Roxburghiaceae, and Dioscoreaceae in the order Dioscoreales. His arrangement was based on the following key.

A. Flowers bisexual:
    B.   Stamens 6; connective produced beyond the anther
           loculi; ovary inferior:
      C.   Fruits elongated with numerous winged seeds;
           ovary-loculi with numerous ovules superposed in
           2 series   Stenomeridaceae
     CC. Fruits short, 1-seeded; ovary-loculi with 2 ovules
                                    Trichopodaceae
    BB. Stamens 4; ovary superior to semi-inferior, 1-locular
                                   Roxburghiaceae
AA. Flowers unisexual; ovary inferior; fruits and seeds
    often winged; usually climbers with tuberous root-
    stocks or thick woody rhizomes; perianth 6-merous
                                        Dioscoreaceae

Following Bentham and Hooker's observations that *Stenomeris* differs widely from the Dioscoreaceae in its type of anther, numerous ovules, and in other characters, Hutchinson proposed the elevation of the genus *Stenomeris* to familial rank. He also created the family Trichopodaceae to include *Trichopus* and *Avetra*. Under Roxburghiaceae (Stemonaceae) he placed the following genera: *Croomia*, *Stichoneuron*, and *Stemona* (*Roxburghia*). Hutchinson's Dioscoreaceae included all the genera of Knuth's tribe Dioscoreae, with the elevation of the subgenus *Testudinaria* to generic level, and the down-grading of *Higinbothamia* as a synonym of *Dioscorea*. As pointed out earlier, Hutchinson up-graded *Petermannia* (included by Knuth in the Dioscoreaceae) to familial rank and placed it under the order Alstroemeriales.

In his comprehensive treatise of the Dioscoreaceae, Burkill (1960) expressed his disapproval of Hutchinson's proposition that the genera *Trichopus* and *Avetra* should constitute the family Trichopodaceae, and that *Stenomeris* should be up-graded as the family Stenomeridaceae. He also disapproved of Engler's (1892) earlier grouping of the 3 genera under the tribe Stenomerideae.

Burkill states that 'Neither suggestion is acceptable; not that they are un-tenable, but that they are too unphilosophical for a subject that is phylo-genetic'. Although he did not offer any morphological reasons, Burkill stated that Hutchinson's classification obscures the phylogeny, and that of Engler implies that *Trichopus* and *Stenomeris* are nearer to each other than their characters suggest. Referring to Knuth's classification, Burkill considered *Higinbothamia*, *Borderea*, and *Epipetrum* as synonyms of *Dioscorea*. He excluded the Australian genus *Petermannia* from the Dioscoreaceae, as indeed had already been suggested by Hutchinson. Burkill proposed the following key for the genera of Dioscoreaceae.

Plants with hermaphrodite flowers—the para-Dioscoreae

Ovules very numerous in each of the 3 loculi (Steno-meridieae)   1. *Stenomeris*

Ovules 2 in each of the 3 loculi (Trichopodeae)

Climber with samara; 5 of the 6 ovules in the ovary aborting   2. *Avetra*

Lowly herb, with a fleshy fruit which liberates its seeds by tearing   3. *Trichopus*

Plants dioecious; ovules 2 in each loculus—the Dioscoreae

Fruit a capsule   4. *Dioscorea*
Fruit a samara, 5 of the 6 ovules aborting   5. *Rajania*
Fruit a berry   6. *Tamus*

As has been said earlier, Hutchinson had up-graded the subgenus *Testudinaria* of Knuth to generic level as was suggested by Bentham and Hooker (1883), mainly because of the much enlarged stem which is woody at the base above ground. Burkill (1952) pointed out that *Testudinaria* did not deserve generic rank but should be considered as a section of the large genus *Dioscorea*. He supported this assertion by pointing out that twining to the left, the anatomy of the stem, and the floral morphology of *Testudinaria* were all characters readily found in *Dioscorea*, especially in the New World species. Burkill's key is the most recent attempt made to define the genera that constitute the Dioscoreaceae.

Perhaps the most valuable taxonomic treatment of the New World species is that of Matuda (1954), covering more than 60 species of Mexican Dio-scoreas (cf. Appendix III). Matuda was also aware of the limitations of Knuth's (1924) classification. In order to avoid greater confusion, he did not alter the sections recognized by Knuth, but in dealing with the Mexican species he constructed his own key based on the male floral structure.

Table I is a summary of the salient morphological characters of the genera investigated.

TABLE 1

Salient morphological characters of the genera investigated

	Dioscorea	Rajania	Tamus	Stenomeris	Avetra	Trichopus	Croomia	Stemona	Stichoneuron
General form	Climber	Climber	Climber	Climber	Evergreen climber	Non-climber short stems	Erect herb	Climber	Low shrub
Leaf arrangement	Generally alternate	Alternate	Alternate	Alternate	Alternate	A leaf terminal on each stem	Alternate	Alternate	Alternate
Inflorescence	Cymes racemes spikes	Cymes racemes spikes	Solitary or racemes	Cymes	Solitary or racemes	Cluster of solitary flowers	Axillary racemes	Cluster of solitary flowers	Racemes
Distribution of sexes	Unisexual	Unisexual	Unisexual	Bisexual	Bisexual	Bisexual	Bisexual	Bisexual	Bisexual
Position of ovary	Inferior	Inferior	Inferior	Inferior	Inferior	Inferior	Superior	Half inferior	Superior
No. of ovules	6	6	6	Numerous	6	6	4–6	2 or more	Numerous
Fruit	Capsule	Samara	Berry	Capsule	Samara	Berry	Capsule	Capsule	Capsule
Seed	Compressed winged	Flat not winged	Ovoid or roundish	Elongated rhombic	Winged	Not winged	Erect ovoid	Erect ovoid or oblong	Erect ovoid
No. of stamens	6	6	6	6	6	6	4	4	4
Perianth	6-merous	6-merous	6-merous	6-lobed	Bell-shaped	6-partite	4-merous	4-merous	4-merous
Placentation	Axile	Axile	Axile	Axile	Axile	Axile	Axile	Axile	Axile
Bulbil	Present	Absent	Absent	Absent	Absent	Absent	Absent	Absent	Absent
Rhizome	Present	Present	Absent	Present	Present	Present	Present	Present	Present
Tuber	Present	Present	Present	Absent	Absent	Present	Absent	Absent	Tuberous root

3. MATERIALS AND METHODS

MOST of the species examined were preserved in a mixture of formalin, acetic acid, and alcohol (FAA) (50 cm³ ethyl alcohol 95 per cent., 5 cm³ glacial acetic acid, 10 cm³ formaldehyde 37–40 per cent., and 35 cm³ water). Since most species are of tropical origin, an effective means had to be worked out to facilitate the transportation of the fixed material. Willing botanists in various parts of the tropics were asked to fix the fresh material in the fixative described above for 2 days. The specimens were then transferred to polythene bags together with a wad of cotton wool soaked in FAA. By this method only a small space was required to pack a large number of specimens.

Because of the difficulty of obtaining freshly fixed material of some critical species, it became necessary to fall back on the use of herbarium specimens. When this was unavoidable, the dried material was first boiled until the original structure had been restored as much as possible. The specimens were then fixed in FAA and treated in the same way as the freshly collected material.

After fixation and prolonged washing of the material in running water, transverse and longitudinal sections were cut on a Reichert sliding microtome, usually at a thickness of 16 μm. The nature of some of the material made it necessary to cut sections up to 90 μm thick.

Sometimes herbarium specimens were treated with laboratory Aerosol in the manner described in detail elsewhere (Ayensu 1967). It is well known that tissues of dried materials are often so greatly damaged or distorted that the treatments outlined above seldom, if ever, restore them to anything like their original form. Although laboratory Aerosol does not restore the tissue completely, it has proved to be the most satisfactory softening agent. When optimum restoration is achieved by this technique even cytological details can be studied.

It was usually possible to obtain good microscopical preparations by sectioning unembedded materials. When ontogenetic studies were undertaken or when very delicate specimens had to be examined the material was embedded in paraffin wax. The standard paraffin-wax embedding technique described by Sass (1958) was used with slight modification. The entire procedure took about a week because gradual infiltration and embedding seemed necessary to prevent distortion of the tissues, especially the phloem.

Sections of embedded material were obtained using a Beck rotary microtome. After the paraffin sections had been fixed to slides, the wax was removed. Both embedded and unembedded sections were stained either in safranin and Delafield's haematoxylin or in safranin and light green. After differentiation and dehydration, the sections were cleared in xylene and mounted in Canada balsam.

Before the permanent preparations were studied, comparable sections were examined in the following types of preparation.

(*a*) Unstained sections mounted in glycerine.

(b) Sections stained in phoroglucinol and concentrated hydrochloric acid to determine the distribution of lignin.

(c) Sections stained in Sudan IV to determine the distribution of suberin and cutin.

(d) Sections mounted in aqueous potassium iodide with a drop of 70 per cent. sulphuric acid to determine the distribution of cellulose, which turns blue and dissolves, and suberin, cutin, and lignin, which turn yellow.

Preparations (b), (c), and (d) were standard microchemical tests performed on all species investigated.

To study the detailed venation of closely related species, the technique described by Arnott (1959) was slightly modified. This technique involved clearing the leaves in sodium hydroxide solution and concentrated chloral hydrate. The materials were then stained in 1 per cent. solution of safranin in 95 per cent. alcohol and mounted in Canada balsam after dehydration in absolute alcohol.

In the study of vascular elements, particularly those of the sieve-tubes and vessels, macerations were largely used. The material was macerated in 5 per cent. chromic acid and a few drops of nitric acid in a warm oven for two to six hours depending on the material. The macerated material was then washed, stained in safranin and Delafield's haematoxylin, differentiated, dehydrated, cleared, and mounted in Canada balsam or glycerine. The mounted specimens were studied histologically to determine the general shape, size, and perforations of the vascular elements. It should be pointed out that broad surveys, as represented by this study, are often beset by limitations of sampling. Reference specimens in herbaria are often much too valuable to enable more than a very limited amount of material to be removed from them for histological investigation. This imposes a severe limitation when measuring the dimensions of individual cells, and the data are usually inadequate for statistical treatment. The measurements recorded in this work are therefore intended only to give some idea of the sizes of the cells being investigated.

To understand the course of vascular-bundle development in the Dioscoreaceae, serial transverse sections of five *Dioscorea* species—*D. alata*, *D. bulbifera*, *D. friedrichsthalii*, *D. opposita*, and *D. prazeri*—have been studied.

One of the difficulties facing those of us involved with the current programme on the systematic anatomy of the monocotyledons, is the selection of strictly comparable portions of the plants to be compared. Metcalfe (1960, 1963) has discussed this question in detail. He pointed out, for example, that the structure of leaves can be examined in sections of the blade taken at right angles to or parallel with the veins. The main difficulty is that local structural differences that occur within a single leaf may lead us to draw incorrect taxonomic conclusions should we fail to restrict all comparisons to the corresponding parts of any two leaves that are being compared. When investigating the Dioscoreales, portions from the mid-section of the blade and mid-section of the petiole, as well as from an internode of the stem were studied. It was rather difficult to treat sections of the tuber and root in such a precise manner since only portions from large specimens were made available to me.

Another major problem that confronts the plant anatomist working on vegetative organs for broad comparative surveys is the difficulty of obtaining materials that are at corresponding levels of development. Our inability to assess whether the materials obtained for such studies are at the same stages of ontogenetic development further complicates the issue.

As far as possible, the names adopted for the species are in accordance with those that are accepted at the Royal Botanic Gardens, Kew (K), and the United States National Herbarium, Washington, D.C. (US), for the Old World and the New World species respectively. For other species where documentary herbarium materials are scattered in widely separated institutions or are even lacking, the names that accompanied the specimens are used unless definite changes in synonymy are known to have been effected.

Microscope slides of the specimens prepared for this investigation have been deposited at the Jodrell Laboratory, Royal Botanic Gardens, Kew, and in the Division of Plant Anatomy, Smithsonian Institution, Washington, D.C. Pickled materials left over from this study will also be deposited at the Jodrell Laboratory, Kew (J).

Some of the photographic illustrations were obtained with a Pentax microscope attachment camera affixed to a Bactil-60 microscope. Others were obtained with a Wild M-20 photomicroscope. In order to obtain photomicrographs of transverse sections of the entire diameters of stems the Leitz micro-attachment (Prado 500) specially modified for projection was used. The screen images, characterized by excellent brilliancy and contrast, were photographed with the Pentax III camera. Ilford FP3 Fine Grain Panchromatic film or Panatomic X film were always used. The line drawings were prepared using a camera lucida.

Table 2 is a list of all the material examined for this study. Specimens marked with asterisks (*) were not described in detail because the representative specimens were badly distorted. However, these specimens were anatomically identified as *Dioscorea* species. The herbarium abbreviations are given on p. 22.

TABLE 2

Specimens of Dioscoreales examined

Species	Collector and number	Geographical origin	Herbarium voucher
		Dioscoreaceae	
Dioscorea alata L.	E. S. Ayensu s.n.	Ghana	—
,, ,,	J. V. Pancho s.n.	Philippines	LB
,, ,,	A. W. Waitt 9	Nigeria	K
,, ,,	J. A. Spence s.n.	Trinidad, W.I.	—
,, ,,	W. L. Stern 2338	Philippines	US
,, ,,	A. C. Tallantire 10	Uganda	—
D. amazonum Mart.	J. S. de la Cruz 4458	Guyana	US
,, ,,	R. de la Froes 21190	Brazil	US
*D. auriculata Poepp.	Bro. Claude-Joseph 3338	Chile	US
D. balcanica Kosanin	E. S. Ayensu s.n.	Hort. Kew	K
*D. bartlettii Morton	F. W. Martin s.n.	Puerto Rico	—
,, ,,	F. Miranda s.n.	Veracruz	—
D. batatas Decne	J. G. Vaughan s.n.	Chelsea Physic Garden	QEC
D. bernoulliana Prain & Burk.	F. W. Martin s.n.	Puerto Rico	—
*D. bridgesii Griseb.	Bro. Claude-Joseph 1402	Chile	US
D. bulbifera L.	H. G. Baker s.n.	Univ. Calif. Bot. Garden, Berkeley	UC
,, ,,	FHI 54884	Nigeria	FHI
,, ,,	J. V. Pancho s.n.	Philippines	LB
,, ,,	—	Hort. Kew	—
,, ,,	A. W. Waitt 11	Nigeria	K
,, ,,	A. C. Tallantire 8	Uganda	—
,, ,,	J. A. Spence s.n.	Trinidad, W.I.	—
D. burchellii Baker	E. E. A. Archibald 7382	Cape Province, S.A.	K
D. campestris Griseb.	F. W. Martin s.n.	Puerto Rico	—
D. carionis Prain & Burk.	P. C. Standley 68065	Guatemala	US
,, ,,	E. Matuda 2817	Mexico	US
D. caucasica Lipsky	E. S. Ayensu s.n.	Hort. Kew	K
D. cayenensis Lamk.	E. S. Ayensu s.n.	Ghana	—
,, ,,	A. W. Waitt 4	Nigeria	K
,, ,,	J. A. Spence s.n.	Trinidad, W.I.	—
,, ,,	A. C. Tallantire s.n.	Uganda	—
D. ceratandra Uline	F. W. Martin s.n.	Puerto Rico	—
D. cochleari-apiculata de Wild	D B. Fanshawe F8254	Zambia	K
D. collettii Hook. f.	Y. Tsiang 9197	Kweichow, China	US
,, ,,	A. Henry 12338	China	US
D. composita Hemsl.	F. Miranda s.n.	Mexico	—
,, ,,	PI 201783	Florida, U.S.A.	—
,, ,,	A. W. Waitt 17	Nigeria	K
,, ,,	E. S. Ayensu s.n.	Hort. Kew	K
,, ,,	J. T. Baldwin, Jr. 14368	Mexico	US
D. convolvulacea Cham. & Schlechtd.	F. W. Martin s.n.	Puerto Rico	—
D. cotinifolia Kunth	E. S. Ayensu s.n.	Hort. Kew	K
,, ,,	B. de Winter s.n.	Pretoria, S.A.	PRE
*D. cubensis Knuth	Bro. Leon 8589	Cuba	US

TABLE 2 (*cont.*)

Species	Collector and number	Geographical origin	Herbarium voucher
*D. cyanisticta Smith	J. A. Steyermark 48855	Guatemala	US
*D. cymosula Hemsl.	Bro. Paul 508	Panama	US
D. deltoidea Wall	E. S. Ayensu s.n.	Hort. Kew	K
D. densiflora Hemsl.	B. A. Krukoff D3	Guatemala	US
	P. H. Gentle 2210	British Honduras	US
D. discolor Kunth	E. S. Ayensu s.n.	Hort. Kew	K
,, ,,	F. Woytkowski 6188	Peru	US
D. divaricata Blanco	J. V. Pancho s.n.	Philippines	LB
D. dregeana (Kunth) Th. Dur. & Sch.	B. de Winter s.n.	Pretoria, S.A.	PRE
D. dugesii Robinson	F. W. Martin s.n.	Puerto Rico	—
D. dumetorum (Kunth) Pax.	A. W. Waitt 7	Nigeria	K
,, ,,	FHI 54885	Nigeria	FHI
,, ,,	A. C. Tallantire 6	Uganda	—
*D. dumetosa Uline	M. Bang 2916	Bolivia	US
*D. dusenii Uline	G. Zenker s.n.	Cameroons	US
D. elephantipes Spreng.	E. S. Ayensu s.n.	Hort. Kew	K
,, ,,	E. S. Ayensu s.n.	Hort. Amsterdam	AMD
D. esculenta (Lour.) Burk.	A. W. Waitt 13	Nigeria	K
,, ,,	J. A. Spence s.n.	Trinidad, W.I.	—
*D. fastigiata Gay	Thos. Morong 1232	Chile	US
D. flabellifolia Prain & Burk.	M. Ramos 1625	N. Borneo	US
,, ,,	M. Ramos s.n.	Philippines	US
D. floribunda Mart. & Gal.	F. W. Martin s.n.	Puerto Rico	—
,, ,,	PI 230618	Florida, U.S.A.	—
,, ,,	PI 201748	Florida, U.S.A.	—
,, ,,	A. W. Waitt 15	Nigeria	K
D. friedrichsthalii Knuth	P.I. Acc. No. 11571	Puerto Rico	—
D. galeottiana Knuth	F. Miranda s.n.	Mexico	—
D. glauca Mühl.	E. S. Ayensu s.n.	Hort. Kew	—
D. gracillima Miq.	R. C. Ching 1459	Chekiang, China	US
,, ,,	M. Togosi 1060	Japan	US
D. guianensis Knuth	B. A. Krukoff 10004	Bolivia	US
,, ,,	A. W. Waitt 21	Nigeria	K
D. hastata Vell.	E. Warming (US 290135)	S. Amer.	US
*D. hastifolia Nees	R. Helms s.n.	N.S.W., Australia	US
D. hemicrypta Burk.	E. S. Ayensu s.n.	Hort. Kew.	K
D. hexagona Baker	Webrandt 3876	Malagasy Republic	US
	Webrandt (US 808310)	Malagasy Republic	US
D. hirtiflora Benth.	E. S. Ayensu s.n.	Hort. Kew	K
,, ,,	D. B. Fanshawe s.n.	Zambia	NDO
*D. hispida Dennst.	Dept. of Agric., Malaya	Malaysia	—
,, ,,	J. V. Pancho s.n.	Philippines	LB
D. lecardii de Wild	A. C. Tallantire s.n.	Uganda	—
D. luzonensis Schauer	W. L. Stern 2339	Philippines	US
*D. macrostachya Benth.	C. L. & A. A. Lundell 8167	Mexico	US
,, ,,	Aguirre & Reko 322	Mexico	US

TABLE 2 (*cont.*)

Species	Collector and number	Geographical origin	Herbarium voucher
D. macroura Harms.	A. W. Waitt 19	Nigeria	K
„ „	E. S. Ayensu s.n.	Hort. Kew	K
*D. matagalpensis Uline	C. L. & A. A. Lundell 7880	Mexico	US
*D. mexicana Scheidw.	F. Miranda s.n.	Mexico	—
*D. microbotrya Griseb.	S. Venturi 1671	Argentina	US
D. minutiflora Engl.	E. S. Ayensu s.n.	Hort. Kew	K
	A. C. Tallantire s.n.	Uganda	—
D. multiflora Mart.	Widgren 988	Brazil	US
„ „	A. F. Regnell 990	Brazil	US
D. mundtii Baker	E. S. Ayensu s.n.	Hort. Kew	—
D. nipponica Makino	E. S. Ayensu s.n.	Hort. Kew	K
*D. opposita Kunth	I. H. Burkill s.n.	Hort. Kew	K
D. oppositifolia L.	H. Santapau s.n.	Madras, India	—
*D. pallens Schlechtd.	C. A. Purpus 122	Mexico	US
„ „	C. A. Purpus 455	Mexico	US
D. pentaphylla L.	G. Edano s.n.	Philippines	US
„ „	J. V. Pancho s.n.	Philippines	LB
„ „	H. Santapau s.n.	Madras, India	—
„ „	C. O. Levine 9/28/17	China	US
*D. piperifolia Humb. & Bonpl.	C. Firman 432	Ecuador	US
D. polygonoides Humb. & Bonpl.	F. W. Martin s.n.	Puerto Rico	—
„ „	D. Wasshausen & E. S. Ayensu 336	Dominica, W.I.	US
D. praehensilis Benth.	A. W. Waitt 27	Nigeria	K
„ „	FHI 54897	Nigeria	FHI
„ „	A. C. Tallantire 7	Uganda	—
„ „	D. B. Fanshawe F8269	Zambia	K
„ „	D. B. Fanshawe F8338	Zambia	K
D. prazeri Prain & Burk.	E. S. Ayensu s.n.	Hort. Kew	K
D. preussii Pax	A. W. Waitt 24	Nigeria	K
„ „	A. C. Tallantire 5	Uganda	—
*D. pringlei Robins.	C. S. Pringle s.n.	Mexico	US
D. quartiniana A. Rich.	A. W. Waitt 23	Nigeria	K
„ „	D. B. Fanshawe s.n.	Zambia	NDO
*D. racemosa (Kl.) Uline	P. H. Allen 1869	Panama	US
*D. remotiflora Kunth	Hinton 6694	Mexico	US
D. retusa Mast.	B. de Winter s.n.	W. Transvaal	PRE
„ „	B. de Winter s.n.	E. Transvaal	PRE
D. rotundata Poir.	E. S. Ayensu s.n.	Ghana	—
„ „	A. W. Waitt 2	Nigeria	K
*D. rupicola Kunth	—	Cult. Hort. Berlin	US
D. samydea Griseb.	L. d'A. F. Carvalho s.n.	Brazil	RB
D. sansibarensis Pax	E. S. Ayensu s.n.	Hort. Kew	K
„ „	B. Verdcourt s.n.	Kenya	EA
„ „	P. B. Tomlinson s.n.	Singapore	—
D. schimperiana Hochst.	I. H. Burkill s.n.	Singapore	—
„ „	B. de Winter s.n.	Pretoria, S.A.	PRE

TABLE 2 (*cont.*)

Species	Collector and number	Geographical origin	Herbarium voucher
D. schimperiana Hochst.	A. C. Tallantire 2	Uganda	—
„ „	D. B. Fanshawe 8189	Zambia	K
*D. semperflorens Uline	Jean Louis 6527	Congo	US
D. sinuata Vell.	L. B. Smith & R. Klein 11131	Brazil	US
„ „	A. Krapovickas 2767	Argentina	US
D. spiculiflora Hemsl.	PI 252684	Florida, U.S.A.	—
„ „	F. W. Martin s.n.	Puerto Rico	—
*D. stellato-pilosa de Wild	Flamigui s.n.	Congo	US
D. stenomeriflora Prain & Burk.	Herb. Calcuttensis 5152	Malaya	US
D. sylvatica Ecklon.	A. W. Waitt 20	Nigeria	K
„ „	B. de Winter s.n.	Pretoria, S.A.	PRE
„ „	E. S. Ayensu s.n.	Hort. Kew	—
„ „	—	Swaziland	—
D. ternata Griseb.	A. Glagiou 14348	Brazil	US
*D. tokoro Makino	Maximowicz s.n.	Japan	US
*D. tomentosa Koenig	H. Santapau s.n.	Madras, India	—
„ „	A. Abraham s.n.	Kerala, India	—
D. trichantha Gleas.	T. G. Tutin 51	Guyana	US
D. trifida L.	H. Piltier 16323	Costa Rica	US
„ „	G. Klug 976	Peru	US
*D. urceolata Uline	Bro. S. Arsene 1394	Mexico	US
D. urophylla Hemsl.	F. W. Martin s.n.	Puerto Rico	—
D. villosa L.	E. S. Ayensu s.n.	Hort. Kew	K
*D. wallichii Hook. f.	A. Abraham s.n.	Kerala, India	—
D. wattii Prain & Burk.	E. S. Ayensu s.n.	Hort. Kew	K
*D. yucatensis Uline	H. H. Bartlett 11560	Br. Honduras	US
D. zingiberensis Wright	E. H. Wilson 2921	Hupeh, China	US
D. sp.	FHI 54898	Nigeria	FHI
Rajania cordata L.	F. W. Martin s.n.	Puerto Rico	—
R. hastata L.	A. H. Curtiss 506	Isla de Pinos, W.I.	K
„ „	E. K. Ekman 2910	Haiti	K
R. mucronata Willd.	E. J. Valeur 905	Dominican Rep.	K
R. tenuiflora Knuth	C. V. Morton & J. Acuna 3020	Cuba	K
Tamus communis L.	C. R. Metcalfe s.n.	Surrey, U.K.	K
„ „	E. S. Ayensu s.n.	Surrey, U.K.	—
„ „	S. Rogers s.n.	Devon, U.K.	—
T. edulis Lowe	A. G. Cabezon s.n.	Tenerife, Canary Is.	TENE

Stenomeridaceae

Stenomeris borneensis Oliver	E. D. Merrill 7301	Philippines	K
S. dioscoreifolia Planch.	G. E. Edano 11116	Philippines	K

Trichopodaceae

Avetra sempervirens Perrier	G. F. S. Elliot 2745	Malagasy Republic	K
„ „	M. H. Humber 28966	Malagasy Republic	P
Trichopus zeylanicus Gaertn.	A. Abraham s.n.	Kerala, India	—

TABLE 2 (cont.)

Species	Collector and number	Geographical origin	Herbarium voucher
Stemonaceae (Roxburghiaceae)			
Croomia pauciflora Torr.	P. B. Tomlinson s.n.	Florida, U.S.A.	—
Stemona curtisii Hook. f.	Haniffi and Nur 4368	Siam	K
*S. kerrii Craib.	Kerr 707	Siam	K
Stichoneuron caudatum Ridley	E. J. Corner 28716	Malaya	K
,, ,,	E. J. Corner 37056	Malaya	K

Herbarium abbreviations

AMB: Hugo de Vries Laboratories, Amsterdam, Netherlands. EA: The East African Herbarium, Nairobi, East Africa. FHI: Department of Forest Research, Ibadan, Nigeria. K: The Herbarium, Royal Botanic Gardens, Kew, U.K. LB: Los Banos College of Agriculture Arboretum, Laguna, Philippines. NDO: Herbarium, Forestry Department, Ndola, Zambia. P: Museum National d'Histoire Naturelle, Laboratoire de Phanérogamie, Paris, France. PRE: National Herbarium, Division of Botany, Pretoria, South Africa. QEC: Queen Elizabeth College Herbarium, London, U.K. RB: Jardin Botanico, Rio de Janeiro, Brazil. TENE: Jarden de Aclimatacion de la Orotava, Tenerife, Canary Islands. UC: University of California, Berkeley, U.S.A. US: National Museum, Smithsonian Institution, Washington, D.C., U.S.A.

4. GERMINATION AND SEEDLING MORPHOLOGY

THE embryo in the mature seed is quite small in proportion to the size of the seed itself. In her description of the seedlings of *Dioscorea villosa*, Smith (1916) showed that on germination the cotyledon increases rapidly in size, filling the entire fissure that is formed within the endosperm. The basal part of the cotyledon elongates, forming a trough-shaped petiole in whose hollow the first foliage leaf lies. The primary root elongates rapidly and soon begins to give off secondary roots. The first foliage leaf elongates, then arches itself until its tip becomes free from the seed coats.

Smith summarizes her study of *D. villosa* with the following conclusions.

   (i) The plane of the first division of the egg is oblong.

  (ii) A spherical 4-celled proembryo is formed.

 (iii) The first foliage leaf is the first organ of the embryo to be differentiated. The growing point of the stem consists, up to the time of germination, of a group of cells in the axil of the first foliage leaf. Both structures are lateral in origin.

 (iv) No 'cotyledonary ring' was observed. The cotyledon originates in a terminal position.

  (v) No structure that is in any way comparable to a second cotyledon is present; the sheath that is described as covering the plumule in all other Dioscoreaceae is wanting.

 (vi) Abundant endosperm is present in the seed.

(vii) The growing point of the stem begins to give off foliage leaves soon after the seed germinates.

(viii) The root of the seed is tetrarch; the hypocotyl is polyarch.

The development of the embryo in the Dioscoreaceae has long been observed to differ from the monocotyledonous types represented by *Alisma*, *Pistia*, *Lilium*, and *Orchis*. Solms-Laubach (1878), who made a detailed study of some species of the Dioscoreaceae and the Commelinaceae, stated that in these families the cotyledon is lateral rather than terminal in origin. The stem tip is terminal in origin but later it is forced to one side by the strong growth of the cotyledon from beneath. Solms-Laubach tentatively suggested that this mode of development of the embryo is so different from that of other monocotyledons that it constitutes a fundamental divergence. He withheld judgement, however, pending the completion of further critical investigations.

Eunus (1952) concluded from his study of *Dioscorea glabra* that the embryo development followed the Asterad (Compositae) type and not the Lilium variation of the Onagrad type which Smith (1916) figured in the case of *D. villosa*.

Rao (1953) described *D. oppositifolia* as having an embryo development of the Polygonum type. He also figured *Trichopus zeylanicus* as having a similar type (Rao 1955). Crété (1953) also studied *D. oppositifolia* with commentary on Rao's (1953) work. Boyd (1932) classified the germination of the Dio-scoreaceae under her Type B. She says of the cotyledon that it is 'a subter-ranean organ consisting of a sheathing base which protects the plumule, an intermediate sheathing region, the elongation of which is responsible for propelling the radicle and cotyledon base deeper into the soils, and a narrower region conveniently termed the stalk . . .'. Boyd also described the first leaf as emerging laterally or at the apex of the sheath, where it narrows into a stalk. The species that Boyd used as representatives of the family included *Tamus communis* and *Dioscorea elephantipes* (*Testudinaria*).

There is much controversy in the literature concerning the number of cotyledons that is characteristic of the Dioscoreaceae. Dutrochet (1835) described the embryo of *Tamus communis* as having 2 cotyledons, viz. one that was conical in form and remained within the seed during germination, the other being closely attached to the globular part of the embryo and becoming recognizable only after germination. Because the vascular bundle arrangement in the aerial stem of the Dioscoreaceae somewhat resembled the dicotyledonous arrangement, he thought this family was better placed between the dicotyledons and the monocotyledons.

In support of Dutrochet's claim, Strasburger (1872) advanced the view that monocotyledons were derived from dicotyledons by the loss of one cotyledon. It was obvious from his analysis that if the Dioscoreaceae could be held to constitute a transition stage between monocotyledons and dicotyledons, the 'second cotyledon' might well represent a stage in the degeneration of one of the cotyledons of the latter group.

In 1839 Jussieu described in *Dioscorea villosa*, *D. cordifolia*, and *Rajania hastata* a structure that was similar to the second cotyledon of *Tamus com-munis* noted earlier by Dutrochet. He, however, suggested that the structure in question was nothing but a sheath formed by the growth of the single cotyledon whose development was coincidental with the elongation of the cotyledonary limb.

Beccari (1870*b*), in agreement with Dutrochet, regarded the Dioscoreaceae as having 2 cotyledons, one being rudimentary. He examined the embryos of *D. bonariensis*, *D. brasiliensis*, *D. sinuosa*, *Rajania cordifolia*, *Tamus com-munis*, and *Trichopus zeylanicus* (Trichopodaceae).

Suessenguth (1921), on the other hand, reported the absence of the di-cotyledonous condition in *D. adenocarpa*, *D. pyrenaica*, and *D. quartiniana*.

More recently Lawton and Lawton (1967) investigated the developing seedlings of 5 *Dioscorea* species, viz. *D. bulbifera*, *D. hirtiflora*, *D. odoratis-sima*, *D. praehensilis*, and *D. preussii*. They described these species as having 2 cotyledons. 'One has an absorbing function and remains within the endo-sperm throughout its functional life and the other, the emergent cotyledon, develops later, being carried out of the seed by the elongating stalk of the absorbent cotyledon, to become the first green leaf of the young plant.'

This vestigial organ, together with the general vascular plan of the stem in the Dioscoreaceae, has led some taxonomists to claim an affinity between this family and the dicotyledons, an affinity that seems unreasonable in view of the over-all structure of the plants. It should be borne in mind that the anomalous 'dicotyledonous' condition of the Dioscoreaceae in the monocotyledons has its counterpart in the 'pseudo-monocotyledons' among the dicotyledonous plants (cf. Hill 1906, 1938, Metcalfe 1936, the papers they cite).

In the early stages of germination in *Peperomia*, Hill (1906) noted that the cotyledons serve as absorbent organs, but soon one of them grows rapidly and is withdrawn from the seed to serve as an expanding assimilating organ. The other organ remains within the seed and never emerges but serves to absorb the reserves stored in the perisperm.

Hill contended that 'This case suggests that evolution along similar lines may have produced the normal seedling habit of such monocotyledonous orders as the Araceae, etc., for it is possible that the absorbent cotyledon and the so-called "first-leaf" may stand in the same relation to each other and be equivalent to the two cotyledons of *Peperomia*'.

Metcalfe (1936), working on the embryology and seedling anatomy of *Ranunculus ficaria*, noted the 1-cotyledon condition of this species within the Ranunculaceae. He concluded that this species had become monocotylous as a result of the suppression of 1 cotyledon and not by the fusion of 2 cotyledons as figured by Sargant (1903). Similarly, the study of the Gesneriaceae by Hill (1938) indicated that the loss or suppression of one of the cotyledons in the monocotylous dicotyledons, is frequently associated with the development of a bulbous habit.

Our knowledge of the development of the tuber is still fragmentary. Archibald (1967) has recently pointed out that there is a fundamental difference in the development of the seedling of the many-tubered species of *Dioscorea* as compared with those that have a solitary perennial tuber. In her study of the seedlings of *D. cotinifolia*, for example, she observed that the first tuber is a small swelling which is formed laterally at the base of the first leaf. The leaf-base (presumably the hypocotyl/epicotyl region) forms the crown that in turn gives rise to horizontal roots, each terminating in a tuber.

More often the development of the tuber of the seedling begins with the initiation of a cambial zone around the vascular tissue in the hypocotyl. This cambial zone is followed by the development of parenchymatous tissue filled with starch. As the tuber swells, a cork cambium develops. Transverse sections through the juvenile tuber show the zonation of the cork cambium, the cortical region, and the central ground tissue with starch and the vascular tissue.

The shapes of the tuber have been attributed to soil texture as well as variability of cambial growth. Archibald (1967) has commented that the final shape of the adult tuber in *D. sylvatica* is very dependent on the physical condition of the soil. She found that in loamy soil the tubers are uniformly disc-shaped with a few basal indentations and the growing point is below soil level. Tubers that grow on scree slopes tend to be subterranean, smooth-skinned, and variously shaped due to the pressure of rocks. In shallow soils Archibald found the tubers to be partially exposed and tessellated above and with irregular lobes in the lower portion below the soil level. Enormous tubers tend to occur in dune sand where they grow up to a metre across.

Reviews of the embryological literature show that studies in this family are few (cf. Johansen 1950, Maheshwari 1950, Davis 1966). It is hoped that future studies involving many species will help to answer some fundamental questions posed by the development of the embryo.

5. THE LEAF

THE leaves of the Dioscoreales are generally alternate, sometimes opposite or whorled, simple or compound, the leaves or leaflets often being acuminate with cordate bases (Figs. 1, 2). The margins are either entire or sinuate. The secondary and tertiary veins are reticulate, thus recalling the venation pattern of most dicotyledons. Burkill (1960) described the typical leaf of *Dioscorea* as having (i) a long petiole with a pulvinus at each end; (ii) a broad lamina with 3 or more arcuate primary nerves of which 3 reach the apex of the leaf; (iii) a water-pore or water-pores on a projecting tip—a tip that is fully developed before the rest of the lamina, ceasing growth and also dying before the rest of the leaf; (iv) reticulate nervation between the primary nerves.

MORPHOLOGICAL VARIATIONS

Although simple leaves are characteristic of the Dioscoreales, compound leaves are known to occur in a few sections of *Dioscorea*, i.e. Lasiophyton, Illigerastrum, Cardiocapsa, Stenocarpa, and Trifoliatae. The evolutionary conversion of the compound to the simple type of leaf has been shown to have occurred in the early history of the order. Burkill (1960), after drawing attention to the range of leaf shapes in *D. quartiniana* (Fig. 1, M–V), went on to show that many new species have been incorrectly proposed because of the failure to realize that such wide morphological variations can occur within a species. He states further that the change from the trifoliate to the simple leaf has taken place along more than one evolutionary line.

PHYLLOTAXY

In the Dioscoreaceae the phyllotaxy falls into 3 main categories. The first, exhibited by *D. opposita*, passes through 3 phyllotactic patterns. It begins with orthodistichy, passes into tristichy, and returns to distichy. The change over from one pattern to the other is very gradual. The second category, which is exhibited by *D. glauca*, begins from an off-spiral condition and passes into a disorderly phyllotaxy (cf. Burkill 1960). The third category is the decussate pattern exhibited by *D. alata* and its allies. Burkill (1960) has explained the phyllotactic pattern in this third category in detail and the reader is advised to consult his work. Besides *Dioscorea*, the phyllotaxy of *Tamus* has been figured in detail (cf. Burkill 1949).

LAMINA

Leaves of all species of Dioscoreaceae exhibit dorsiventral organization with a well-developed lamina. The area of the lamina is usually of the order of 30–250 cm² with much larger leaves in such species as *D. sansibarensis*. Although there is a basic anatomical uniformity in the family, differences in detailed structure do exist at the species level (see Table 3, p. 31).

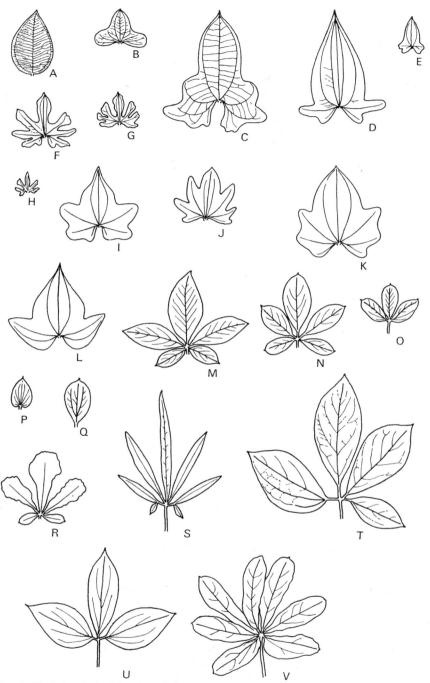

FIG. 1. Variation in leaf forms and the arrangement of primary veins in some *Dioscorea* species (after Burkill 1960) (all × ⅐ except M–V). A, *Dioscorea smilacifolia*, leaf margin entire; three primary veins shown without any accessory primaries. B, *D. sylvatica*. C, *D. sansibarensis* (young leaf). D, E, *D. rupicola*. F–H, *D. undatiloba*. I, *D. bryoniifolia*. J, *D. diversifolia*. K, *D. nipponica*. L, *D. membranacea*. M–T, V, *D. quartiniana*, variations in leaf forms. (× ⅓) U, presumed form of ancestral leaf

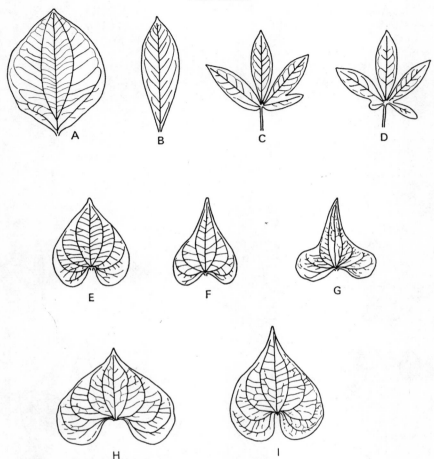

FIG. 2. A–D, Compound leaves (after Burkill 1960) ($\times \frac{1}{3}$). A, *Dioscorea dumetorum*, terminal leaflet with the three primary veins parting above. B, *D. crotalariifolia*, terminal leaflet in which only one vein reaches the apex. C, D, *D. crotalariifolia*, showing lobing on the lateral leaflets. E–I, Lamina of *Tamus communis* showing variations in the outlines of individual leaf bases.

Epidermis

Most of the Dioscoreales have a 1-layered epidermis, but occasionally a multiple epidermis occurs on the adaxial side as demonstrated in *D. luzonensis* (Fig. 5. K, p. 40). The subepidermal cells are presumed to have arisen as a result of periclinal division of the protoderm, thus distinguishing them from hypodermal cells that originate from the ground tissue. The epidermal cells show a wide range of variation in size and shape. Some of the largest cells are to be seen in *D. campestris* (Fig. 5. J) and some of the smallest in *D. macroura*. The cells are either cuboidal or rectangular. The adaxial epidermal cells in surface view are either straight (e.g. *D. macroura*, Fig. 14. B, p. 88), slightly sinuous (e.g. *D. samydea*), or markedly sinuous (e.g. *D. sansibarensis*, Fig. 15. A, p. 89). The abaxial cells are either slightly sinuous as in *D. samydea* (Fig. 13. A, p. 87) and *D. campestris* (Fig. 10. B, p. 81) or conspicuously sinuous as in *D. sansibarensis* (Fig. 15. B) and *D. macroura* (Fig. 14. A). Generally speaking, adaxial cells have straight walls while abaxial cells have sinuous walls. In some species, such as *D. hexagona*, *D. tomentosa*, *D. urophylla*, *D. zingiberensis*, and *Rajania tenuiflora*, epidermal cells on both surfaces exhibit straight walls. In other species, such as *D. burchellii*, *D. sansibarensis*, *Avetra sempervirens*, and *Tamus communis*, epidermal cells on both surfaces show sinuous walls. *Trichopus zeylanicus* exhibits deeply sinuous cell walls on both surfaces and thus differs from all other species investigated.

In transverse section the epidermal cells can be seen to have straight anticlinal walls. There are slight differences in thickness between the periclinal and anticlinal walls, the outer periclinal walls being the thickest. The epidermal cells are coated externally by a thin or thick layer of cuticle which may be either undulating or ridged. In species such as *D. densiflora* where thick cuticles occur, there is a tendency for the cuticle to extend inwards between the epidermal cells. The cuticle covering the epidermal cells around the main veins is generally thick and ridged.

Among the salient features of the epidermal cells of the species investigated is the occurrence of cuticular striations. In most species these striations occur most frequently on epidermal cells that surround the stomata. Inconspicuous striations occur on adaxial epidermal surfaces of species such as *D. ceratandra*, *D. dregeana*, *D. hirtiflora*, *D. macroura*, *D. polygonoides*, *D. preussii*, *D. quartiniana*, *D. schimperiana*, and *D. villosa*. The striations radiate from around the stomata in either broken or continuous undulating lines. In *D. bulbifera*, for example, the striations are quite pronounced on the costal cells and also on the cells surrounding the stomata. Striations on the costal epidermal cells run parallel with the long axis, while those of the intercostal cells give a radiating effect.

Stomata occur mainly in the abaxial surfaces of the lamina, but in a few species such as *D. campestris* and *D. bulbifera* they are to be seen in the adaxial surfaces also (see Table 3, p. 31). Although stomata are less numerous on the adaxial than on the abaxial surface, there is no support for Raghavan's (1960) assertion that they are confined to the abaxial surface in all members of the Dioscoreales. The distribution of stomata is irregular, for they are usually absent from the costal regions and appear less numerous along the periphery of the leaf than elsewhere. The axes of the stomata are randomly directed, thus presenting the same orientation as that which is to be seen in many dicotyledonous leaves. The size of stomata shows some degree of uniformity within species. In most of the species investigated they average 39×27 μm. There are other species with stomata averaging 18×18 μm (e.g. *D. discolor*), 21×21 μm (e.g. *D. dugesii*), and 45×45 μm (e.g. *Avetra sempervirens*). The guard cells are bean-shaped as seen in surface view. In transverse section the walls facing the pore are thickened and, more especially around the tapered ends, have either very short or no projecting ledges. The guard cells occur at the same level as the adjacent epidermal cells except in species such as *D. multiflora* where the guard cells are slightly sunken.

The anomocytic (ranunculaceous) type of stoma is found throughout the Dioscoreales. Unfortunately the term 'anomocytic' is not wholly satisfactory because there are so many varieties of this type. Unlike the paracytic type of stomata in which each guard cell is accompanied on the outer side by a lateral subsidiary cell, and the tetracytic type in which both 2 lateral and 2 polar subsidiary cells occur, the anomocytic type exhibits no morphologically distinct subsidiary cells and no distinctive arrangement of the contiguous epidermal cells. Nevertheless, the *Dioscorea* species that have been studied reveal a considerable range of variation in the positions of epidermal cells in relation to the guard cells. The term 'anomocytic' is still less satisfactory when used with reference to *Avetra* and *Trichopus* because, although the stomata of these genera fall within the definition of anomocytic, they differ from those belonging to other genera included in the Dioscoreales. (See Table 3.)

Stebbins and Khush (1961) considered the organization of the stomatal complex in the leaves of monocotyledons (including 2 species of *Dioscorea*), and its bearing on their phylogeny. These workers concluded that the Dioscoreales are related to other families of the Liliales because of their anomocytic type of stomatal organization. Although the possession of anomocytic stomata is generally accepted by botanists as a taxonomic character, the apparent distinct variations of stomatal organization generally grouped under the anomocytic type will require further critical comparative studies before final decisions can be reached.

Mesophyll

The mesophyll in the Dioscoreales is generally dorsiventral in structure. The palisade tissue, which occurs only on the adaxial side of the lamina, consists of 1 or 2, and never more than 2 (except occasionally near leaf margins), layers of cells. The innermost layer tends to be less easily distinguishable from the spongy tissue. The palisade cells are generally elongated, cylindrical, and vertically orientated in transverse section. In *D. luzonensis* (Fig. 5. K, p. 40), for example, the cells are 3·5 to 4 times higher than wide, but in *D. campestris* (Fig. 5. J) they are 1·5 to 2·5 times higher than wide. The cells are generally compactly arranged; those of the innermost layer in the species having 2 layers are generally of fairly uniform size and are shorter than those of the outer layer. The spongy tissue, occupying about half to two-thirds of the thickness of the mesophyll, has cells of irregular size and shape, and the cells are either compactly or loosely arranged.

Vascular system

The type of vascular bundle in the Dioscoreales leaf is basically collateral with adaxial xylem and abaxial phloem. This is clearly demonstrated in the midrib. The phloem tissue in transverse section appears as a crescentiform group of isolated units or strands, the number of which varies in different species. In *D. dregeana* (Fig. 3. A, p. 34), *D. macroura* (Fig. 3. D), *D. campestris* (Fig. 3. E), *D. bulbifera* (Fig. 3. F), and *D. samydea* (Fig. 3. B), 3, 4, 5, 6, and 7 phloem units are observed in each species respectively.

TABLE 3

Anatomical characters of mature leaves

Species	Stomata		Size in μm	Epidermal cell walls		Cuticular striations	Trichomes		Tannins	Crystals
	Ad	Ab		Ad	Ab		Hairs	Glands		
Dioscoreaceae										
Dioscorea alata	-	+	39×27	st	sls	+	-	+	+	+
D. balcanica	±	+	45×24	st	sls	+	-	+	+	+
D. bernoulliana	-	+	24×21	st	sls	+	-	+	+	+
D. bulbifera	±	+	39×21	st	st	+	-	+	+	+
D. burchellii	±	+	42×24	s	s	+	-	+	+	+
D. campestris	-	+	39×27	st	sls	+	-	+	-	+
D. cayenensis	-	+	45×30	sls	sls	+	-	+	+	+
D. ceratandra	-	+	30×21	st	sls	+	bi	+	+	+
D. cochleari-apiculata	-	+	33×18	st	sls	+	-	+	-	+
D. composita	-	+	45×30	st	sls	-	-	+	+	+
D. convolvulacea	-	+	30×18	st	sls	-	uni	+	-	+
D. cotinifolia	-	+	39×27	st	s	-	-	+	+	+
D. deltoidea	-	+	33×24	st	sls	+	-	+	+	+
D. discolor	-	+	18×18	st	st	±	uni/bi	+	-	+
D. dregeana	-	+	30×21	st	s	±	uni	+	-	+
D. dugesii	-	+	21×21	st	sls	-	-	+	+	+
D. dumetorum	-	+	42×21	st	s	+	uni/bi	+	-	+
D. elephantipes	-	+	33×18	sls	sls	+	-	**+**	+	+
D. esculenta	-	+	39×27	st	sls	-	T-s	+	+	+
D. floribunda	-	+	42×30	st	sls	+	-	+	+	+
D. friedrichsthalii	-	+	30×24	st	sls	-	-	+	+	+
D. galeottiana	-	+	45×30	st	s	-	uni	+	-	+
D. hastata	-	+	42×28	st	s	+	uni/bi	+	+	+
D. hemicrypta	-	+	36×24	sls	sls	+	-	+	+	+
D. hexagona	-	+	45×36	st	st	-	-	+	+	+

TABLE 3 (cont.)

Species	Stomata			Epidermal cell walls		Cuticular striations	Trichomes		Tannins	Crystals
	Ad	Ab	Size in µm	Ad	Ab		Hairs	Glands		
D. hirtiflora	—	+	30×21	st	s	+	*	+	+	+
D. lecardii	—	+	45×27	st	sls	+	—	+	+	+
D. luzonensis	—	+	33×21	st	sls	+	—	+	+	+
D. macroura	—	+	45×21	st	s	+	—	+	+	+
D. mundtii	—	+	30×18	sls	s	+	uni	+	+	+
D. nipponica	—	+	36×27	sls	s	+	—	+	+	+
D. polygonoides	—	+	30×24	st	sls	+	—	+	+	+
D. praehensilis	—	+	42×30	st	sls	+	—	+	+	+
D. prazeri	—	+	32×21	st	sls	—	T-s	+	+	+
D. preussii	—	+	36×27	st	sls	+	bi	+	—	+
D. quartiniana	—	+	39×30	st	sls	+	bi	+	—	+
D. retusa	—	+	30×21	st	sls	+	—	+	+	+
D. rotundata	—	+	45×27	sls	sls	+	—	+	+	+
D. sanydea	—	+	39×24	sls	sls	+	—	+	+	+
D. sansibarensis	—	+	30×15	s	s	+	*	+	+	+
D. schimperiana	—	+	37×24	st	s	+	—	+	+	+
D. spiculiflora	—	+	30×24	st	sls	+	—	+	—	+
D. sylvatica	—	+	36×21	st	sls	+	bi	+	+	+
D. tomentosa	—	+	39×27	st	st	+	uni	+	+	+
D. trifida	—	+	45×24	st	sls	+	—	+	+	+
D. urophylla	—	+	30×21	st	sls	+	uni/mul	+	—	+
D. villosa	—	+	33×24	st	sls	+	—	+	+	+
D. wattii	—	+	27×21	sls	sls	+	—	+	+	+
D. zingiberensis	—	+	39×27	st	st	—	uni	+	+	+
Rajania cordata	—	+	39×27	st	sls	+	—	+	—	+
R. hastata	—	+	42×36	st	s	+	uni	+	+	+
R. mucronata	—	+	42×24	st	sls	+	uni	+	—	+

TABLE 3 (cont)

R. tenuiflora	−	+	36×18	st	st	+	−	+	+	+
Tanus communis	−	+	30×21	sls	s	−	−	+	+	+
T. edulis	−	+	42×36	sls	s	−	−	+	+	+
Stenomeridaceae										
Stenomeris borneensis	−	+	45×33	sls	sls	−	−	bi.g	−	+
S. dioscoreifolia	−	+	45×30	sls	sls	−	−	bi.g	−	+
Trichopodaceae										
Avetra sempervirens	−	+	45×45	st	s	−	−	−	−	+
Trichopus zeylanicus	−	+	33×30	vs	vs	+	−	c.g.	−	+
Stemonaceae										
Croomia pauciflora	±	±	45×31	s	s	−	−	−	−	+
Stemona curtisii	±	±	48×33	sls	sls	−	−	−	+	+

Abbreviations

Ad, adaxial   uni, unicellular   s, sinuous   +, present
ab, abaxial   bi, bicellular   sls, slightly sinuous   −, absent
*, stellate   mul, multicellular   vs, very sinuous   ±, infrequent or not pronounced
c, crescentiform   g, gland   st, straight   T-s, T-shaped

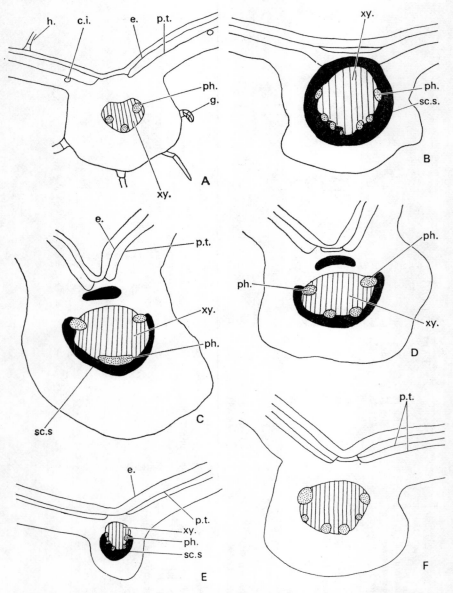

FIG. 3. Outlines of T.S. leaf midribs of *Dioscorea* showing distribution of sclerenchyma and number of phloem units within the vascular bundle (×40). A, *Dioscorea dregeana*. B, *D. samydea*. C, *D. sansibarensis*. D, *D. macroura*. E, *D. campestris*. F, *D. bulbifera*.
c.i., crystal idioblast; e., epidermis; g., gland; h., hair; ph., phloem; p.t., palisade tissue; sc.s., sclerenchyma sheath; xy., xylem.

The distribution of sclerenchyma in the Dioscoreaceae appears in a variety of patterns. In *D. dregeana* (Fig. 3. A) and *D. bulbifera* (Fig. 3. F), the vascular bundles of the midribs are not associated with fibres. In other species such as *D. campestris* (Fig. 3. E) thick-walled fibres occur only on the abaxial side of the vascular bundle of the midrib. Two separate fibre arcs are encountered in *D. sansibarensis* (Fig. 3. C) and *D. macroura* (Fig. 3. D), while in *D. samydea* (Fig. 3. B) the vascular bundle is completely surrounded by fibres.

PETIOLE

The petiole is usually long with a pulvinus at each end, the basal pulvinus being jointed and twisted. A few species have short petioles as in *D. hexagona* and *D. heteropoda*. Completely sessile leaves have not been observed.

The outlines of the petioles of most of the Dioscoreales species are pentagonal in transverse section. In some species the outlines are crescentiform; in others they are almost circular. Petioles with pentagonal outlines are either winged at all corners as in *D. alata* (Fig. 4. D) or only at the corners orientated towards the adaxial side as in *D. macroura* (Fig. 4. A).

Epidermis

The epidermis of the petiole is similar to that of the stem. In transverse sections the cells are either rectangular, cuboidal, circular, or conical, compactly arranged and with cytoplasmic contents of variable densities. The cuticle is either thin or thick, undulating or ridged. Stomata are present and resemble in detail those described for the leaf.

Cortex

The cortex is composed of collenchymatous and chlorenchymatous cells. Subjacent to the epidermis there are generally 1–3 layers of either lamellar or lacunar collenchyma cells followed by chlorenchyma cells of variable size. Passing from the outside to the centre of the section there is a gradual transition from smaller to larger chlorenchyma cells. Occasionally an endodermoid layer separates the cortex from the vascular cylinder.

Vascular system

The vascular bundles are arranged in a ring, generally with the largest vascular bundle towards the abaxial side of the petiole. The vascular bundles are basically collateral, and just as was observed in the leaf, the number of phloem units within each vascular bundle is variable. There are generally 3 phloem units in each bundle, but bundles having 2, 4, and 7 phloem units respectively have been observed in *D. retusa*, *D. cochleari-apiculata*, and *D. bulbifera*. The number of vascular bundles in each petiole is also variable but constant in each species. Petioles of many species have 6 vascular bundles of which 3 are major. Petioles with 7, 9, or 11 bundles are exhibited, for example, in *D. campestris* (Fig. 4. C), *D. sansibarensis*, and *D. dregeana* (Fig. 4. H) respectively.

The distribution of sclerenchyma in the Dioscoreaceae petioles falls into

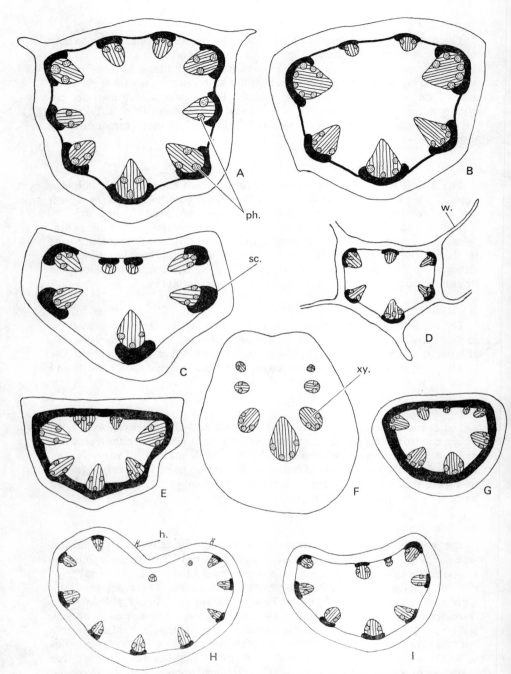

FIG. 4. Outlines of T.S. petioles showing the general vascular plan and the distribution of sclerenchyma (all × 16 except C, × 40). A, *Dioscorea macroura*. B, *D. bulbifera*. C, *D. campestris*. D, *D. alata*. E, *D. samydea*. F, *D. cochleari-apiculata*. G, *D. quartiniana*. H, *D. dregeana*. I, *D. retusa*.

h., hair; ph., phloem; sc., sclerenchyma; w., wing; xy., xylem.

three main patterns: (1) arcs of sclerenchyma on the outer face (phloem end) of each vascular bundle thus abutting on the cortex, e.g. *D. campestris* (Fig. 4. C), *D. dregeana* (Fig. 4. H), and *D. retusa* (Fig. 4. I); (2) a cylinder of sclerenchyma enclosing all the vascular bundles, e.g. *D. quartiniana* (Fig. 4. G) and *D. samydea* (Fig. 4. E); (3) a combination of categories (1) and (2), e.g. *D. bulbifera* (Fig. 4. B), *D. macroura* (Fig. 4. A), and *D. sansibarensis*. Sclerenchyma is completely absent from other species and hence the vascular bundles are embedded in thin-walled parenchymatous tissue, e.g. *D. cochleari-apiculata* (Fig. 4. F).

6. THE STEM

GENERAL MORPHOLOGY

THE aerial stems of the Dioscoreales are annual, rounded or winged, and with or without spines or hairs. Perrier de la Bathie (1924) and Hauman (1916) have described *Avetra sempervirens* and *Dioscorea multiflora* respectively as having persistent stems. Burkill (1960) disagreed and argued that with the perennial humidity, as in Upper Assam, *D. wattii* is virtually evergreen as it sends up a new stem to displace the old, and therefore a slight extension of this process can easily be interpreted as perennial growth.

Archibald (1967) stated that of the 8 species of *Dioscorea* that she studied, occurring in the most southerly part of South Africa, 3 species, and possibly 2 others, were known to have aerial stems that persisted for at least 2 years. Dr. Archibald has assured me that this phenomenon can be made clear by following the development of the aerial shoot during the seasonal changes in a typical 'annual' species and comparing it with what happens in the 'perennial' species. She further contends that with the 'persistent' aerial stem only the uppermost parts are deciduous; the lower laterals and main stem remain dormant during the winter and some of the lower leaves also remain green during this period. When the growing season starts, new shoots are produced from axillary buds either on the main stem or lower laterals. Aerial stems persisting for more than 1 season and giving rise to the new season's growth in this way have been observed in *D. cotinifolia* and *D. sylvatica*, where the growing season starts in August to September, and in *D. mundtii*, an autumn-flowering species in which the growing season starts in January. Dr. Archibald is, however, not sure how long the main stems persist. In *D. cotinifolia* she has observed that specimens produced new main shoots from the tubers in 1963, and produced laterals from aerial buds in 1964 and again in 1965. She stated further that 'in *D. sylvatica* aerial shoots collected in the fields show on the main stem the stumpy remains of previous aerial branches for at least two and possibly five previous periods of growth'.

The stems reach considerable heights; 120–225 m for *D. bartlettii* and over 396 m for *D. mangenotiana* (cf. Burkill 1960). The latter figure has been questioned since the maximum growth period of the stem is 12 months and, as Burkill pointed out, the biggest Dioscoreas cannot spread over the top of forests as giant species of *Vitis* do. In the present work measurements of the available stems show a wide range in diameter. The smallest diameter was recorded for *D. mundtii* (0·5 mm), the largest was recorded for *D. cochleari-apiculata* and *D. sansibarensis* (12 mm), the average diameter of all species studied being 5 mm. Miège recorded a diameter of 4 cm for *D. mangenotiana* but there is a strong possibility that the region measured formed part of the underground portion of the stem; moreover, as Burkill has stated, a 4-cm diameter for a typical stem of *Dioscorea* is quite out of the ordinary. *Trichopus* differs markedly from other genera of the order in having many short stems, each bearing 1 leaf, and in the complete absence of any trace of the climbing habit.

The direction of twining of the vines has been used as a sectional character. For example, in sections Enantiophyllum and Lasiophyton, twining is said to be clockwise and anticlockwise (right- and left-hand helices) respectively. Because of the much confused descriptions of the direction of climbing an explanation will not be out of place. As Burkill (1960) pointed out, when an observer faces the growing plant, twining is clockwise (dextrorse) if the vine mounts towards the right hand and anticlockwise (sinistrorse) if the vine mounts towards the left hand.

To what extent environment or genetics influence the direction of climbing is not clearly known. Allard (1945, 1947) and Copeland (1916), working on the growth behaviour of *Dioscorea*, observed that twining and nutation may not occur in darkness unless some support is available, thus demonstrating selective adaptation. Doubts have therefore been expressed concerning the taxonomic reliability of the direction of twining. Burkill (1960) has stated that the direction of twining is generally constant for Old World species. He noted on the other hand that the direction did not appear to be sufficiently fixed in New World species to be taxonomically reliable. In his work he cited various recorded exceptions. *D. elephantipes* and *D. humilis* twine in both directions on different parts of the same plant. *D. baya* has been observed to twine anticlockwise in exception to the characterization of the section Enantiophyllum. The reverse is true of *D. inopinata* of the section Opsophyton. In the Trichopodaceae and Stenomeridaceae, clockwise and anticlockwise twining are exhibited in *Avetra* and *Stenomeris* respectively. Although most of the stems of the order are twiners, they exhibit orthotropic qualities, and this phenomenon is responsible for keeping the lower part of the stem erect. It has been observed that when twining fails orthotropism reasserts itself.

GENERAL ANATOMY. INTERNODE

Epidermis

The epidermis consists of thick- or thin-walled rectangular, cuboidal, conical, or rounded cells with cytoplasm and distinct nuclei. In some species such as *D. ternata* the epidermal cells are replaced by brachysclereids. These are stone-cells having a short, somewhat isodiametric appearance. The cuticle is generally thin and ridged or undulating. A few species exhibit very thick cuticle, e.g. *D. multiflora* (Fig. 5. D). The stomata are similar in structure to those of the leaf, but they are very infrequent in the stem. *D. multiflora* exhibits sunken stomata.

Cortex

Transverse sections of the stem reveal that the cortical cells are of various sizes and shapes, generally with intercellular spaces between them. Thus the thickness of the cortex varies from species to species. The cortex is about 3–5 cells thick in most species, but in others it is composed of more layers of cells (*D. burchellii*, 11–15; *Tamus communis*, 8–15; and *D. prazeri*, 6–8). In

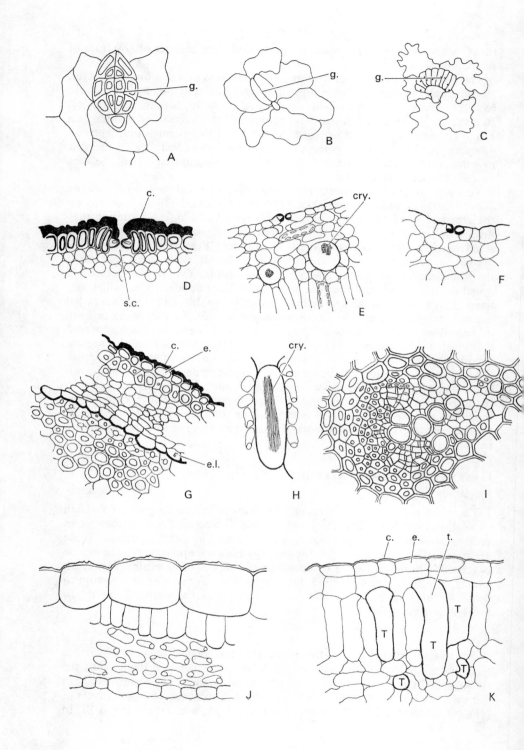

some species, e.g. *D. densiflora*, the cortex and the epidermis are separated by a zone of sclerenchyma. The cortical cells are generally chlorenchymatous. Distinct radial arrangement of cells does not occur, although a suggestion of such an arrangement has been observed in some species. Sclerification of the cortex is observed in some species of the order. In other species such as *D. alata* we can observe the development of collenchymatous cells, often containing raphide bundles, subjacent to the epidermis of the prominent wings.

Lying in the inner boundary of the cortex, one generally observes an endodermoid layer (Fig. 5. G). This zone of cells is so called because, although the cells exhibit U-shaped thickenings that are often characteristic of a mature endodermis, no true casparian strips have been observed when the cells are young. As Esau (1953) pointed out, in the original concept of the stele, the term 'endodermis' was applied to the inner layer of the cortex, regardless of whether this layer had any distinctive morphological characteristics or not. The common usage now is to restrict the term 'endodermis' to the innermost layer of the cortex only when the young cells exhibit casparian strips. Any layer of cells in a similar position (i.e. lying in the inner boundary of the cortex), lacking such wall modification but showing some other structural or histochemical resemblance to the true endodermis may be called an *endodermoid layer of cells*. In *D. bulbifera* (Fig. 16. E, F, p. 91; Pl. V. F) the endodermoid layer is represented by a very distinctive layer of brachysclereids which distinguishes it from all other species of the Dioscoreales. Below the endodermoid layer in most species are fibre-like layers 2–many cells deep that encircle the central cylinder.

Vascular bundles

One feature that serves to distinguish the Dioscoreales from all other monocotyledons is the type of vascular bundle that occurs in the stem. In an earlier paper (Ayensu 1965) the writer emphasized the peculiarity and the uniqueness of the vascular bundle type in this family. It is rather surprising that when Cheadle and Uhl (1948a, b) used vascular bundles of monocotyledons to develop their ideas concerning phylogeny, they somehow overlooked the very distinctive form in the Dioscoreales.

The vascular bundles of the stems of the Dioscoreales (except *Trichopus*

FIG. 5. (all ×165). A, Multicellular gland on unicellular stalk observed on leaves of Dioscoreaceae species. B, Bicellular gland on unicellular stalk observed on leaves of Stenomeridaceae species. C, Crescentiform gland on unicellular stalk observed in Trichopodaceae except *Avetra* which has Dioscoreaceae gland type (A). D–G, T.S. small portions of stems (D and G) and leaves (E and F) showing stomata (D and E), crystals (E), thickness of the cuticle, and the presence of an endodermoid layer (G). H, Raphide bundle in a mucilaginous idioblastic cell. I, T.S. vascular bundle of type to be found in petioles of Dioscoreaceae. J, K, T.S. small portions of leaves illustrating the type and size of epidermal cells, the mesophyll and the distribution of tannin (T).
A, *Dioscorea alata*. Gland. B, *Stenomeris dioscoreifolia*. Gland. C, *Trichopus zeylanicus*. Gland. D, *D. multiflora*. Stem. E, *D. dregeana*. Leaf. F, *D. quartiniana*. Leaf. G, *D. dregeana*. Stem. H, *D. campestris*. Crystals. I, *D. campestris*. Petiole. J, *D. campestris*. Leaf. K, *D. luzonensis*. Leaf.
c., cuticle; cry., crystals; e., epidermis; e.l., endodermoid layer; g., gland; s.c., stomatal chamber; t., tannin cells.

TABLE 4

Characters of the cauline vascular bundles of stems investigated

	No. of pairs of large metaxylem vessels	Average diameter of large vessels (μm)	No. of phloem units on inner side of meta-xylem vessels	Average diameter of large sieve-tubes (μm)
	Dioscoreaceae			
Section Dematostemon				
Dioscorea campestris	1	98	1	42
Section Brachyandra				
D. hexagona	1	140	2	Obliterated
Section Sphaerantha				
D. multiflora	1	294	1	126
D. guianensis	1	140	1	70
Section Chondrocarpa				
D. samydea	1	364	2	196
Section Opsophyton				
Subsection Macrourae				
D. macroura	1	462	2	140
D. sansibarensis	½	420	2	140
Subsection Euopsophyton				
D. bulbifera	3	350	2	98
Subsection Isocantha				
D. burchellii	1	112	1	70
D. cotinifolia	1	98	1	28
D. mundtii	1	70	1	42
D. trichantha	1	420	2	182
Section Trigonobasis				
D. convolvulacea	1	182	1	70
D. galeottiana	1	280	1	140
Section Stenocarpa				
D. ternata	½	210	2	98
Section Lasiophyton				
D. dregeana	1	196	2	84
D. dumetorum	2	280	2	112
Section Trieuphorostemon				
D. pentaphylla	1	336	2	154
D. tomentosa	1	280	2	112
Section Botryosicyos				
D. cochleari-apiculata	1–2	140	2	112
D. quartiniana	1–2	308	2	112
D. retusa	1	210	2	70
Section Macrogynodium				
D. bernoulliana	1	140	1	70
D. dugesii	1	210	2	70
D. trifida	1	420	2	180
D. urophylla	1	294	2	140
Section Apodostemon				
D. friedrichsthalii	1	238	1	140
D. spiculiflora	1	154	1	70

TABLE 4 (*cont.*)

	No. of pairs of large metaxylem vessels	Average diameter of large vessels (μm)	No. of phloem units on inner side of meta-xylem vessels	Average diameter of large sieve-tubes (μm)
Section Macropoda				
D. balcanica	1	126	2	56
D. deltoidea	1	154	1	42
D. prazeri	1	252	1	84
D. villosa	1–2	112	1	56
D. zingiberensis	1	210	1	112
Section Heterostemon				
D. composita	1	252	1	98
D. composita (very large specimen)	1	812	1	336
D. floribunda	1	266	1	154
Section Combilium				
D. esculenta	1	350	2	126
D. flabellifolia	1	490	2	266
Section Oxypetalum				
D. carionis	1	406	1	238
D. densiflora	1	504	1	252
Section Brachystigma				
D. sinuata	1	224	1	126
Section Lychnostemon				
D. ceratandra	1	84	1	56
D. polygonoides	1	350	1	168
Section Macrocarpaea				
D. preussii	1	560	2	182
Section Cryptantha				
D. hastata	1	306	1	126
Section Sarcantha				
D. amazonum	1	392	1	294
Section Lasiogyne				
D. discolor	1	378	1	224
Section Orientali-asiaticae				
D. collettii	1	252	1	84
D. gracillima	1	196	1	70
Section Asterotricha				
D. schimperiana	1	434	2	196
Section Enantiophyllum				
D. alata	2	518	2	210
D. cayenensis	1–2	448	2	210
D. luzonensis	2	630	2	210
D. minutiflora	1	350	2	154
D. rotundata	2	322	2	140
Section Syntepaleia				
D. hirtiflora	2	266	2	98

TABLE 4 (*cont.*)

	No. of pairs of large metaxylem vessels	Average diameter of large vessels (μm)	No. of phloem units on inner side of meta-xylem vessels	Average diameter of large sieve-tubes (μm)
Section Stenocorea				
D. stenomeriflora	1	322	2	126
Section Eustenophora				
D. nipponica	2	210	1	70
Subgenus Testudinaria				
D. elephantipes	2	168	1	84
D. hemicrypta	1–2	84	1	42
D. sylvatica	1–2+	322	2	140
Rajania cordata	1	98	2	42
R. hastata	1	126	2	42
R. mucronata	1	196	2	70
R. tenuiflora	1	154	2	56
Tamus communis	1	168	1	84
T. edulis	1	224	1	84
Stenomeridaceae				
Stenomeris borneensis	2	252	1	112
S. dioscoreifolia	2	350	1	140
Trichopodaceae				
Avetra sempervirens	2–3	238	1	84
Trichopus zeylanicus	Does not follow general plan			
Stemonaceae				
Croomia pauciflora		,,	,,	
Stemona curtisii		,,	,,	
Stichoneuron caudatum		,,	,,	

and Stemonaceae) are disposed in 2 circles. The bundles of the outer circle (common vascular bundles) have a V-shaped arrangement of metaxylem vessels and tracheids together with at least 2 phloem units terminating the flanges of the V, and a third phloem unit at the converging ends of the V. The bundles of the inner circle (cauline vascular bundles) have an elliptical arrangement of metaxylem vessels and tracheids with either 1 or 2 large phloem units on the inner side of the innermost pair of large metaxylem vessels. There is at least 1 additional phloem unit at the outer end which is enclosed by tracheids and small vessels. The number of vascular bundles as seen in a transverse section varies within the same species.

The number of large metaxylem vessels within a vascular bundle varies with the species. In *D. bulbifera* there are 3 pairs of large metaxylem vessels with an average diameter of 350 μm (Pl. V. F). In *D. mundtii* only 1 pair of vessels occurs with an average diameter of 70 μm. The number of phloem units within an individual vascular bundle also varies with the species. In *D. wattii* (Fig. 6. A; Pl. XIII. A) and *D. dumetorum* (Figs. 6. C; 17. D, p. 97; Pl. VII. B) 2 phloem units occur on the inner side of the large metaxylem vessels while only 1 phloem unit has been observed in *D. discolor* (Fig. 6. B; Pl. XI. E). For complete listing of species see Table 4.

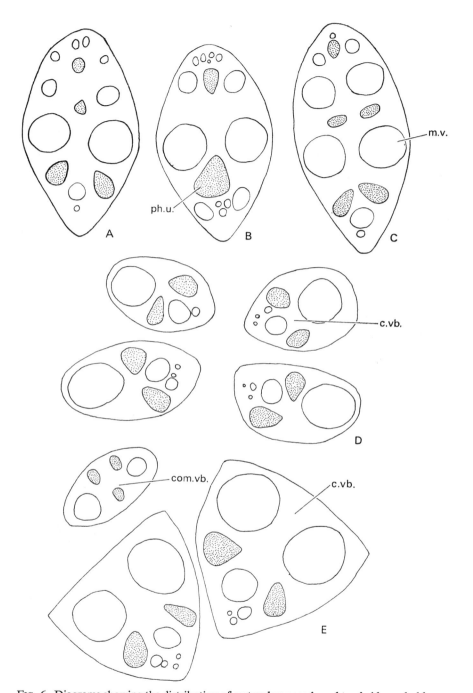

Fig. 6. Diagrams showing the distribution of metaxylem vessels and tracheids, and phloem strands in the cauline vascular bundles of stems (×40). A, *Dioscorea wattii*. B, *D. discolor*. C, *D. dumetorum*. D, *D. sansibarensis*. E, *D. macroura*.

Com.vb., common vascular bundle; c.vb., cauline vascular bundle; m.v., metaxylem vessel; ph.u., phloem unit.

A strikingly distinct arrangement is to be seen in many species where each phloem unit within the vascular bundle is encircled by 1–4 rows of sclerenchyma cells, generally consisting of fibres. Mason (1926) concluded that the distribution of sclerenchyma around the phloem units must result in a considerable measure of physiological isolation. Sclerenchyma sheaths have also been observed to encircle the vessels in some species, e.g. *D. trichantha* (Pl. VI. C).

Sometimes the entire vascular bundle is completely surrounded by sclerenchyma, e.g. in *Stenomeris*, *Avetra*, and some species of *Dioscorea*. In other species the vascular bundles are generally embedded in thick-walled parenchyma cells that are either cuboidal or rectangular as seen in longitudinal sections. Some of the rectangular parenchyma cells resemble fibres in that they are about 15 times longer than wide, but unlike most ordinary fibres they have square ends. Fibres with thick walls and tapered ends also occur in the Dioscoreales, but a large proportion of the fibres encountered in this order have square ends.

The width of the pith in the family shows a wide range of variation, which limits its taxonomic importance. Nevertheless, the 2 species of *Tamus*, for example, can be easily separated from each other because the pith of *T. communis* is very wide in relation to the total diameter of the stem while the pith of *T. edulis* is about one-third of the total diameter of the stem (Pl. XIV. D, E). The pith cells are sometimes filled with starch grains and tannin, e.g. *D. luzonensis* (Pl. XII. E). Occasionally sclerosed tyloses, resulting from various traumatic responses, occur in the vascular bundles and the pith parenchyma, e.g. in *D. samydea* (Fig. 13. E, F, p. 87; Pl. V. C) and *D. amazonum* (Pl. XI. D).

DEVELOPMENT OF PRIMARY VASCULAR ELEMENTS

Before considering the differentiation of the primary phloem and xylem in *Dioscorea*, it must be pointed out that our knowledge concerning procambial differentiation in monocotyledons is meagre when it is compared with the corresponding information available concerning the dicotyledons. The subject has been reviewed and discussed in detail by Esau (1965).

To understand the ontogeny of the vascular bundles in the Dioscoreaceae, serial transverse sections have been studied of 5 *Dioscorea* species—*D. alata*, *D. bulbifera*, *D. friedrichsthalii*, *D. opposita*, and *D. prazeri*.

The apical meristem of the shoot and the tissue immediately below it are relatively homogeneous with respect to cell size and general staining reaction of the cytoplasm. The meristematic cells are covered with a distinct layer of dermatogen. At this stage it is difficult to recognize the cells whose derivatives will become the future procambial strands.

At a slightly lower level below the stem apex the outline of the stem begins to appear pentagonal and at this stage it is easy to recognize the 5 procambial strands beneath the apical meristem when the ground meristem (future pith) becomes vacuolated and enlarged. At this point the homogeneity of the meristematic tissue is broken. The regions of the future vascular strands retain their 'true' meristematic characteristics much longer than the ground meristem.

When the procambial strands have become fully apparent, further periclinal and anticlinal divisions take place within them. As each procambial strand increases in size it assumes an elliptical shape in transverse section.

The first vascular tissue to differentiate is the protophloem. This appears towards the periphery of the procambial strand. At the same time, further periclinal divisions within the strand lead to a somewhat radial arrangement of the cells. A few micrometres below this level, the elements of the protoxylem appear on the same radius as the protophloem and orientated towards the inner boundary of the procambium.

This pattern of development of the primary vascular elements confirms earlier studies of other monocotyledons that have been described by Esau (1943, 1965). It is noteworthy that the radial arrangement of cells that occurs between the protophloem and the protoxylem is a result of the periclinal divisions of the meristematic cells, and the radially arranged cells are not derived from cambium as suggested for this family by Arber (1918, 1925).

When the protophloem and the protoxylem are nearly fully differentiated, 1 large metaxylem vessel appears almost midway between the protoxylem and protophloem. Almost at the same time another large metaxylem vessel appears adjacent to the first one. After the establishment of the second metaxylem vessel, either 1 or 2 phloem units appear. Although they have been studied only in mature tissue, such species as *D. sansibarensis* and *D. ternata* probably develop their 1 large metaxylem vessel at this stage.

It is well known that individual vascular strands of monocotyledons are nearly always collateral at first. Occasionally the strands become amphivasal when the xylem extends around and completely encloses the phloem. In most genera of the Dioscoreales, the mature vascular strands cannot be described simply as collateral, amphivasal, or amphicribral.

THE COURSE OF VASCULAR BUNDLES IN THE STEM

The nodal anatomy of the Dioscoreaceae cannot be understood unless we first make it clear that there are some very complex and peculiar assemblages of specialized vascular cells situated in the stems at the level of the nodes. These conglomerates of highly specialized vascular elements have been described in the literature as 'glomeruli'. Before proceeding further it is necessary to consider their structure in rather more detail.

We may take Mason's (1926) article as a convenient starting-point for this discussion. Mason's contribution was written when he was studying the rate of sugar transport in *Dioscorea alata*. Earlier, Falkenberg (1876) had referred to the glomerulus of the node as an 'imperfect knot' in his study of *D. villosa*. Mason noted that the phloem was of a markedly abnormal type. He further observed that the sieve-tubes of the successive internodes did not join with each other directly except through a glomerulus that was composed of a great number of oblong, thin-walled, distinctly nucleate parenchymatous cells running almost parallel with each other. Behnke (1965a) questioned the presence of nuclei in the glomerulus cells but present studies show that nuclei occur at certain stages in the ontogeny of these cells (Fig. 7. A).

In his study of the ontogeny of the stem of *Tamus communis*, Burkill (1949) disproved Mason's claim that glomeruli are absent from the nodes of *T. communis*. Present studies reveal that glomeruli are certainly present in the nodes of *Tamus* (Pl. III. C) but, although they cannot be easily overlooked, it should be emphasized that the glomeruli in this genus are not so pronounced as those in most species of *Dioscorea* (Pl. II. A–C; Pl. III. A, B).

A study by Happ (1950) on the nodes of Dioscoreaceae based on serial sections remains unpublished. The study is cited by Braun (1957), but has not been seen by the author.

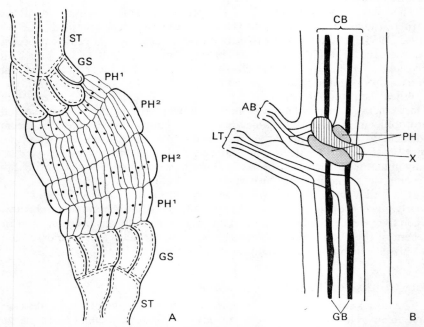

FIG. 7 (after Ayensu 1969). A, Schematic diagram of the phloem-glomerulus. B, Schematic representation of the stem showing the relationship and the position of the xylem- and phloem-glomeruli in the region of the leaf insertion.
AB, axillary bud. CB, cauline vascular bundles. GB, glomerulus bundles. GS, glomerulus sieve-tubes. LT, leaf trace. PH, phloem. PH₁, phloem-glomerulus cells (first-order). PH₂, phloem-glomerulus cells (second-order). ST, sieve tube. X, xylem.

Brouwer (1953) published his account of the arrangement of the vascular bundles in the nodes of Dioscoreaceae and presented a diagram of the elements of the node. Brouwer concluded that the sieve-tubes of two successive internodes were connected in the following sequence: sieve-tubes, 'funiculus cells', 'bast tubulus cells', glomerulus cells, 'bast tubulus cells', 'funiculus cells', and sieve-tubes. Brouwer, following Mason (1926), concluded that the phloem-glomerulus cells (*a*) were densely filled with cytoplasm; (*b*) had a persistent nucleus with nucleolus; and (*c*) lacked sieve-areas.

A comprehensive study of the nodal anatomy of *Dioscorea batatas* and *Tamus communis* was conducted by Braun (1957). He concluded that (*a*) the xylem-glomerulus consists of very numerous short tracheids of various sizes, the orientation of which is difficult to trace; (*b*) the phloem-glomerulus, which is divided into several partial glomeruli, is composed of a new type of translocatory cell, called phloem-glomerulus cells; and (*c*) the phloem-glomerulus cells possess thin walls without sieve-pores and without visible pitting; they are distinguished from parenchyma cells by their lack of starch. Behnke's (1965c) electron microscopic studies show that sieve-areas are, in fact, present in the phloem-glomerulus cells.

The present study, involving more species than were available to earlier investigators, essentially supports and extends their conclusions.

Xylem-glomerulus

Serial sections and macerations, made during the present study, reveal that the mature xylem-glomerulus is mainly composed of short tracheids of variable shape closely fitted together, thus resembling the individual parts of a jigsaw puzzle. These peculiar tracheids are confined to the node and have large bordered pits. In the internodes, water presumably moves freely from vessel element to vessel element through the scalariform perforation plates. Exactly how materials are translocated through the nodal region has not been seriously investigated.

The width of the glomerulus in the nodes is correlated with the phyllotaxy. In the species having simple, alternate leaves, a single glomerulus occupies about one-third of the area of the node. In an opposite (or decussate) arrangement, the glomerulus occupies about two-thirds of the nodal area. In species that exhibit a whorled arrangement, the glomerulus occupies almost the whole of the nodal area.

The glomerulus tracheids vary in width and length within a species. Widths varying from 40 to 110 μm, and lengths from 80 to 260 μm have been recorded for different species. These tracheids are closely fitted together, and have numerous pit-pairs on their common walls. The exact pathway of the contiguous tracheids between successive internodes is very complicated and variable within a species (Pls. II, III). Longitudinal sections and macerations of the node give a partial elucidation of the complicated sequence of the tissue structures. As Braun (1957) interpreted D. batatas and Tamus communis, a vessel just about to enter a node is attached to 1, 2, or 3 cells which Braun referred to as 'vessel-like tracheids'. The end wall of the vessel-like tracheid (VT) facing the vessel (V) has a reticulate perforation plate, while the other end wall has bordered pits (Fig. 8, A, B). The elements that constitute the bulk of the xylem-glomerulus lie between the vessel-like tracheids. The tracheids of the first group (T_1) are closely fitted to those of the second group (T_2) and to other successive tracheid groups, thus establishing the normal communication between them. The lengths of the tracheids vary from one node to another within a species. In this respect variation in tracheid length does not have any taxonomic value. Those of the first few groups (T_1–T_3) are shorter than those of T_4 and T_5. It has also been observed that the tracheid groups increase in number from T_1 to T_5. This presumably enlarges the water-conducting tissues and their capacity is increased still further by the complex arrangement of many xylem-glomeruli at a node. Each glomerulus is S-shaped and longitudinally orientated. A diagram of a theoretical unit of a xylem-glomerulus (Fig. 8. A) is presented for the sake of simplicity, but the full complexity of it is demonstrated by Plates II and III.

854376X   E

Phloem-glomerulus

The construction of the phloem-glomerulus (Fig. 7. A) follows essentially the scheme presented for the xylem-glomerulus (Fig. 8. A). The phloem-glomerulus is made up of what Braun (1957) named 'glomerulus sieve-tubes' (GS). Earlier, the same tissues had been called 'funiculus cells' by Brouwer (1953) and 'funnel-cells' by Mason (1926). Recently, Behnke (1965a) has called the same tissues 'connecting sieve-tubes'. Essentially, these tissues are

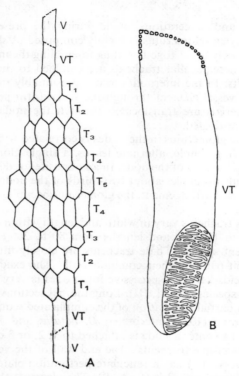

Fig. 8. (after Ayensu 1969). A, Schematic diagram illustrating the arrangement of the elements (T) of xylem-glomeruli in the nodal region of stems of *Dioscorea* and *Tamus*. V, vessel; VT, vessel-like tracheid. B, Vessel-like tracheid showing a reticulate perforation plate (lower) and bordered pits (upper).

composed of somewhat funnel-shaped, thin-walled cells having numerous small simple pits on the end walls adjoining the phloem-glomerulus cells (PH). They differ from ordinary sieve-tubes in having the sieve-plates restricted to the ends adjoining the sieve-tubes. The glomerulus sieve-tubes adjoin the cells that make up the bulk of the phloem-glomerulus. These cells were designated 'phloem-glomerulus cells' of the first (PH_1), second (PH_2), and third (PH_3) orders by Braun (1957). Cells similar to PH_1 and PH_2 respectively were previously termed 'bast tubulus cells' and 'glomerulus cells' and were later called 'nodal sieve-tubes' and 'nodal sieve-elements' by Behnke (1965a). The PH_3 of Braun may actually be the overlapping ends of PH_2 and PH_1.

The cells of PH_1 and PH_2 have thin walls (about 1 μm thick) with simple pits that can hardly be seen with a light microscope. Whether the walls are interconnected by cytoplasmic threads (plasmodesmata) or by any other means has not been demonstrated with the light microscope. Electron-microscope studies by Behnke (1965a, b, c) show that plasmodesmata are present in the cells of PH_1 and PH_2. It is certain, however, that these phloem cells are specialized and differ from sieve-tubes and sieve-cells of ordinary phloem tissue. Microchemical tests reveal the absence of starch grains from the phloem-glomerulus cells; the surrounding parenchyma cells possess starch. The histochemistry of the phloem will have to await critical studies.

DESCRIPTION OF VASCULAR BUNDLES IN THE STEM

The following description of the vascular bundles in the stem axis is based on the author's personal observations.

Cleared and stained portions of the tip of young stems reveal that at the node (Fig. 7. B) 3 major vascular bundles (LT) enter the stem from the petiole and run through the underlying internode as peripheral vascular bundles. These leaf-trace bundles are V-shaped.

The vascular bundles of the stem axis lying radially at the point of entry of the leaf-traces, and those of the inner and outer circles, become enlarged and unite to form xylem- and phloem-glomeruli (Fig. 7, X, PH). These glomeruli lie obliquely above each leaf insertion at the same level as the axillary bud (AB). Opposite the vascular bundles of the outer circle in the internode they lie near the outside of the stem and project into the base of the axillary bud or the lateral shoot. Five cauline vascular bundles leave a glomerulus and pass into the internode above (CB), but only 2 enter it from below (GB). The latter are the characteristic large vascular bundles which are arranged in the gaps between the 3 leaf-trace bundles, which lie on the inside of the stem furrows. Hence the 5 cauline vascular bundles forming the circle are made up of the 2 vascular bundles from the glomerulus (GB) and the 3 vascular bundles of the leaf-trace (LT).

The vascular bundles of the axillary buds are connected to the glomerulus directly. Just before they reach the glomerulus, each divides into an upper xylem branch and a lower phloem branch, which join the upper and lower regions of the glomerulus respectively. Occasionally the lower phloem branch subdivides into 2 with one establishing itself above the xylem branch.

The optical shuttle method (cf. Zimmermann and Tomlinson 1966) was used to film serial sections of 4 species of the Dioscoreaceae, *Dioscorea composita, D. friedrichsthalii, D. polygonoides,* and *Tamus communis.* With the aid of a data analyser projector the course of the vascular bundles of the mature stem was analysed frame by frame starting from an internode, through a node, to the next internode.

Dioscorea composita is used here to illustrate the pathways observed in the species mentioned above. (1) Starting from the base of an internode from the middle portion of the plant and proceeding upwards it can be seen that 8 common and 8 cauline vascular bundles maintain their characteristic appearance and shape (Pl. IX. E) until a position about 850 μm from the nodal region is reached. At this point there is a change in the 2, or in some special cases the 4 cauline vascular bundles facing towards the leaf insertion. Here the large phloem units on the inner side of the innermost pairs of metaxylem vessels begin to break down and anastomose. (2) At about 1·5 mm above our starting-point (1) the innermost protoxylem elements of the same cauline bundles begin to anastomose. (3) Immediately above the point where the xylem elements of the cauline bundles begin to anastomose the phloem elements from the 2 or 4 cauline bundles exhibit the typical appearance of a phloem-glomerulus. (4) Again passing upwards the next stage to be observed is the development of the xylem-glomerulus. (5) After passing through stages (3) and (4), the phloem units and the xylem elements of the common vascular bundles begin to amalgamate to form xylem- and phloem-glomeruli. (6) The large metaxylem vessels which, until now, have not become involved in the structural changes in the cauline vascular bundles, begin to lose their identity by merging into the xylem-glomerulus. (7) The more centrally located phloem-glomerulus passes out radially between the remnants of the 2 adjacent cauline bundles and joins the outer one of these towards the glomerulus of the common bundle organized in the same radial direction. (8) The phloem-glomeruli formed from the remaining common bundles that we have not yet considered pass towards the point at which the petiole is inserted. This takes place while the changes described in (7) are going on. (9) The xylem-glomerulus formed within the cauline bundles is formed slightly above the phloem-glomerulus described in (8), thus completing the breakdown and the incorporation of the large metaxylem vessels in the plexus. (10) The phloem units at the outer end of the cauline vascular bundles are unaffected by the processes of the anastomoses that take place in the node. Instead, the position of the phloem units is altered only slightly and this is due to the stresses set up as the xylem- and phloem-glomeruli pass outwards. (11) At about the stage when the outward passage of the glomeruli has been completed, the reorganization of the tissues on the inner side of the cauline bundles begins. This reorganization is rapidly followed by the return of the outer half of the cauline bundle into its original position. At this point the elliptical shape of the bundles observed in transverse sections of the internode is restored. (12) The reorganization of the common bundles follows the process described for (11). (13) At 12·48 mm above the node the reorganization is complete and the internodal structure with the usual 8 common and 8 cauline bundles is completely restored.

Although the number of bundles varies with species, and the alternation of common and cauline bundles is an established feature, it can be seen that 2 common bundles occasionally run side by side. This irregularity can be accounted for as follows. At the node 2 cauline bundles attached to the plexus occupy positions in the spaces on either side of the middle common bundle and the lateral common bundles. The ratio of two cauline and three common bundles is corrected a little down the stem by the elimination in the plexus of one of the lateral common bundles. Hence in the internode there are almost always 1 or more common bundles above those required to maintain its 1 to 1 ratio of common and cauline bundles. This irregularity is detected only in the internode because the common bundles never unite during their course in the internode. Likewise, the cauline bundles of some specimens of *Dioscorea macroura*, *D. preussii*, and *D. sansibarensis* sometimes split into 2 in such a way that all the vascular elements above the pair of innermost metaxylem vessels form a separate unit radially above it.

Discussion

The structure of the xylem- and phloem-glomeruli in the nodes of the Dioscoreaceae seems to be unique among the monocotyledons. Further-more, the presence of tracheids and the distinct type of sieve elements in the node have considerable implications regarding the evolutionary history of these tissues in the angiosperms.

The anatomical studies of the xylem by Bailey and Tupper (1918) showed that the most logical phylogenetic sequence is the derivation of vessels from tracheids in the angiosperms. Cheadle (1943a, b), working with the xylem of monocotyledons, confirmed Bailey's work. In the light of this theory it is interesting to draw attention to the essentially primitive tracheal elements in the node of the Dioscoreaceae. The bulk of the xylem-glomerulus is made up of tracheids, which are considered primitive in the phylogenetic sense. Similarly, the cells of the phloem-glomerulus are considered to be of a rela-tively primitive type (cf. Braun 1957, and the papers he quotes).

It is important to note that the structure of the node is less specialized than that of the internode as this has a bearing on the views of Bailey (1956), who wrote as follows: 'It is now clearly demonstrated that evo-lutionary modification of the xylem of stems and roots is *not necessarily* closely synchronized with phylogenetic trends in the specialization of the angiospermic flower. Either trend of evolution may be accelerated or retarded in relation to the other.' This can be extended by saying that vessel develop-ment in an individual part of an organ can be delayed or advanced within that particular part as demonstrated in the node and internode of the Dio-scoreaceae respectively.

This study shows that in the midst of the complex nodal vascular system lies an orderly and systematic mechanism that permits the transport of assimilatory materials through the stems of the Dioscoreaceae as outlined under the course of vascular bundles in the stem (p. 47).

The complexity of the phloem-glomerulus in the Dioscoreaceae raises some fundamental questions about the current hypotheses on transport mechanisms in plants. Esau, Currier, and Cheadle (1957) summarized the hypotheses as (*a*) mass or pressure flow; (*b*) mass flow together with activities of paren-chyma cells associated with the phloem which account for the turgor gradients necessary for mass flow; (*c*) transport of solutes in the sieve-tube along proto-plasmic interfaces; (*d*) accelerated solute movements in sieve-tubes resulting apparently from some special kind of cytoplasmic movement or flow; (*e*) independent solute movement resulting from one or more as yet unknown active transfer processes that occur in the sieve-element cytoplasm.

The unique anatomical characteristics of the phloem-glomerulus in this family seem to suggest that perhaps more than one of the above methods is responsible for the movement of assimilatory substances in the Dioscoreaceae. Arisz's (1952) suggestion that every substance moves its own way, and that different mechanisms may be involved in translocation, should be considered in the light of the anatomical variation in the phloem of this family.

7. BULBIL, TUBER, AND RHIZOME

GENERAL MORPHOLOGY

THE chief aerial storage organ of the Dioscoreaceae is the bulbil. The morphological nature of bulbils has been much discussed. Dale (1901) and Goebel (1905) argue that the bulbil and the tuber are morphologically identical, and that the bulbil should be considered as an arrested condition of the tuber. Burkill (1960) defined the bulbil as a branch of the aerial stem, and this I wholly support. Its main function is that of dispersal. Of the 3 buds that generally appear in the leaf axils of the bulbil-bearing Dioscoreas, usually 1 becomes a bulbil. In *Dioscorea alata* 2 buds sometimes become bulbils and these may coalesce at the base. It has also been observed that rarely and under extremely moist conditions, bulbils consist partly of tissues having the morphological characteristics of roots. In his study of *Ranunculus ficaria*, Metcalfe (1938) demonstrated that bulbils (axillary tubercles) sometimes exhibit a mixture of root and stem characteristics. Burkill, who studied *D. bulbifera* in nature, reported that this species is usually bulbiliferous, but that bulbils are much more abundant on some specimens than on others. At the same time this species lacks a storage tuber.

There is a marked difference in bulbil shape between the African and Asiatic species of *Dioscorea*. The African species generally have rounded bulbils while those of the Asiatic species become more angular as they grow larger. Varieties of some Asiatic species exhibit elongated, narrow bulbils.

The tuber and the rhizome are common features of the Dioscoreaceae, but the terminology of what constitutes a tuber or a rhizome has been much confused. In order to clarify this position, Burkill (1960) restricted the term rhizome to organs that are thick, horizontal, and cauline. If one used the term in this sense, he pointed out that the underground stem of *Paris quadrifolia* is not a rhizome but a stolon because it lacks thickness. The underground stem of *Aspidistra*, however, is a rhizome because it has all three features. Both *Paris* (Trilliaceae of Hutchinson) and *Aspidistra* belong to the subfamily Asparagoideae, but the tribe Aspidistreae has characters that seem to be allied to such species of *Dioscorea* as *D. nipponica*.

Discussing the growth habits of monocotyledons, Holttum (1955) pointed out that the underground storage organs of *Dioscorea* exhibit morphological complexities and a peculiar mode of development that is not obviously of the basic sympodial monocotyledon pattern. Nevertheless, he found that rhizomatous species of *Dioscorea* exhibit growth patterns that most closely resemble those of other monocotyledons.

Large tubers of *Dioscorea* were not available for the present study, but Raghavan's (1960) morphological studies of Indian Dioscoreas reveal that tubers exhibit a great variety of growth habit and morphology. *D. deltoidea* grows horizontally, lying near the surface of the soil; *D. hispida* has lobed tubers; *D. tomentosa* and *D. pentaphylla* have branching tubers 1–2 m long, deeply buried in the soil. Some varieties of *D. pentaphylla* (e.g. var. *communis*

Prain and Burk.) have large tubers, not elongated, covered with dead roots. In the section Enantiophyllum, such species as *D. alata, D. belophylla, D. hamiltonii, D. oppositifolia, D. puber*, and *D. wallichii* have tubers ranging from 1 to 3 m long which are generally deeply buried.

Tubers from both leaf cuttings and seedlings appear to develop in the same way, as shown by Martin and Ortiz (1963). In both kinds undifferentiated tissue is produced first and is the main source of tubers, adventitious roots, and shoots. Burkill's (1937) developmental study of the tubers of *D. sansibarensis* demonstrated a similar type of growth to that described by Martin and Ortiz (1963).

The various interpretations of the mode of origin of the storage organs of the Dioscoreaceae cannot be fully understood without comparative studies of living plants.

GENERAL ANATOMY

Bulbil

Despite the differences in size and sometimes in shape, the anatomy of the bulbil resembles that of the tuber. The epidermis is 1-layered but in mature bulbils it is generally replaced by cork. Subjacent to the epidermis or the corky layer is the cortical region of 8–15 layers, the cells of which are variable in shape, and they turn brownish when mature. A 5–8-layered zone of meristematic cells, which become suberized in mature bulbils, separates the cortex from the ground parenchyma. The outer portion of the ground tissue contains very few starch grains but exhibits numerous idioblasts containing raphide bundles, and tannin cells. Towards the central portion of the ground tissue, raphide bundles and tannin cells are less numerous but the number and size of starch grains increase. The cells of the central ground parenchyma are larger than those of the outer region. Vascular bundles are collateral, distributed irregularly in the outer portion of the ground tissue near the meristematic zone.

As already pointed out (p. 54), the morphological nature of the bulbil has been in dispute. Dale (1901) concluded after her investigation of *Dioscorea sativa* that the bulbil and the tuber are morphologically identical. Goebel (1905) also supported this view by pointing out that the bulbil is an arrested condition of the tuber. Burkill (1960) disagreed with Dale and Goebel. He regarded the tuber as being morphologically equivalent to either the whole or a part of the hypocotyl after it has become swollen. The bulbil, on the other hand, is interpreted as a whole branch that fails to become elongated. On this shortened branch the leaves are not laid down in an orderly sequence and the vascular bundles, like those in a tuber, pursue an irregular course.

The present study shows that the bulbil and the tuber are quite similar. Whether their modes of origin and development are identical is outside the scope of the present study.

Tuber (see also Root, p. 58)

In most previous anatomical studies of the vegetative organs of the Dioscoreaceae the tuber has often been neglected although this organ is undoubtedly the most economically important part of the plant. Efforts to rectify this situation are reflected in the studies by Martin and Ortiz (1963). These investigators studied young tubers of *Dioscorea floribunda* and *D. spiculiflora*, and made the following observations. (1) The cells below the epidermis of the initial bulge of the hypocotyl (i.e. that part of the hypocotyl destined to develop into the tuber) give rise to the first cork. (2) The central core of storage parenchyma of the tuber contains irregularly arranged vascular bundles. (3) Towards the periphery there is a prominent cortex of uniform thickness containing a well-defined cambium-like layer ('cambium'). (4) The cells arising from this 'cambium' are compactly arranged in rows and radiate outwards. (5) The cells at the periphery of the 'cambium' are eventually suberized and become 'storied cork' such as is seen in some genera of the Agavaceae. They noted also that with further development of the tuber the storied cork was isolated from the living cells and ceased activity. In conclusion, they pointed out that all further growth of the tuber may be considered as resulting from continued activity of the 'cambium', which in itself is an extension and specialization of the primary thickening meristem.

The occurrence of cork in the tubers of some species of the Dioscoreaceae had earlier been reported by von Mohl (1845), de Bary (1884), Kny (1886), Cordemoy (1893), and Goebel (1905). These investigators also determined that cambium and secondary thickening appear in tubers of some species of *Dioscorea*, *Tamus*, and *Testudinaria*.

In order to distinguish tubers of the Dioscoreaceae that have cambium from those in which there is none, de Bary (1884) divided the species of this family into three categories. Each of these is characterized by one of the following sets of swollen storage organs: (1) tuberous swollen roots as in *Dioscorea batatas*; (2) rhizomes with scaly leaves, and composed of many internodes, as in *D. villosa*; (3) leafless tubers, resulting from the swelling of the first epicotyledonary internode of the seedling, as in *Tamus communis*, *Testudinaria*, and many species of *Dioscorea*. Of these three categories de Bary pointed out that only the tubers of category (3) have a cambium and secondary thickening.

Tubers of *Dioscorea* and *Tamus* that were available for the present study showed a striking uniformity in their general anatomy. The epidermal cells are not easily identifiable in either T.S. or L.S. The first cork of primary origin is composed of loosely and irregularly arranged cells. In some species, e.g. *D. luzonensis*, the cells are suberized. The cambium produces storied cork which is composed of tightly compressed suberized cells in radial rows. The cork cells are 4–6-layered in some species, e.g. *D. cochleari-apiculata*, but they are many-layered in others, e.g. *D. schimperiana*.

The cortex consists of large, often rounded or somewhat oval-shaped parenchyma cells separated by intercellular spaces. Occasionally, the cortical cells are storied and many-layered as demonstrated in *D. luzonensis*. The cortex generally becomes compressed with age. No endodermis is clearly distinguishable, but the innermost cortical cells are often devoid of starch.

The inner ground tissue is composed of either thin- or thick-walled parenchyma cells which are filled with starch grains. The cells lose their radial arrangement towards the centre of the tuber.

Collateral vascular bundles are sporadically distributed throughout the inner ground tissue. The xylem consists of wide tracheids having numerous bordered pits and associated parenchyma. The phloem consists of sieve-tubes, companion cells, and phloem parenchyma. Of all the species investigated vessels were found only in *D. luzonensis*.

The parenchyma cells surrounding the vascular bundles show the greatest concentration of starch grains, which are relatively infrequent structures in the cortex. Tannin and raphide bundles often occur in both the inner and outer parenchyma cells.

Rhizome

The development of rhizomes in the Dioscoreaceae is limited to a few species. This is borne out by the taxonomic accounts of the family by Knuth (1924) and Burkill (1960). Materials from *Dioscorea caucasica* and *Rajania cordata* were examined in the present study.

The epidermis is composed of thick-walled cuboidal cells, compactly arranged, and with cytoplasmic contents. Hairs are often to be seen on the epidermis of *R. cordata*. Subjacent to the epidermis are 3–4 layers of cells constituting the outer cortex. These cells are also compactly arranged and contain cytoplasm. In mature specimens the outer cortex is suberized and the cell walls much thickened. The inner cortical cells, 6–12-layered, are of variable size, but those of *D. caucasica* are fairly uniform. An endodermoid layer separates the cortex from the vascular cylinder. This layer is replaced by sclerenchyma represented by 2–3 layers of fibres in *D. caucasica*.

Numerous starch grains of variable size and shape fill the parenchyma cells surrounding the vascular bundles. Idioblasts containing raphide bundles occur in the cortex and pith of *R. cordata*, but were not seen in *D. caucasica*. Tannin cells are present, but seem to be restricted principally to the cortex.

8. THE ROOT

GENERAL MORPHOLOGY (see also Tuber, p. 55)

BECAUSE of the difficulties of obtaining ample material of underground organs, very little root material was available for detailed morphological studies. Our limited knowledge of the behaviour of living roots has been furnished by Burkill (1960). The Dioscoreaceae possess two kinds of roots—long exploring roots, most of them spreading horizontally in the top soil, and rootlets that are mainly short-lived. In the section Paramecocarpa the short roots are lignified internally, thus sloughing off the cortex. Thorns are developed on these roots and are said to help to protect the tuber. In the sections Combilium and Enantiophyllum the lateral roots of some species are also converted into protective thorns. Perhaps the most notable species with spine-bearing roots is *Dioscorea praehensilis*. Coursey (1967) has recently stated that yams, on the whole, have comparatively weak rooting systems.

The morphological relationship between the root and the tuber is not clearly understood. Queva (1894c) came to the conclusion that the tubers of *D. illustrata* and *D. discolor* had lost the morphological nature of roots. He based his opinion on the fact that numerous vascular bundles are scattered in the tubers. He further explained that when a tuber forms at the extremity of a root, as in *D. illustrata*, the multipolar bundle of the root enlarges greatly and is then continued as a large number of vascular strands. These strands gradually acquire the structure of unipolar bundles radially orientated, with xylem on the inside and phloem on the outside. The apex conserves its structure, and the transformation goes no further. This presents the appearance of a morphologically defined organ, a root of which the apical meristem enlarges without changing its basic appearance, but produces an organ of different morphological nature. On the basis of developmental studies, Goebel (1905) took the view that the tubers of Dioscoreaceae (including those arising from roots) stood morphologically midway between stem and root. Lindinger (1907) considered this opinion unsound, by arguing that tubers formed by *D. batatas* are not morphologically equivalent to the tubers of *D. discolor*; whereas the former could be called 'stems', he saw no justification for denying the tuber of *D. discolor* its morphological value of root. He pointed out further that tubers of *D. discolor*, *D. eburnea*, and *D. illustrata* consist of two physiologically distinct regions, one being cylindrical, with the structure of an absorbing root, and the other consisting of the apex of the former, which is developed as a tuberous storage organ. The anatomical differences between the two regions can be attributed to the change in function.

GENERAL ANATOMY

Like that of the tuber, the anatomy of the root has received relatively little attention. Morot (1882) described the occurrence of vessels in roots of *Dioscorea*. Siedler (1892) drew attention to the distinctive 1-layered hypodermis of *D. bonariensis*. Scott's (1897) study of the spinous roots of *D.*

praehensilis and *D. spinosa* showed that the spines contain no vascular elements, which indicates that they are merely outgrowths from the external tissues of the root. A more elaborate study of *D. praehensilis* was undertaken by Hill and Freeman (1903), who concluded that there was no definite calyptrogen layer such as had been credited to the Dioscoreaceae by Bucherer (1889). They indicated that the number of xylem and phloem poles is quite high, 30 being not uncommon in *D. praehensilis*, that sieve-areas occur on the lateral walls of the larger sieve-tubes, and that a well-marked endodermis is present at the innermost limit of the cortex. They observed also that the first portions of the vascular strands to thicken are the regions immediately external to the phloem groups. It was found that the external regions of the phloem groups were encased by arcs of fibres. Hill and Freeman also examined roots of *Tamus communis* and concluded that lignification is general and that regions external to the phloem groups do not stand out as the first to be markedly lignified. Blunden, Hardman, and Trease (1963) presented a detailed description of the root as part of their anatomical studies of *D. belizensis*.

Present studies of roots of about 2 mm diameter reveal that the piliferous layer is composed of irregular cells, mostly somewhat rectangular in shape as viewed in T.S. but elongated longitudinally. Root-hairs are generally present but, owing to their fragile nature, they break down quite easily in mature roots. The exodermis consists of 1 layer of thick-walled compactly arranged cells. In mature roots the cells have suberized walls.

Subjacent to the exodermis is the cortex, which constitutes between half and two-thirds of the root diameter. The cells of the cortex are of irregular size with intercellular spaces. In mature roots the cell walls are thin and slightly lignified. Large simple pits occur in the cell walls. The innermost cortical cells are much smaller than those towards the periphery.

The endodermis is 1-layered, composed of longitudinally elongated cells with characteristic U-shaped thickenings on the inner and radial walls, and simple pits. In some species, e.g. *D. ceratandra*, *D. cochleari-apiculata*, and *D. polygonoides*, the cell walls of the endodermis are slightly thickened on all surfaces.

The pericycle varies between 2 and 4 layers. The fibrous cells are strongly lignified in mature specimens and have simple-pitted walls. Occasionally, the inner layer is interrupted by tracheary elements.

The stele is variable: 6-arch in *D. caucasica*, 7-arch in *Tamus*, 8-arch in *D. ceratandra*, 12-arch in *D. alata*, 18-arch in *D. cochleari-apiculata*, 20-arch in *D. schimperiana*, and 32-arch in *D. luzonensis*. The xylem consists mainly of vessels and associated parenchyma. The large vessels are situated towards the centre of the root. The phloem is composed of sieve-tubes, companion cells, and phloem parenchyma. Each phloem unit is partly or almost wholly surrounded by fibres.

The pith consists of thick-walled, often lignified cells with simple pits. The pith region generally constitutes about one-third of the central cylinder. Tannin often occurs sporadically in some of the pith cells. Raphide bundles are also present in the cortex and pith parenchyma.

9. CONDUCTING ELEMENTS

In order to gain a full appreciation of the histology of the vascular tissues of the Dioscoreales, the vegetative organs were macerated by the procedure outlined in Chapter 3 (p. 16). The observations were first made on unstained materials mounted in glycerine and later confirmed by studies of stained permanent preparations.

Xylem Elements

Since the occurrence and distribution of vessels and tracheids are of phylogenetic interest, special attention was paid to ensuring their correct morphological interpretation. Vessels in the Dioscoreaceae are generally wide with long scalariform end plates, but within an individual species some vessels exhibit end walls with reticulate perforation plates (Pl. IV. A).

In a broad survey of certain trends of vessel specialization in the mono-cotyledons, Cheadle (1943a) described the end wall of a vessel as 'transverse' when it lies at right angles to the length of the vessel element, as 'slightly oblique' when it is not more than twice as long as the diameter of the vessel element, as 'oblique' when it is 2–5 times the diameter of the vessel element, and as 'very oblique' when the end wall is more than 5 times the diameter of the vessel element. In the present investigation all the vessel perforations in the Dioscoreales are found to be oblique. (For the corresponding classification of sieve-tube members see p. 61.)

Pitting is mostly alternate, and the pit apertures are generally elliptical and tend to be limited by the border. The protoxylem elements are made up essentially of tracheids with secondary thickenings consisting mainly of helically wound bands and very oblique imperforate end walls.

In a survey of the occurrence and types of vessels in various organs of the monocotyledons, Cheadle (1942) divided the families that he studied into the following four categories: (1) families whose members have no vessels and little or no thickening of the xylem elements; (2) families whose members have vessels restricted to the roots; (3) families that have both (a) some members with vessels only in the roots and (b) some members with vessels in the roots and also in some other organs of the plant; (4) families with vessels throughout the plant. Cheadle included the Dioscoreaceae in the fourth of these categories. The present studies do not fully support Cheadle's conclusion, for vessels were observed in roots, stems, and petioles of all the species. They are absent from the lamina, bulbils, and tubers except in *Dioscorea luzonensis*, where at least a few vessels were observed in the tuber. Cheadle showed that he was aware that his conclusion might not be of universal application when he stated that 'It is perhaps unjustifiable to place this family (Dioscoreaceae) among those which have vessels throughout the plant, for only aerial stems were available for study'. Cheadle's study was based on 3 species of *Dioscorea*. The present study indicates that the Dioscoreaceae should be placed in category (3) rather than (4).

The tracheids in the tubers were seen mostly to have wall thickenings varying from scalariform to reticulate, but in the same species, tracheids with pitted walls were also observed. The end walls of the tracheids generally vary from 'slightly oblique' to 'oblique'.

In a detailed study of vessel members in stems of *D. alata*, Shah, Unni-krishnan, and Poulose (1967) made diagrammatic representations of the variation in size and shape of these elements. They also studied the nature, number, inclination, and distribution of perforation plates of the vessels. Earlier, Shah *et al.* (1966) studied vessel member length–diameter and perforation plate–vessel member length relation in the same species. It should be pointed out that these findings are by no means confined to *D. alata*. Present investigations show that the variation patterns of vessel elements described by Shah *et al.* (1967) occur in all the species of Dioscoreaceae, Stenomeridaceae, and *Avetra* (Trichopodaceae).

The phylogenetic sequence of vessel development in different organs of a monocotyledonous plant has also been discussed by Cheadle (1942, 1944). He concluded that vessels appear first in the roots, then in the stem, and lastly in the leaves. He also noted that in *Dracaena* and *Cordyline* some species have vessels in the roots and leaves but not in the stems. Likewise, the author (Ayensu 1968*b*) observed a similar condition in the Velloziaceae. It is interest-ing to find that a somewhat similar situation obtains in the Dioscoreaceae where vessels occur in roots and stems but not in bulbils, tubers, and rhi-zomes.

PHLOEM ELEMENTS

The phloem of the Dioscoreales consists of large sieve-tubes, companion cells, and phloem parenchyma. The sieve-tube members have very oblique end walls with highly complex compound sieve-plates and numerous sieve-areas (Pl. IV. B). In classifying the various positions of the end wall as it meets the side walls of a sieve-tube member in the monocotyledons as a whole, Cheadle and Whitford (1941) recognized the following categories, which closely resemble, although they differ slightly from, the corresponding classes for vessel elements (see p. 60): (1) 'transverse' if the end wall is at right angles to the side wall; (2) 'slightly oblique' if the length of the end wall is greater than but not more than twice the diameter of the sieve-tube member; (3) 'oblique' if the end wall is 2 to 5 times the diameter of the tube; (4) 'very oblique' when the end wall is more than 5 times the diameter of the sieve-tube member.

When the results of the present investigation of the Dioscoreales are con-sidered in relation to Cheadle and Whitford's data for the monocotyledons which they surveyed, it can be noted that the sieve elements of the Dio-scoreales all fall into category (4).

The compound sieve-plates of the Dioscoreales were studied in detail during the present investigation and it was found that there are connecting strands between adjacent cells, although they are locally indistinct. The strands are surrounded by clear areas representing the callus cylinders. The sieve-areas on the side walls of the sieve-tube members have smaller callus cylinders than those of the sieve-plates.

The companion cells are shorter than the sieve-tube members with densely stained cytoplasmic contents. The phloem parenchyma cells between the companion cells and the sieve-tubes are thin-walled and densely pitted and they resemble in many respects the parenchyma of the ground tissue.

10. TRICHOMES

MORPHOLOGICAL comparison of trichomes in a fairly natural taxon such as the Dioscoreales helps to define lesser taxa within the order. Staudermann (1924) has already demonstrated that trichomes can provide useful taxonomic characters in the monocotyledons. This has been confirmed in other volumes of the *Anatomy of the monocotyledons* and Metcalfe (1963), in drawing attention to the importance of trichome studies, pointed out that on the whole these dermal appendages are less common in monocotyledons than in dicotyledons. Among the monocotyledons, this limits their taxonomic usefulness to families in which they occur. Metcalfe illustrated his observations by studies of hair structure in grasses, palms, and sedges.

Two types of trichomes, which are glandular and non-glandular respectively, occur in the Dioscoreales. In the present study the term 'glandular trichomes' is used with reference to epidermal or subepidermal appendages that exhibit either a unicellular stalk with a bicellular to multicellular head, or internal glands. Non-glandular trichomes (hairs) are tubular or branched epidermal appendages, which may be either unicellular or multicellular.

GLANDS

Five types of glandular trichomes have been observed in the Dioscoreales: (1) multicellular glands each consisting of a unicellular stalk and a bulb-like head divided by anticlinal and periclinal walls (Fig. 5. A, p. 40); (2) bicellular glands similar to (1) but having elliptical heads divided longitudinally into two (Fig. 5. B); (3) multicellular glands similar to (1) but having crescentiform heads with anticlinal partitions only (Fig. 5. C); (4) extra-floral nectaries or honey-glands which are embedded in the parenchyma of aerial vegetative organs such as leaves, petioles, and stems; (5) a peculiar kind of acuminate gland deeply embedded in the mesophyll of the leaf tip; it is confined to the section Opsophyton of *Dioscorea*.

The occurrence and distribution of the various types of glands are as follows. Type (1) is present in most genera of the tribe Dioscoreae; (2) is confined to the genus *Stenomeris* of the Stenomeridaceae; (3) is restricted to *Trichopus* which belongs to the Trichopodaceae; (4) occurs in some species of *Dioscorea*. The very interesting and peculiar acuminate glands of type (5) merit special discussion. Orr (1923) recognized this distinctive form of gland in *Dioscorea macroura* and made an extensive study of its anatomy and histology. In the present study this same specialized type of acumen has been demonstrated in *D. sansibarensis*. Orr observed that the mucilaginous secretion that fills the lumina of these glands harbours a species of bacterium. It is believed that the constant association of a bacterium with the secretory glands of the 2 species may have some physiological significance.

The glands appear in transverse section as 2 dark, kidney-shaped areas (Pl. IV. C). They are embedded in the mesophyll, and their cell walls are irregular in outline because of the infolding of the wall-layers. Each gland is connected to the surface of the acumen by way of longitudinal slits. The epithelium of these slits is endodermoid in nature and possesses a heavily cuticularized outer layer.

The roof of the gland cavity is formed as a result of the shifting of the epithelial layers of the slits. As was observed by Orr, the epithelial layer is continued downwards to form the curved floor of the crypt, from which the secretory tissue of the gland is developed. Underlying the cutinized epithelium there are 2–3 layers of smaller, thin-walled cells, which form a compact sheath partially enclosing the gland and separating it from the mesophyll.

The secretory tissue of the gland consists of a large number of vermiform, filamentous outgrowths, each developing from one epithelial cell. In the mature glands these filamentous outgrowths consist of longitudinally elongated cells which are almost circular in transverse section. The cells have thin walls but the basal cell of each filament shows some cuticularization in its lateral walls. Nuclei of the filamentous cells are quite prominent.

The mode of development and other points of physiological interest have been described by Orr (1923).

HAIRS

Non-glandular hairs are restricted to a few species within the order and take a variety of forms. In the genus *Dioscorea* most species of sections Trigonobasis, Macropoda, Cryptantha, and Eustenophora have unicellular hairs occurring mainly on the abaxial surfaces of the leaves and concentrated along the primary and secondary veins. The hairs are less numerous on petioles and stems. Some species of the genus *Rajania* possess unicellular hairs.

T-shaped hairs (the arms of the T being about 5 to 8 times as long as the stalk) are particularly characteristic of the sections Combilium and Macrocarpaea. Stellate hairs are confined to sections Asterotricha and Syntepaleia. Stiletto hairs, which have been reported by Burkill (1960) for some species of the section Enantiophyllum, were not observed in the species examined.

Hairs generally occur in the tribe Dioscoreae except in *Tamus*, but their absence is conspicuous in the Stenomeridaceae.

11. CELL INCLUSIONS
(ERGASTIC SUBSTANCES)

STARCH

PERHAPS the most important cellular content of the Dioscoreales is starch. The genus *Dioscorea* is the most valuable source of commercial starch obtained from this order. The grains exhibit a variety of size and form. Most grains measure between 15 and 70 μm in length and are 10 to 45 μm across. They are generally simple, always isolated and flattened. In outline they are pear-shaped, elliptical, or somewhat rounded. Occasionally rod-shaped grains are to be observed. The broad end of most pear-shaped grains is truncated, but the grains taper to rather indistinct points at the opposite ends. The hilum is usually near the narrow end and it is seldom encountered in the centre of the grain. When the starch grains are studied under a phase-contrast microscope the eccentricity of the hilum is clearly demonstrated. Similarly, the eccentric rings are quite distinct under phase. Polarized light was also used to confirm the position of the hilum since the dark areas that appear on the grains with crossed Nicol prisms intersect at that point.

The grains do not form aggregates, but in the tuber they may either be concentrated around the vascular bundles or be evenly distributed in the ground parenchyma.

The possible taxonomic usefulness of variations in the size and shape of the starch grains has been suggested by Rao and Beri (1952, 1955). These investigators have shown that in *D. sativa* and *D. anguina*, 95 per cent of the grains are triangular, with a few that are oval, while in *D. alata* 80 per cent of the grains are oval, the rest being triangular. They likewise found the grains of *D. hispida* to be oval, while those of *D. bulbifera* are triangular. Rao and Beri concluded that the above features may offer an easy method of distinguishing the species they investigated. Comprehensive reviews of *Dioscorea* starches have been published by Seidemann (1964), Holló (1964), Greenwood-Barton (1961), and Miège (1948, 1957). A study of the starch of *D. alata* and *D. batatas* was earlier conducted by Decrock (1908).

CRYSTALS

Crystals of the four following kinds occur in the Dioscoreales: (*a*) raphides, (*b*) rectangular crystals, (*c*) cuboidal crystals, and (*d*) styloids. The commonest type is the raphide bundle; each of these is usually embedded in an idioblast containing mucilaginous substances.

Raphide bundles are to be found in the mesophyll of leaves, in the cortex and pith parenchyma of petioles, stems, and roots, and in the ground parenchyma of bulbils and tubers. They are usually more abundant in leaves and bulbils than in other vegetative organs. (Fig. 5.H, p. 40.)

Rectangular and cuboidal crystals have been observed in the leaves of some species of *Dioscorea*. These crystals have proved to be particularly useful

in section Opsophyton, where cuboidal crystals are restricted to the leaf of
D. macroura and rectangular crystals to the leaf of *D. sansibarensis*.

The presence of styloids in the Dioscoreales is very limited. Of all the
species investigated styloids have been observed only in *D. tomentosa*,
Stemona curtisii, and *S. kerrii*.

TANNIN (Fig. 5.K, p. 40)

The presence of tannin has been recorded in many vegetative organs of the
Dioscoreales (see Table 3 and the descriptions of the anatomy of the genera).
The tanniniferous cells show a wide range of form and size within a species.
Tannin occurring in the palisade tissue, for example, generally assumes the
elongated shape of the cells, while that of the spongy tissue exhibits either
cylindrical, cuboidal, or shapes resembling the pieces of a jigsaw puzzle. In
unstained preparations mounted in glycerine the tannin secretions appear
either as a solid mass, as granules, or as rounded particles in either ground
parenchymatous cells or idioblasts.

The distribution of tannin in many species of the order does not easily
lend itself to systematic treatment. However, within the subgenus *Testudinaria*
of *Dioscorea* the presence of the jigsaw puzzle type should not be overlooked.
The presence of a similar type of tanniniferous cells in unrelated sections within *Dioscorea* reduces its taxonomic significance.

12. GENERAL TAXONOMIC CONCLUSIONS BASED ON ANATOMICAL EVIDENCE

THE anatomical analysis of the vegetative organs of the Dioscoreales has revealed the need for numerous alterations in taxonomic concepts. The most important of these include the exclusion of *Trichopus* from the family, as indicated in a recent paper (Ayensu 1966), and the transfer of *Petermannia* to the family Liliaceae (Tomlinson and Ayensu 1969). As pointed out in the Taxonomic Review (pp. 6–13), *Trichopus* had always presented a problem to the taxonomist on the question of its assignment. Within the family Dioscoreaceae the two tribes recognized by Knuth (1924, 1930)—Dioscoreae and Stenomerideae—appear unnatural, on the basis of their anatomy not being easily distinguishable by any constant feature or combination of features.

Certain anatomical and histological features relating to the present study appear to be of greater value than others when utilized in drawing conclusions for systematic purposes. Some salient anatomical characters are outlined in Table 4 (p. 42). Initially, the sections of the genus *Dioscorea* can be divided into two major groups: (A) sections having one major phloem unit on the inner side of the innermost pair of large metaxylem vessels in the stem, and (B) sections having two major phloem units in the corresponding position. These groups are listed in Table 5.

Furthermore, if the characters outlined in Table 3 (p.31) are combined with those in Table 4, even more regrouping of Knuth's sections (Table 5) could be suggested. The subsections of section Opsophyton are quite distinct anatomically and therefore merit special comments.

TABLE 5
Grouping of sections of Dioscorea (*after Knuth 1924*)

Group A Sections with one major phloem unit	Group B Sections with two major phloem units
Dematostemon	Brachyandra
Sphaerantha	Chondrocarpa
Opsophyton	Opsophyton
(Subsection Isocantha)	(Subsections Macrourae and Euopsophyton)
Trigonobasis	
Apodostemon	Stenocarpa
Macropoda	Lasiophyton
Heterostemon	Trieuphorostemon
Oxypetalum	Botryosicyos
Brachystigma	Macrogynodium
Lychnostemon	Combilium
Cryptantha	Macrocarpaea
Sarcantha	Asterotricha
Lasiogyne	Enantiophyllum
Orientali-asiaticae	Syntepaleia
Eustenophora	Stenocorea

(1) Subsection Isocantha belongs to Group A, while subsections Macrourae and Euopsophyton come under Group B. (2) Euopsophyton can be separated from Macrourae because the former exhibits a distinctive distribution of brachysclereids around the vascular cylinder of both the petiole and the stem, and also because it has 3 pairs of large metaxylem vessels within each cauline vascular bundle of the stem. It is therefore suggested that Euopsophyton be elevated to sectional rank. (3) The subsection Macrourae should likewise be elevated to sectional rank because of the unique arrangement of the metaxylem vessels in the stem and the presence of distinctive acuminate leaves. The 2 species of the subsection Macrourae, *Dioscorea macroura* and *D. sansibarensis*, can be distinguished anatomically. Transverse sections of the stem of *D. macroura* show that each of the main cauline vascular bundles has two metaxylem vessels together with 2 phloem units. On the other hand, only 1 large metaxylem vessel occurs in each of the main cauline bundles of *D. sansibarensis*. Studies of the leaf epidermis show that the adaxial anticlinal cell walls are sinuous in *D. sansibarensis* and straight in *D. macroura*. Furthermore, rectangular and cuboidal crystals occur in the 2 species respectively. Therefore, on anatomical grounds the view put forward by Burkill (1960) that *D. macroura* is a synonym of *D. sansibarensis* is not supported.

In this light it is interesting to examine Prain and Burkill's (1936) explanation of their disagreement over Knuth's (1924) section Opsophyton. In his conspectus of the genus *Dioscorea*, Knuth treated the section defined by Uline (1898) as a subsection Euopsophyton after adding a group of African species for which Uline had suggested the name Isocantha. Prain and Burkill argued that the subsection Isocantha recognized by Knuth included certain species with their seeds winged like those of *D. bulbifera*. These species differ among themselves as regards the direction in which their stems twine, but agree with each other and differ from Opsophyton as originally delimited by Uline in having clustered flowers. This floral feature prevented Prain and Burkill from accepting Knuth's treatment.

Furthermore, along with his subsections Euopsophyton and Isocantha, Knuth included in Opsophyton another African subsection Macrourae. Prain and Burkill concluded that the species of subsection Macrourae agreed with those of subsection Isocantha and differed from Opsophyton in having seeds encircled by wings. This feature again prevented Prain and Burkill from accepting Knuth's treatment. Prain and Burkill suggested that Isocantha should be retained as Uline originally proposed.

Using the same characters outlined in Tables 3 and 4, Knuth's sections (Table 5) could be regrouped as indicated in Table 6.

Apart from section Opsophyton which has already been discussed, the seven other regroupings shown in Table 6 will now be considered in relation to the respective classifications by Knuth, Prain and Burkill, and Matuda. Appendix II (p. 160) is a key to the Old World sections of *Dioscorea* by Burkill (1960).

(1) The sections Apodostemon and Heterostemon as recognized by Knuth cannot be distinguished from each other on anatomical and histological grounds (see Tables 3 and 4). Knuth (cf. Appendix I, p. 156) separated the above sections on the grounds that the 6 stamens of Apodostemon are equally long while Heterostemon has 3 short and 3 long stamens. Matuda (cf.

TABLE 6

Regrouping of sections of Dioscorea

Section	Group A	Section	Group B
A.	Dematostemon	A.	Brachyandra
B.	Sphaerantha	B.	Chondrocarpa
C.	Isocantha	C.	Macrourae
D.1.	Apodostemon	D.	Euopsophyton
D.2.	Heterostemon	E.	Stenocarpa
E.1.	Trigonobasis	F.1.	Lasiophyton
E.2.	Macropoda	F.2.	Trieuphorostemon
E.3.	Cryptantha	F.3.	Botryosicyos
E.4.	Eustenophora	G.	Macrogynodium
F.1.	Oxypetalum	H.1.	Combilium
F.2.	Brachystigma	H.2.	Macrocarpaea
F.3.	Lychnostemon	I.1.	Asterotricha
G.1.	Sarcantha	I.2.	Syntepaleia
G.2.	Lasiogyne	J.	Enantiophyllum
G.3.	Orientali-asiaticae	K.	Stenocorea

Appendix III, p. 163), on the other hand, separated the same sections because Apodostemon has 6 short filaments while Heterostemon has 6 long ones.

When considered separately the systems of Knuth and Matuda seem acceptable, but when the two systems are compared there are obvious ambiguities in that stamens which Knuth considered to be long are treated as short by Matuda.

(2) The sections Trigonobasis, Macropoda, Cryptantha, and Eusteno-phora are considered here to be close associates because of the similar anatomy of their stems and the presence of unicellular hairs. Matuda's section D (p. 163) consists of Trigonobasis and Polyneuron. The association of Polyneuron with Trigonobasis cannot be discussed from the anatomical standpoint since stem material of Polyneuron was not available.

(3) It seems desirable to unite the sections Oxypetalum, Brachystigma, and Lychnostemon because their anatomy is similar. This suggested regrouping seems to agree very well with Matuda's section E based on floral morphology. Matuda has criticized the classification of Knuth's (cf. Appendix I) sections 29, 30, 31, 32, and 33 on the grounds that they were based on tenuous distinctions.

(4) The sections Sarcantha, Lasiogyne, and Orientali-asiaticae are sufficiently alike in their anatomy to justify uniting them.

(5) It also seems desirable to combine the sections Lasiophyton, Trieu-phorostemon, and Botryosicyos because of the similar anatomy of their stems and the presence of bicellular hairs on their leaves. In their treatment of species of *Dioscorea* from the east, Prain and Burkill (1936) suggested that Lasiophyton and Trieuphorostemon should be placed together because of their similar floral morphology.

(6) The similar vascular anatomy and the presence of T-shaped hairs in Combilium and Macrocarpaea suggest that they should be included in one

section, although Burkill (1960) suggested that the resemblance between the two sections may probably be no more than an example of parallel evolution. The composition of Matuda's section B (p. 163) is not supported on anatomical grounds because sections Combilium and Euopsophyton belong to my Group B, while section Heterostemon belongs to Group A (see Table 6).

Section Macrogynodium is also included in Matuda's section B. The question is therefore raised whether there is any affinity between Macrogynodium and Combilium. On anatomical grounds it can be argued that there are similarities between them, but not close enough to justify their inclusion in one section.

(7) Sections Asterotricha and Syntepaleia should be considered as one on the basis of the vascular anatomy and the stellate hairs. Burkill (1960) suggested that the section Enantiophyllum may also be related to Asterotricha because of the stiletto hairs of the former.

The regroupings suggested above (Table 6) generally support the conclusions of Matuda (1954) and Burkill (1960). The chief objection to Knuth's classification of his sections has been his reliance mainly on the fertile stamens as sectional characters. Burkill argued that reduction of fertile stamens is not a reliable criterion on which to base the composition of sections because similar reductions also occur in various sections such as Enantiophyllum, Rhacodophyllum, Stenophora, and Lasiophyton. Discounting Knuth's sections based on staminal sterility, Burkill suggested the reduction of section Strutantha to Cryptantha and Periandrium to Sarcocapsa. He further suggested the transfer of species with compound leaves which were originally assigned to section Apodostemon to section Trifoliatae.

The various suggested regroupings based on the present anatomical studies coupled with those already recommended by Matuda (1954), Prain and Burkill (1936), and Burkill (1960), indicate that a major revision of Knuth's sections is most desirable.

Although studies of the vegetative anatomy appear to be of value at the intersectional level, they do not, except in a limited way, offer much information of taxonomic value at the intrasectional level. One outstanding exception to this is *Dioscorea bulbifera* (Pl. V. F), whose endodermoid layer in the stem is replaced by a highly distinctive layer of brachysclereids and which is therefore easily separable from all other species in the family.

The genus *Rajania* (Pl. XIV. B) is unquestionably a close associate of *Dioscorea*. From an anatomical standpoint, the 2 genera cannot be separated. Similarly, the genus *Tamus* (Pl. XIV. D, E) cannot be distinguished from either *Rajania* or *Dioscorea*. On the other hand, the 3 genera can easily be separated from each other by their fruit characters. Capsules, samaras, and berries occur in *Dioscorea*, *Rajania*, and *Tamus* respectively. The value of the fruit characters was very early recognized by systematists as useful in separating the 3 genera. Brown (1810), who proposed the family name, was aware of the importance of the capsular fruit in *Dioscorea*. Bentham and Hooker (1883), Knuth (1924, 1930), and Burkill (1960) also made use of the fruiting characters in differentiating the 3 genera.

The genus *Stenomeris* was considered by Bentham and Hooker (1883) to differ widely from the rest of the Dioscoreaceae in its type of anther and the presence of numerous ovules. Hutchinson (1959) expressed ideas similar to those discussed by Bentham and Hooker. He went on to separate *Stenomeris* from the Dioscoreaceae and created a new family—Stenomeridaceae. This new family was also criticized by Burkill on the same grounds as the Trichopodaceae. From a purely anatomical viewpoint, there appears to be no justification for the proposal of Hutchinson. The histology of the vascular tissues and the general anatomy of the vegetative organs of *Stenomeris* hardly differ from those of *Avetra, Dioscorea, Rajania,* or *Tamus.*

A comparison of the anatomy and morphology of the monotypic genus *Trichopus* (Ayensu 1966) with that of the Dioscoreaceae shows that although certain characters are common to all genera, the totality of evidence supports the exclusion of *Trichopus* from the Dioscoreaceae. It is therefore suggested that Hutchinson's family Trichopodaceae should be retained, but that *Avetra* (Pl. XV. A), which differs considerably from *Trichopus* (Pl. XIV. F; Pl. XV. B), should be excluded from it.

The genus *Petermannia* has long been suspected (cf. Bentham and Hooker 1883; Knuth 1924, 1930; Schlittler 1949) as having very doubtful relationship with the Dioscoreaceae. However, none went as far as to remove it from the family. It was not until Hutchinson's (1934) arrangement of the monocotyledons (according to his concept of their phylogeny) that a new family, Petermanniaceae, was established for the single genus. The vascular bundles of the stem and the general vascular plan differ from the other genera placed in the Dioscoreaceae. The bundles are collateral, and sporadically distributed in the central cylinder; the smaller vascular bundles are confined to the outer limits of the vascular cylinder; xylem- and phloem-glomeruli are totally lacking in the nodal regions of the stem (Tomlinson and Ayensu 1969).

A comparison of the above characters with those outlined earlier (p. 39) for the Dioscoreaceae as a whole suggests that Hutchinson's removal of *Petermannia* from the Dioscoreaceae is also fully justified.

The comparison of the anatomical descriptions of the monotypic genus *Avetra* and the genera of the Dioscoreaceae clearly indicates that this genus belongs in the family. As indicated above, Hutchinson (1959) created the family Trichopodaceae to include *Trichopus* and *Avetra*. Burkill (1960) expressed his disapproval of Hutchinson's new family, saying that the taxon is 'phylogenetically unphilosophical'. The present anatomical study supports Burkill, for the anatomy of *Trichopus* differs considerably from that of *Avetra*, whose anatomy and indeed general morphology resemble those of the other genera of the Dioscoreaceae excluding *Petermannia*.

A comparative study of the Stemonaceae shows that the 3 genera, viz. *Croomia* (Pl. XVI. A), *Stemona* (Pl. XVI. B), and *Stichoneuron* (Pl. XVI. C), can easily be separated from one another especially when the vascular plans of the stem are considered. *Croomia* has 8–11 amphivasal vascular bundles arranged in one ring. Holm (1905) recorded up to 13 bundles in his material. *Stemona* has common and cauline bundles, the outer ring of 13 collateral bundles with a V-shaped arrangement of vessels and tracheids and the inner ring consisting of 13 amphivasal bundles with elliptically arranged metaxylem vessels and tracheids, the largest vessels orientated towards the periphery of the vascular cylinder. Lachner-Sandoval (1892) recorded a variable number of vascular bundles in the 3 species he investigated. *Stichoneuron* has an outer ring of 20 collateral bundles with a U- or V-shaped arrangement of metaxylem vessels and tracheids, and an inner ring of 5 amphivasal bundles nearly evenly spaced and close to the outer limits of the thin-walled, parenchymatous tissue. The total absence of crystals from the stem of *Croomia*, the presence of styloids and raphide bundles in *Stemona*, and the occurrence of raphide bundles in *Stichoneuron* separate the genera from each other. Lachner-Sandoval recorded prismatic crystals but no raphides in *Roxburghia japonica*.

In contrast to the other families of Hutchinson's (1959) Dioscoreales, that is, Dioscoreaceae, Stenomeridaceae, and Trichopodaceae (excluding *Trichopus*), the genera of the Stemonaceae have vegetative anatomical characters indicative of a less intimate relationship with the rest of the families of the order.

A comparison of the 3 genera of the Stemonaceae shows, however, that *Stemona* is perhaps the closest genus to the Dioscoreaceae, the structural similarity being the general vascular plan with the V-shaped arrangement of metaxylem vessels and tracheids for the common bundles and the elliptical arrangement of the metaxylem vessels and tracheids of the cauline bundles. Lachner-Sandoval (1892) recorded the presence of large sieve-tubes with very oblique end walls and numerous sieve-fields in the species he investigated. However, the subdivision of the phloem into several distinct strands and the large sieve-tubes with complicated compound sieve-plates of the Dioscoreaceae differ considerably from those of *Stemona*. Lachner-Sandoval concluded that, although the passage of the vascular bundles in the stem of *Roxburghia* (*Stemona*) exhibited some resemblances to that of *Dioscorea*, the latter genus differed considerably from the former in its embryo and venation.

From the preceding discussion it is clear that the anatomical studies have furnished considerable data which can resolve some of the conflicts in the various taxonomic systems. The distinctive anatomy of the Dioscoreaceae tends to confirm that *Avetra*, *Dioscorea*, *Rajania*, *Stenomeris*, and *Tamus* belong to the family. The anatomical characters support the view that *Trichopus* and *Petermannia* should be excluded from the Dioscoreaceae.

Cytological considerations

Reference to the cytological literature reveals that chromosomal studies in the Dioscoreaceae are quite meagre, although attempts are being made to correct this situation.

It is now generally accepted that the basic number in *Dioscorea* is 10. The first published count of $2n = 20$ was reported by Nakajima (1933) for *D. gracillima* and *D. tokoro*. He also reported counts of $2n = 40$ for *D. japonica* and *D. discolor*. Later Smith (1937) reported counts of $2n = 20$ for *D. caucasica* and *D. quinqueloba*, $2n = 40$ for *D. macroura*, $2n = 60$ for *D. villosa*, $2n = 61$ for *D. reticulata*, and $2n = 64$ for *D. fargesii*.

In studies of polyploidy in *Dioscorea*, Sharma and De (1956) and Raghavan (1958) have concluded that although at one extreme there are species such as *D. caucasica* and *D. tokoro* with $2n = 20$, and at the other extreme such species as *D. oppositifolia* and *D. cayenensis* having $2n = 140$, there is good evidence that species of *Dioscorea* are characterized as having $2n$ as derivatives of 10, and thus indicating the probability of a homogeneous and single line of evolution within the genus.

It has been recorded in Darlington and Wylie's (1955) work that the basic number for *Tamus communis* is 12. Ramachandran (1968) has found that the basic number for *Trichopus* is 14, providing additional evidence for its separation.

Palynological considerations

Erdtman (1952) described the pollen grains of the Dioscoreales as more or less heterogeneous. Generally the grains are 1-sulcate, 2–3-sulcate, or 4 (5?)-foraminoidate, the longest axis being 18 to 45 μm. Under the tribe Dioscoreae he described the pollen grains of such genera as *Dioscorea*, *Borderea*, *Rajania*, and *Tamus*. For the family Stenomeridaceae he studied *Stenomeris*, for Trichopodaceae *Avetra*, for Stemonaceae *Croomia* and *Stemona*, and for Petermanniaceae *Petermannia*. Erdtman concluded that the pollen grains of *Avetra* deviate considerably from those of *Stenomeris*. He stated further that the grains in both genera differ from those of the Dioscoreaceae–Dioscoreae. On *Petermannia* he observed that the grains were more or less different from those of the rest of the order. Erdtman has indicated the need for further pollen studies and that such work is in progress.

Phytochemical considerations

As pointed out in the introduction, interest in the chemistry of the Dioscoreaceae has centred round the tuber as a potential source of precursors for cortisone synthesis. The sapogenin that has been found to be relatively specific for *Dioscorea* is diosgenin. Relationships have been discovered between the configuration of the steroid ring in *Dioscorea* and certain other plant groups. For example, it is known that some species of *Agave* (Agavaceae) yield *trans*-derivatives, while others give *cis*-compounds. The same happens in *Yucca* (Agavaceae) and *Dioscorea* (Swain 1963). Unfortunately little work has so far been done to improve our knowledge of the Dioscoreaceae. However, there are indications that future biochemical work will be useful, as shown by Hegnauer (1963).

Palaeobotanical considerations

Although fossil evidence is insufficient, findings indicate that the Dioscoreaceae appeared along with the Liliaceae during the Cretaceous period. The earlier liliaceous forms are of the *Smilax* type which are usually confused with the Dioscoreaceae even in their extant forms.

The present distribution of *Dioscorea* demonstrates that the Atlantic Rift that occurred at the end of the Cretaceous period divided the family into two, thereby separating the New World species, especially those along the coasts of Brazil and the Argentine, from those of the Old World, particularly along the coasts of Africa. Burkill (1960) expressed a desire to make a comparative study of the Dioscoreaceae found on either side of the Atlantic Rift in an attempt to integrate all the sections of *Dioscorea*. Unfortunately he was unable to pursue his objective. He expressed his awareness of the superficial nature of the studies of the family in South America and in Africa at the time of his publication. Burkill also realized that Knuth's monograph, while informative, was not constructed so as to be helpful in this respect.

Comparative anatomical studies of the stem in this present work seem to show good accord with most of the existing sections of *Dioscorea* found on either side of the Rift. In Table 5 (p. 67) are two major groupings of sections of *Dioscorea* available for this study. Group A consists of all sections whose cauline vascular bundles have 1 large phloem unit on the inner side of the innermost pair of metaxylem vessels. Group B, on the other hand, is composed of those sections having 2 large phloem units on the inner side of the innermost pair of metaxylem vessels. Since the New World sections fall under Group A and those of the Old World occur in Group B, on anatomical grounds it would seem that divergence in the development of the vascular bundles of *Dioscorea* was a consequence of the separation of the two groups.

Phylogenetic considerations

As a basis for his last major work, Burkill (1960) entered into a long and complex discussion about the course by which the 'proto-Liliales' gave rise to the Dioscoreaceae through a hypothetical taxon which he named the 'proto-Dioscoreaceae'. The families that have often been associated with the Dioscoreaceae are the Amaryllidaceae, Stemonaceae (Roxburghiaceae), Taccaceae, and Liliaceae. Solms-Laubach (1878), Uline (1898), and Knuth (1924) state that on the basis of embryology and general morphology, the Dioscoreaceae are nearest to the Amaryllidaceae. Burkill rejected this proposition because he thought that the Taccaceae and Stemonaceae are phylogenetically nearer. He pointed out that although the progress of evolution has obliterated the stages by which all 3 families emerged from the proto-Liliales, the area over which the above families are distributed can be used for measuring their evolutionary success. The Dioscoreaceae, Taccaceae, and Stemonaceae occur in hot, wet areas while the Amaryllidaceae are characteristic of dry cool regions (Fig. 9). Burkill claims, furthermore, that the Dioscoreaceae and Stemonaceae began to compete whenever stems became extended by assuming the twining habit. The Taccaceae achieved the same end when their leaves became enlarged. The Amaryllidaceae, on the other hand, could neither enlarge their leaves nor extend their stems because of the short growing seasons in the areas in which they grow.

Unfortunately the Amaryllidaceae, a family composed of over 80 genera with approximately 700 species, have not been subjected to critical anatomical and histological studies in recent years. However, Queva (1894*b*) claims on the basis of his comparative anatomical studies that the Taccaceae are more closely related to the Dioscoreaceae than is any other family.

Of the 2 families Stemonaceae and Taccaceae, perhaps the former is closer to the Dioscoreaceae. Assessment of the anatomical characters of the three genera (viz. *Croomia*, *Stemona* (*Roxburghia*), and *Stichoneuron*) shows that *Stemona* is the closest to the Dioscoreaceae (Ayensu 1968*a*). The 2 families are similar in having distinct common and cauline vascular bundles in the organization of their stems. However, the disposition and histology of the phloem strands in the Dioscoreaceae differ considerably from those of *Stemona*. Lachner-Sandoval (1892) recorded the presence of large sieve-tubes with very oblique end walls and numerous sieve-fields in the species he investigated, but the subdivisions of the phloem into several distinct groups and the large sieve-tubes with complicated compound sieve-plates of the Dioscoreaceae are totally lacking in *Stemona*.

In his appraisal of the relationships within the assemblage of the families in Fig. 9, Burkill (1960) suggested that Stemonaceae and Dioscoreaceae

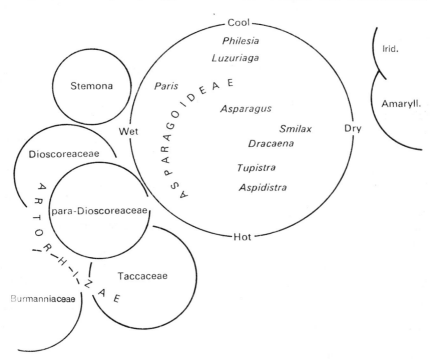

FIG. 9. Diagram suggesting how families closest to the Dioscoreaceae have been evolved from the proto-Liliales such as the Asparagoideae. (After Burkill 1960.)

both originated from some stock of proto-Liliales. The reasoning that under-lies this conclusion was based on the following considerations.

The genus *Stemona*, though discovered many years earlier, was first described by Loureiro (1790) when he named his species *S. tuberosa*. (A similar plant was also called *Roxburghia gloriosoides* Banks.) Later Smith (1807) described the same plant and assigned it to the Asparagi of de Jussieu (1789). Sims (1812) wrote that the genus fell between the Liliaceae and Asclepia-daceae, but on the basis of morphology it was later reassigned to the Tac-caceae by Reichenbach (1828). Endlicher (1837) in his *Genera Plantarum* remarked that in *Stemona* the lower part of the stamen, which had earlier been named a 'nectarial body', was a member of the perianth to which the stamen was attached. Smith (1807) had called it a filament. Burkill, concurring with Smith, stated 'This body is rendered unusual by a prolongation of the connective and that brings it into one view with the para-Dioscoreaceae (viz. *Stenomeris, Avetra* and *Trichopus*), and the few species of *Dioscorea* which have apiculate anthers'.

Burkill (1960) has found the ovary of *Stemona* to be half inferior, a condition intermediate between the fully inferior ovary of the other genera of the Stemonaceae and the superior ovary of the Dioscoreaceae.

Further discussions on the relations of *Dioscorea* and the other genera within the order have been given by Huber (1969).

Summary

The present anatomical and histological investigations have proved to be significant in demonstrating that the Dioscoreaceae (excluding *Trichopus* and *Petermannia*) are a natural taxon. The unifying anatomical characters are as follows: (1) the presence in the aerial stem of two types of vascular bundles. The first of these is the common bundle having a V-shaped group of metaxylem vessels and tracheids together with 1 phloem unit at the converging ends of the V and 2 phloem units terminating the flanges of the V. The second type is the cauline bundle which exhibits an elliptical group of metaxylem vessels and tracheids, with 1 or 2 phloem units on the inner side of the innermost pair of vessels and at least 1 phloem unit at the outer end. (2) The presence of xylem- and phloem-glomeruli in the nodal regions of the stem of most species. (3) The presence of very large sieve-tubes with complicated compound sieve-plates within the phloem units.

The pattern of development of the primary vascular elements has shown that the distinctive cauline vascular bundles of the stem, believed to be confined to the Dioscoreaceae, have developed from bundles of the collateral type that is common to most monocotyledons.

The anatomy and indeed the exomorphic characters of the genus *Trichopus* give no indication that this genus belongs to the Dioscoreaceae (*sensu stricto*). On the other hand, the present findings add credence to the establishment of Hutchinson's Trichopodaceae, provided that the dioscoreaceous genus *Avetra* may be excluded.

Knuth's classification of his sections of *Dioscorea* has for the most part been criticized by Prain and Burkill, Matuda, and Burkill on morphological grounds.

The regrouping of the sections of *Dioscorea* suggested by the present studies of the vegetative anatomy generally support the findings of Matuda and Burkill. Comparative studies suggest that the sections recognized by Knuth can be divided into two major groups as shown in Table 5 (p. 67). Furthermore, the following suggestions are proposed based on anatomical findings.

(1) Subsection Isocantha should be elevated to sectional rank.
(2) Subsections Euopsophyton and Macrourae should be elevated to sectional ranks.
(3) Sections Apodostemon and Heterostemon should be combined in one section.
(4) Sections Trigonobasis, Macropoda, Cryptantha, and Eustenophora are sufficiently alike to be treated as one taxon.

(5) Sections Oxypetaulm, Brachystigma, and Lychnostemon should constitute one section.

(6) Sections Sarcantha, Lasiogyne, and Orientali-asiaticae are similar in their anatomy and should be included in one section.

(7) Sections Lasiophyton, Trieuphorostemon, and Botryosicyos should be combined in one section.

(8) Sections Combilium and Macrocarpaea share certain features which suggest their close relationship.

(9) Sections Asterotricha and Syntepaleia should be combined.

Studies of vegetative anatomy appear to be of value at the intersectional level, but they do not offer much information of taxonomic value at the intrasectional level.

The genus *Stenomeris* belongs to the family Dioscoreaceae, and it is suggested that Stenomeridaceae should be reduced to synonymy.

Vegetative anatomy is not wholly reliable for separating the closely related genera *Dioscorea*, *Rajania*, and *Tamus*, but morphological studies show that they can be separated on differences of their fruits.

The two major groupings proposed for the sections of *Dioscorea* clearly suggest that there has been a divergence in the development of this genus. It is suggested that this may have taken place during the Cretaceous period, when parts of the genus on either side of the Atlantic became separated from one another.

The genera of the Stemonaceae (Roxburghiaceae) are not closely related to each other; furthermore, these genera show no apparent relationship on structural grounds (with the possible exception of *Stemona*) to the genera of Dioscoreaceae. Notwithstanding the anatomical and histological difference noted, perhaps the only link between the 2 families is through *Stemona* (Stemonaceae).

Although the data derived from other botanical disciplines (cytology, palynology, embryology (cf. p. 23), and phytochemistry) are insufficient to be of help in formulating conclusions on the systematics and phylogeny of the Dioscoreales, there are indications that future studies along these lines might prove to be quite useful.

Table 7 is a summary of the taxonomic subdivision of the order Dioscoreales as conceived by various authors. The last column is a grouping which I consider to be most clearly defined on the basis of my anatomical diagnoses.

TABLE 7

Systems of major classifications of the Dioscoreales

Bentham and Hooker (1883)	Knuth (1930)	Hutchinson (1959)	Burkill (1960)	Suggested classification based on anatomy
DIOSCOREACEAE	DIOSCOREACEAE	DIOSCOREALES	DIOSCOREACEAE	DIOSCOREALES
NORMAL GENERA *Dioscorea* *Testudinaria* *Rajania* *Tamus*	Tribe I DIOSCOREAE *Dioscorea* *Higinbothamia* *Borderea* *Epipetrum* *Rajania* *Tamus*	DIOSCOREACEAE *Dioscorea* *Rajania* *Tamus* *Testudinaria*	DIOSCOREAE *Dioscorea* *Rajania* *Tamus*	DIOSCOREACEAE *Avetra* *Dioscorea* *Rajania* *Stenomeris* *Tamus*
ABNORMAL GENERA *Stenomeris* *Trichopus* *Oncus* *Petermannia*	Tribe II STENOMERIDEAE *Stenomeris* *Trichopus* *Petermannia* *Avetra*	TRICHOPODACEAE *Trichopus* *Avetra* STENOMERIDACEAE *Stenomeris* STEMONACEAE (ROXBURGHIACEAE) *Croomia* *Stemona* *Stichoneuron*	PARA-DIOSCOREAE *Stenomeris* *Avetra* *Trichopus*	TRICHOPODACEAE *Trichopus* STEMONACEAE (ROXBURGHIACEAE) *Croomia* *Stemona* *Stichoneuron*

PART II
THE ANATOMY OF THE INDIVIDUAL GENERA AND SUBGENERA OF THE DIOSCOREALES

DIOSCOREACEAE

THE following characters occur in all species examined in the sections of the Dioscoreaceae.

(*a*) Glands on the leaf surface as well as the petiole are bulb-like, multicellular, and appear on short unicellular stalks.

(*b*) The stomata are anomocytic on all organs in which they occur.

(*c*) Palisade cells occur only towards the adaxial surface.

(*d*) The vascular bundles in the leaf are collateral with adaxial xylem and abaxial phloem.

(*e*) The xylem in the leaf consists mainly of tracheids and associated parenchyma; the phloem is composed of sieve-tubes, companion cells, and phloem parenchyma.

(*f*) The vascular bundles of the stem are basically arranged in a ring, with common and cauline bundles alternating.

(*g*) The common vascular bundles of the stem are basically V-shaped and the cauline bundles are elliptical.

(*h*) The number of phloem units within the V of the common bundle varies from 1 to 7.

(*i*) The number of large metaxylem vessels varies in the cauline bundles; the number of phloem units on the inner side of the innermost pair of large metaxylem vessels is either 1 or 2. However, the number of phloem units appearing elsewhere within the same bundle may vary from 1 to 4 with at least 1 phloem unit at the outer end.

(*j*) In the stem the xylem consists of vessels, tracheids, and associated parenchyma; the phloem is composed of sieve-tubes, companion cells, and phloem parenchyma.

(*k*) Xylem- and phloem-glomeruli occur in all the species investigated.

DIOSCOREA L.

The genus *Dioscorea* was divided into 4 subgenera by Knuth (1924) based on the seed and tuber characters (cf. Appendix I). Subgenus I Helmia was divided into 17 sections. Subgenus II Dioscorea was divided into 39 sections.

Subgenus III Stenophora was divided into 2 sections. Subgenus IV Testudinaria was treated as a section. The key characters used in separating the sections are outlined in Appendix I (p. 156).

Representative specimens for all the sections were not available for study. However, one or more specimens from each subgenus were examined.

Dioscorea is the largest genus in the Dioscoreaceae and according to Knuth (1930) there are about 600 species in the genus. In recent years most taxonomists consider the genus as having not more than 200 species. The reason for this conservative estimate is based on the fact that the flowers are unisexual and many male and female members of the same species have been described as separate species.

SUBGENUS I HELMIA (Kunth) Benth.

Section DEMATOSTEMON

Leaf surface Fig. 10. A, B, C.

Hairs absent; **glands** present mainly on abaxial surface. **Stomata**: average size 39×27 μm, mainly confined to abaxial surface; each stoma surrounded by 2–4 epidermal cells. Adaxial anticlinal cell walls straight, abaxial walls slightly sinuous.

Lamina T.S. Figs. 3.E, p. 34; 10.D.

Dorsiventral. **Cuticle** thin and undulating on both surfaces, slightly thicker around main veins. **Epidermis**: adaxial cells mainly rectangular with thin, straight anticlinal walls and cytoplasmic contents; abaxial smaller than adaxial cells. **Stomata**: walls of guard cells facing pore thickened and with no projecting ledges. **Mesophyll**: palisade tissue always 1-layered. Cells of spongy tissue mainly elongated axially, lying parallel to surface of lamina and occupying half of mesophyll. **Vascular bundle** of midrib much larger than remainder. Xylem groups alternating with 5–6 phloem units. **Bundle sheath** poorly developed around main veins, but vascular bundle of midrib partly surrounded by 3–5 rows of fibres. **Crystals**: idioblasts containing raphide bundles occurring in mesophyll. **Tannin** cells absent.

Petiole surface

Hairs absent; **glands** present. **Stomata** as in lamina.

Petiole T.S. Figs. 4.C, p. 36; 10. E.

Outline pentagonal. **Cuticle** thick and undulating. **Epidermis** composed of thin-walled, cuboidal cells with cytoplasmic contents. **Vascular bundles** 7, arranged in a circle, each bundle partly surrounded by an arc of 2–4 layers of fibres, embedded in thin-walled parenchymatous tissue. Lignified parenchyma cells, 1–2-layered, occupying interfascicular regions. Xylem consisting of tracheids, vessels, and associated parenchyma. Phloem composed of small sieve-tubes. **Crystals**: idioblasts containing raphide bundles present. **Tannin** cells absent.

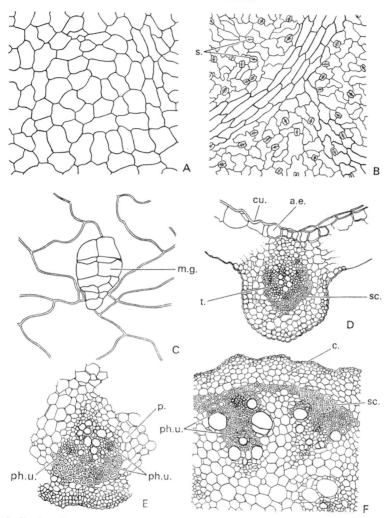

Fig. 10. Section Dematostemon. *Dioscorea campestris* (all ×185 except C, ×330). A, Adaxial epidermis, surface view. B, Abaxial epidermis, surface view. C, Multicellular gland. D, T.S. leaf midrib. E, T.S. portion of petiole showing one of the vascular bundles. F, T.S. small portion of stem showing common and cauline vascular bundles.

a.e., adaxial epidermis; c., cortex; cu., cuticle; m.g., multicellular gland; p., parenchyma; ph.u., phloem unit; s., stoma; sc., sclerenchyma; t., tracheal element.

Stem T.S. Fig. 10. F; Pl. V. A.

Hairs absent; **glands** as in lamina. **Cuticle** thick and undulating. **Epidermis** of thin-walled, rounded cells. **Cortex** consisting of 3–6 layers of chlorenchyma cells of variable size. **Endodermoid layer** separating cortex from thick-walled parenchyma. **Vascular bundles**: common bundles V-shaped, 1 phloem unit at converging ends of V, but seldom at flanges of V. Cauline bundles elliptical;

1 pair of large vessels, average diameter 98 μm. One large phloem unit on inner side of the single pair of large metaxylem vessels; average diameter of sieve-tubes 42 μm. **Pith** area constituting two-thirds of central cylinder. **Crystals**: idioblasts containing raphide bundles present. **Tannin** cells absent.

Tuber T.S.

Epidermis thick-walled, outline of cells not easily identifiable. **Cork**: first cork of primary origin; cells irregularly arranged. Storied cork of secondary origin, 6-layered; cells in radial rows, suberized. Outer ground tissue of large, rounded or irregular, thin-walled cells; mainly radially arranged. **Vascular bundles** collateral, sporadically distributed in central ground tissue. Xylem consisting of short tracheids with scalariform to reticulate thickenings. Phloem composed of small sieve-tubes and companion cells. **Starch grains** of variable size, mostly spherical, few elliptical, hilum off-centre, grains concentrated around vascular bundles. **Crystals**: raphide bundles distributed at random. **Tannin** cells absent.

MATERIAL EXAMINED

Dioscorea campestris Griseb.; Puerto Rico; F. W. Martin s.n. Leaf, petiole, stem, tuber (J).

Section BRACHYANDRA

Leaf surface Fig. 11. A, B.

Hairs absent; **glands** present on both surfaces. **Stomata**: average size 45×36 μm, mainly confined to abaxial surface; each stoma usually surrounded by 3–4 epidermal cells. Adaxial and abaxial anticlinal cell walls mostly straight.

Lamina T.S. Fig. 11. C, D.

Dorsiventral. **Cuticle** thin and undulating on both surfaces; slightly thicker and ridged around main veins. **Epidermis**: adaxial cells mainly rectangular with thin, wavy anticlinal walls and cytoplasmic contents; abaxial smaller than adaxial cells. **Stomata**: walls of guard cells facing pore slightly thickened and with no projecting ledges. **Mesophyll**: palisade tissue 2-layered, occasionally 3-layered towards margins, innermost layer less differentiated. Cells of spongy tissue somewhat rounded and occupying about half of mesophyll. **Vascular bundle** of midrib much larger than remainder. Commissural bundles frequently observed. Xylem groups alternating with 2–3 phloem units. **Bundle sheath** poorly developed around main veins, but vascular bundle of midrib surrounded by up to about 3–5 rows of fibres. **Crystals**: idioblasts containing raphide bundles numerous, occurring in mesophyll. **Tannin** abundant in both palisade and spongy cells.

Stem T.S. Fig. 11. E, F.

Hairs and **glands** absent; **stomata** as in lamina. **Cuticle** thin and undulating. **Epidermis** of thick-walled cuboidal cells. **Cortex** consisting of 2–3 layers of chlorenchyma cells of variable size. **Endodermoid layer** separating cortex

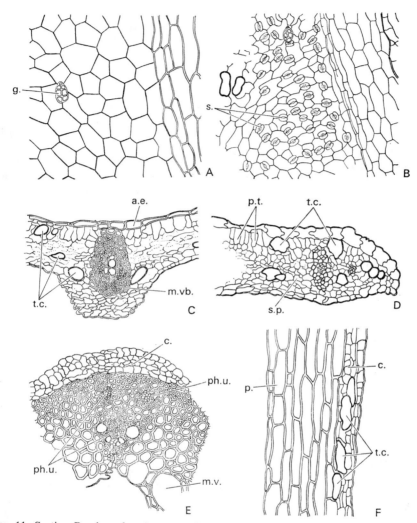

Fig. 11. Section Brachyandra. *Dioscorea hexagona* (×185). A, Adaxial epidermis showing a multicellular gland, surface view. B, Abaxial epidermis, surface view. C, T.S. leaf midrib. D, T.S. leaf margin. E, T.S. part of stem. F, L.S. stem showing tannin cells in cortex. a.e., adaxial epidermis; c., cortex; g., gland; m.vb., midrib vascular bundle; m.v., metaxylem vessel; p., parenchyma; ph.u., phloem unit in common vascular bundle; p.t., palisade tissue; s., stoma; s.p., spongy parenchyma; t.c., tannin cells.

from thick-walled fibres. **Vascular bundles:** common bundles V-shaped, with 1 phloem unit at converging ends of V, and 2 phloem units terminating flanges of V. Cauline bundles elliptical; 1 pair of large vessels, average diameter 140 μm. Phloem unit(s) crushed in material examined. **Pith** area constituting half of central cylinder. **Crystals:** idioblasts containing raphide bundles present. **Tannin** cells present in cortex.

84   DIOSCOREACEAE

MATERIAL EXAMINED

Dioscorea hexagona Baker; Malagasy Republic; Webrandt 3876 and (US 808210) (US). Leaf, stem.

Section SPHAERANTHA

Stem T.S. Fig. 12. A–D; Pl. V. B.

Hairs and **glands** absent. **Stomata** present, sunken. **Cuticle** very thick (40 μm) and ridged. **Epidermis** of thick-walled cells of variable size, with cytoplasmic contents; cells often radially arranged. **Cortex** consisting of 6–10 layers of cells of variable size. Cells subjacent to epidermis often thick-walled. **Endodermoid layer** separating cortex from thick-walled fibres. **Vascular bundles:** common bundles V-shaped with 1 phloem unit at converging ends of V, and 2 phloem units terminating flanges of V. Cauline bundles elliptical; 1 pair of large vessels, average diameter 217 μm. One large phloem unit on inner side of the single pair of large vessels and close to centre of pith. Average diameter of large sieve-tubes 98 μm. **Pith** area constituting one-fourth of central cylinder. **Crystals:** idioblasts containing raphide bundles absent. **Tannin** cells few.

TAXONOMIC NOTES

The anatomy of the stem of *Dioscorea guianensis* and *D. multiflora*, particularly the type of radially orientated epidermal cells and the very thick cuticle, suggests that the 2 species are closely related.

MATERIAL EXAMINED

Dioscorea guianensis Knuth: (i) Bolivia; B. A. Krukoff 10004 (US). (ii) Nigeria; A. W. Waitt 21 (K).
D. multiflora Mart.: (i) Brazil; A. F. Regnell 990 (US). (ii) Brazil; Widgren 988 (US) (J).

Section CHONDROCARPA

Leaf surface Fig. 13. A, B.

Hairs absent; **glands** present on both surfaces. **Stomata:** average size 39 × 24 μm, mainly confined to abaxial surface; each stoma surrounded by 3–5 epidermal cells. Adaxial and abaxial anticlinal cell walls slightly sinuous.

Lamina T.S. Figs. 3.B, p. 34; 13. C.

Dorsiventral. **Cuticle** thin, undulating and with prominent striations on both surfaces, thicker around main veins. **Epidermis:** adaxial cells mainly rectangular with thin, mostly straight, anticlinal walls and cytoplasmic contents; abaxial smaller than adaxial cells. **Stomata:** walls of guard cells facing pore slightly thickened and with no projecting ledges. **Mesophyll:** palisade tissue always 2-layered. Innermost layer poorly developed. Cells of spongy tissue mainly spherical and occupying about half of mesophyll. **Vascular bundle** of midrib much larger than remainder; tracheal elements consisting mainly of tracheids, but with few vessels. Xylem groups alternating with

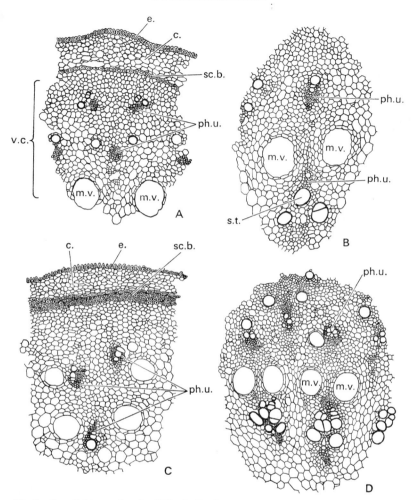

FIG. 12. Section Sphaerantha (×185). A, B, *Dioscorea guianensis*, T.S. small portion of stem: A, common vascular bundle; B, cauline vascular bundle. C, D, *D. multiflora*, T.S. portion of stem: C, common vascular bundle; D, cauline vascular bundle.

c., cortex; e., epidermis, thick walled; m.v., metaxylem vessel; ph.u., phloem unit of common vascular bundle; sc.b., sclerenchyma band (endodermoid layer) separating vascular cylinder from cortex; s.t., sieve-tube; v.c., vascular cylinder.

c. 8 phloem units. **Bundle sheath** poorly developed around main veins, but vascular bundle of midrib surrounded by 2–5 rows of fibres. **Crystals**: idioblasts containing raphide bundles occurring in mesophyll. **Tannin** cells present especially on abaxial side of main vascular bundles.

Petiole surface

Hairs absent; **glands** present. **Stomata** as in lamina.

Petiole T.S. Figs. 4.E, p. 36; 13. D.

Outline pentagonal. **Cuticle** thick and undulating. **Epidermis** composed of thick-walled, cuboidal cells with cytoplasmic contents. **Vascular bundles** 7, arranged in a circle, each bundle subtended by about 3–4 layers of fibres, embedded in thick-walled parenchymatous tissue. Lignified parenchyma cells, in 2–5 layers, occupying interfascicular regions. Xylem consisting of tracheids, vessels, and associated parenchyma. Phloem composed of small sieve-tubes. **Crystals**: idioblasts containing raphide bundles present. **Tannin** cells present.

Stem T.S. Pl. V. C.

Conspicuously winged in 2 places. **Hairs** absent; **glands** and **stomata** as in lamina. **Cuticle** thin and undulating. **Epidermis** of thick-walled, rounded cells. **Hypodermis**: 1 layer of brachysclereids. **Cortex** consisting of 10–12 layers of chlorenchyma cells of variable size. **Endodermoid layer** separating cortex from thick-walled parenchyma. **Vascular bundles**: common bundles V-shaped, with 1 phloem unit at converging ends of V, and 2 phloem units terminating flanges of V. Cauline bundles elliptical; 1 pair of large vessels, average diameter 364 μm. Two large phloem units on inner side of the single pair of large vessels and close to centre of pith. Average diameter of large sieve-tubes 196 μm. **Pith** area constituting one-third of central cylinder. **Crystals**: idioblasts containing raphide bundles present. **Tannin** cells present.

SPECIAL NOTE

Tyloses occur in some vessels and large sieve-tubes (Fig. 13. E, F). Hypodermis consisting of 1 distinct layer of brachysclereids present in stem.

MATERIAL EXAMINED

Dioscorea samydea Griseb.; Brazil; L. d'A. F. Carvalho s.n. (RB). Leaf, petiole, stem (J).

Section OPSOPHYTON

Subsection 1. MACROURAE

Leaf surface Figs. 14. A, B; 15. A, B.

Hairs absent; **glands** present mostly on abaxial surface. **Stomata**: average size 38 × 18 μm, mainly confined to abaxial surface; each stoma surrounded by 2–5 epidermal cells. Adaxial anticlinal cell walls straight or curved and abaxial walls sinuous in *D. macroura*, but adaxial and abaxial walls sinuous in *D. sansibarensis*. Leaf acumen distinct.

Lamina T.S. Figs. 3.C, D, p. 34; 15. C.

Dorsiventral. **Cuticle** thin and undulating on both surfaces, thicker around main veins. **Epidermis**: adaxial cells with thin anticlinal walls and cytoplasmic contents; abaxial slightly smaller but frequently more elongated than adaxial cells. **Stomata**: walls of guard cells facing pore thickened and with no projecting ledges. **Mesophyll**: palisade tissue always 2-layered, innermost layer poorly differentiated. Cells of spongy tissue of irregular size and occupy-

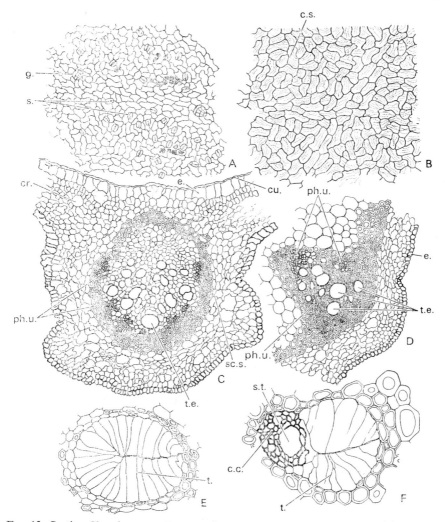

FIG. 13. Section Chondrocarpa. *Dioscorea samydea* (all × 185 except F, × 270.) A, Abaxial epidermis, surface view. B, Adaxial epidermis, surface view. C, T.S. leaf midrib. D, T.S. portion of petiole. E, T.S. stem vessel showing tylosis. F, T.S. stem sieve-elements showing similar tylosis.

c.c., companion cells; cr., crystal chamber; c.s., cuticular striation; cu., cuticle; e., epidermis; g., gland; ph.u., phloem unit; s., stoma; sc.s., sclerenchyma sheath; s.t., sieve-tube; t.e., tracheal element; t., tylosis.

ing about two-thirds of mesophyll. **Vascular bundle** of midrib much larger than remainder. Xylem groups alternating with 3–4 phloem units. **Bundle sheath** of midrib well developed, 2–5-layered. Thick-walled parenchyma almost surrounding bundle sheath. **Crystals:** idioblasts containing raphide bundles associated with mucilage occurring in mesophyll; cuboidal and

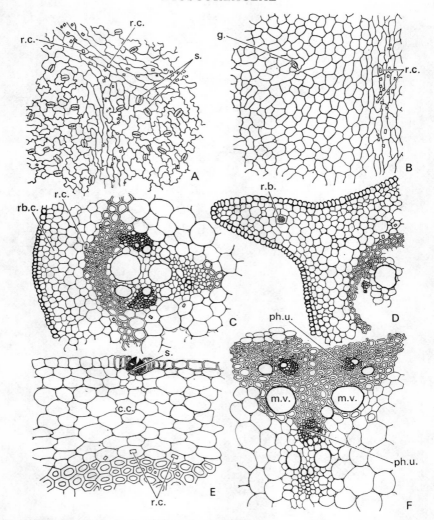

Fig. 14. Section Opsophyton, Subsection Macrourae. *Dioscorea macroura.* Rhomboidal crystals present in all organs (×185). A, Abaxial epidermis, surface view. B, Adaxial epidermis, surface view. C, T.S. portion of petiole. D, T.S. portion of petiole showing one of two wings on adaxial side. E, T.S. very small piece of stem showing outer tissues. F, T.S. common vascular bundle from stem.

c.c., cortical cell; g., gland; m.v., metaxylem vessel; ph.u., phloem unit; r.b., raphide bundle; rb.c., raphide bundle cavity; r.c., rhomboidal crystal; s., stoma.

rectangular crystals present in *D. macroura* and *D. sansibarensis* respectively. **Tannin** cells present.

Petiole surface

Hairs absent; **glands** present. **Stomata** few.

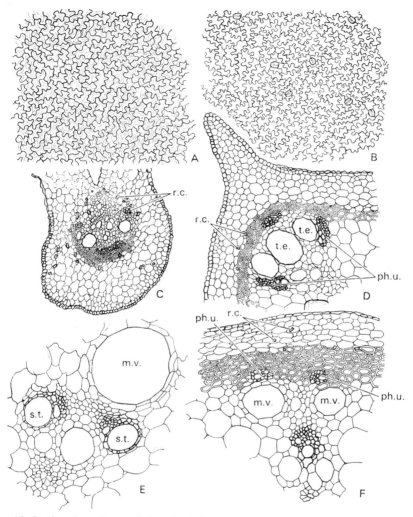

Fig. 15. Section Opsophyton, Subsection Macrourae. *Dioscorea sansibarensis* (×185). A, Adaxial epidermis, surface view. B, Abaxial epidermis, surface view. C, T.S. leaf midrib. D, T.S. portion of petiole showing one of the two wings on adaxial side. E, T.S. cauline vascular bundle with only one large metaxylem vessel and two phloem units. F, T.S. showing a common vascular bundle from stem.

m.v., metaxylem vessel; ph.u., phloem unit; r.c., rhomboidal crystal; s.t. sieve-tube; t.e., tracheal elements.

Petiole T.S. Figs. 4.A, p. 36; 14, C, D; 15. D.

Outline somewhat pentagonal, with 2 wings on adaxial side. **Cuticle** thin and ridged. **Epidermis** composed of thin-walled, cuboidal cells with cytoplasmic contents. **Vascular bundles** 9, arranged in a circle, each bundle subtended by an arc of 2–5 layers of thick-walled parenchyma cells and embedded in thin-walled parenchymatous tissue. Lignified parenchyma in 1–3 layers occupying interfascicular regions. Xylem consisting of tracheids, vessels, and associated parenchyma. Phloem composed of small sieve-tubes. **Crystals**: idioblasts containing raphide bundles and rhomboidal crystals present. **Tannin** cells absent.

Stem T.S. Figs. 14. E, F; 15. E, F; Pl. V. D, E.

Hairs absent; **glands** and **stomata** few, as in lamina. **Cuticle** thin and undulating. **Epidermis** of thin-walled, rectangular cells. **Cortex** consisting of chlorenchyma cells of variable size, in 5–7 layers. **Endodermoid layer** separating cortex from 4–6 layers of thick-walled parenchyma cells. **Vascular bundles**: common bundles V-shaped, with 1 phloem unit at converging ends of V, and 2 phloem units terminating flanges of V. Cauline bundles of *D. macroura* also with V-shaped group of metaxylem vessels; 1 pair of large vessels (single large vessel in *D. sansibarensis*), average diameter 441 μm. Two phloem units on inner side of the large vessels close to centre of pith. Several bundles with no fixed arrangement occurring between outermost and innermost bundles. Average diameter of large sieve-tubes 140 μm. **Pith** area constituting about half of central cylinder. **Crystals**: idioblasts containing raphide bundles and rhomboidal crystals present in cortex. **Tannin** cells present.

TAXONOMIC NOTES

The acumen of leaves of this subsection separates it from all other sections investigated.

MATERIAL EXAMINED

Dioscorea macroura Harms: (i) Nigeria; A. W. Waitt 19 (K). (ii) Hort. Kew; E. S. Ayensu, s.n. (K).
D. sansibarensis Pax: (i) Hort. Kew; E. S. Ayensu, s.n. (K). Leaf, petiole, stem. (ii) Kenya; B. Verdcourt, s.n. (EA). Leaf, petiole, stem. (iii) Singapore; P. B. Tomlinson, s.n. (J).

Subsection 2. EUOPSOPHYTON
Leaf surface Fig. 16. A, B.

Hairs absent; **glands** present on both surfaces. **Stomata**: average size 39×21 μm, almost confined to abaxial surface, few observed on adaxial surface; each stoma usually surrounded by 3–4 epidermal cells. Adaxial and abaxial anticlinal cell walls straight.

Lamina T.S. Figs. 3.F, p. 34; 16. C, D.

Dorsiventral. **Cuticle** thin and undulating on both surfaces, thin and ridged around main veins. **Epidermis**: adaxial cells with thin, mostly straight, anticlinal walls and cytoplasmic contents; abaxial smaller than adaxial cells. **Stomata**: walls of guard cells facing pore thickened and with no projecting ledges. **Mesophyll**: palisade tissue always 2-layered, innermost layer poorly

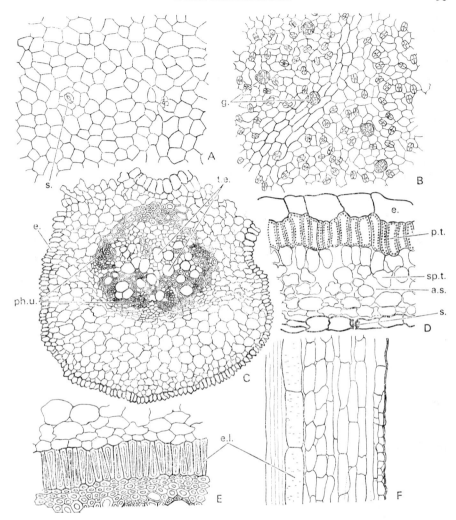

FIG. 16. Section Opsophyton, Subsection Euopsophyton. *Dioscorea bulbifera* (× 168). A, Adaxial epidermis, surface view. B, Abaxial epidermis, surface view. C, T.S. leaf midrib. D, T.S. portion of leaf. E, T.S. distinctive sclerenchyma separating cortex from vascular cylinder in stem. F, L.S. stem showing cortex and sclerenchyma cells.

a.s., air space; e., epidermis; e.l., endodermoid layer of lignified parenchyma; g., gland; ph.u. phloem unit; p.t., palisade tissue with choroplasts; s., stoma; sp.t., spongy tissue; t.e., tracheal element.

differentiated. Cells of spongy tissue of irregular size and occupying about half of mesophyll. **Vascular bundle** of midrib much larger than remainder. Xylem groups alternating with 6 phloem units. **Bundle sheath** of midrib and other vascular bundles poorly developed. **Crystals:** idioblasts containing raphide bundles present. **Tannin** cells observed.

Petiole surface

Hairs absent; **glands** present. **Stomata** as in lamina.

Petiole T.S. Fig. 4.B, p. 36.

Outline pentagonal. **Cuticle** thin and ridged. **Epidermis** composed of thin-walled, cuboidal cells. **Vascular bundles** 7, arranged in a circle, each bundle subtended by arcs of tayers of 1–2 brachysclereids and 2 layers of thick-walled fibres, and embedded in thin-walled parenchymatous tissue. Lignified parenchyma in 2–3 layers occupying interfascicular regions. Xylem consisting of tracheids, vessels, and associated parenchyma. Phloem composed of small sieve-tubes,companion cells, and phloem parenchyma. **Crystals**: idioblasts containing raphide bundles and rhomboidal crystals present. **Tannin** cells present.

Stem T.S. Fig. 16. E, F; Pl. V. F.

Bicellular finger-like projections present; **glands** and **stomata** as in lamina. **Cuticle** thin and ridged. **Epidermis** of thin-walled, rectangular or cuboidal cells. **Cortex** consisting of 8–15 layers of chlorenchyma cells of variable size. **Endodermoid layer** represented by a highly distinctive layer of brachysclereids, separating cortex from 4–5 layers of fibres. **Vascular bundles**: common bundles V-shaped, with 1 phloem unit at converging ends of V, and 2 phloem units terminating flanges of V. Cauline bundles elliptical; 3 pairs of large vessels, average diameter 350 μm; 2 large phloem units on inner side of inner-most pair of large vessels and close to centre of pith, and another phloem unit at outer end. Average diameter of large sieve-tubes 98 μm. **Pith** area constituting one-third of central cylinder. **Starch grains** present in pith parenchyma. **Crystals**: idioblasts containing raphide bundles present. **Tannin** cells present.

TAXONOMIC NOTES

The representation of the endodermoid layer by a highly distinctive layer of brachysclereids separates this species from all other species investigated in this family.

MATERIAL EXAMINED

Dioscorea bulbifera L.: (i) Nigeria; FHI 54884 (FHI). (ii) Univ. Calif. Bot. Gard.; H. G. Baker, s.n. (UC). Leaf, petiole, stem. (iii) Philippines; J. V. Pancho, s.n. (LB). (iv) Nigeria; A. W. Waitt 11 (K). (v) Uganda; A. C. Tallantire 8. (vi) Trinidad, W. I.; J. A. Spence, s.n. (vii) Hort. Kew.

Subsection 3. ISOCANTHA

Leaf surface

Hairs absent; **glands** present mainly on abaxial surface. **Stomata**: average diameter 37×23 μm, mainly confined to abaxial surface; each stoma surrounded by 3–4 epidermal cells. Adaxial and abaxial anticlinal cell walls in *D. burchellii* sinuous; adaxial walls in *D. cotinifolia* straight; and adaxial walls slightly sinuous, abaxial walls sinuous in *D. mundtii*.

Lamina T.S.

Dorsivental. **Cuticle** thin and undulating on both surfaces, slightly thicker around main veins. **Epidermis:** adaxial composed of large rectangular cells with thin, straight, anticlinal walls. Abaxial cells smaller than adaxial cells. **Stomata:** walls of guard cells facing pore thickened and with no projecting ledges. **Mesophyll:** palisade tissue always 1-layered, not well differentiated in *D. cotinifolia*. Cells of spongy tissue mainly elongated, lying parallel to surface of lamina and occupying about two-thirds of mesophyll. **Vascular bundle** of midrib much larger than remainder. Xylem groups alternating with 2–3 phloem units. **Bundle sheath** of all vascular bundles poorly developed. **Crystals:** idioblasts containing raphide bundles present. **Tannin** cells present.

Petiole surface

Hairs absent; **glands** present. **Stomata** as in lamina.

Petiole T.S.

Outline pentagonal, nearly crescentiform in *D. burchellii*. **Cuticle** thin and ridged. **Epidermis** composed of thin-walled cuboidal cells. **Vascular bundles:** 6 (8 in *D. burchellii*), arranged in a circle, each bundle subtended by an arc of 2–3 layers of fibres and embedded in thin-walled parenchymatous tissue. 1–2 layers of lignified parenchyma occupying interfascicular regions. Xylem consisting of tracheids, vessels and associated parenchyma; phloem composed of small sieve-tubes, companion cells and phloem parenchyma. **Crystals:** idioblasts containing raphide bundles present. **Tannin** cells present.

Stem T.S. Pl. VI. A–C.

Hairs absent; **glands** and **stomata** as in lamina. **Cuticle** thick and ridged. **Epidermis** of thin-walled, rounded cells with cytoplasmic contents. Epidermis replaced by a layer of brachysclereids and hypodermis of thick-walled parenchyma cells in *D. trichantha*. **Cortex** consisting of 2–6 layers of chlorenchyma cells of variable size. **Endodermoid layer** separating cortex from 2–3 layers of lignified parenchyma. **Vascular bundles:** common bundles V-shaped, with 1 phloem unit between flanges of V; *D. trichantha* having somewhat U-shaped arrangement of 4 metaxylem vessels alternating with phloem units. Cauline bundles elliptical; 1 pair of large vessels, average diameter for *D. burchellii*, *D. cotinifolia*, and *D. mundtii* 93 μm; average diameter for *D. trichantha* 420 μm. One phloem unit on inner side of the single pair of large vessels (2 phloem units in *D. trichantha*) and close to centre of pith, and another phloem unit at outer end. Average diameter of large sieve-tubes 47 μm; 182 μm in *D. trichantha*. **Pith** area constituting about two-thirds of central cylinder. **Crystals:** idioblasts containing raphide bundles present. **Tannin** cells present.

TAXONOMIC NOTES

The presence of 2 phloem units on the inner side of the pair of large vessels in the cauline vascular bundles, and the replacement of the epidermis by a layer of brachysclereids with a distinct hypodermis, separate *D. trichantha* from the other species of this subsection.

MATERIAL EXAMINED

Dioscorea burchellii Baker; Cape Province, S. Africa; E. E. A. Archibald 7382 (K).

D. cotinifolia Kunth: (i) Pretoria, S. Africa; B. de Winter, s.n. (PRE). (ii) Hort. Kew; E. S. Ayensu, s.n. (K). Leaf, petiole, stem.

D. mundtii Baker; Hort. Kew; E. S. Ayensu, s.n. Leaf, petiole, stem.

D. trichantha Gleas.; Guyana; T. G. Tutin 51 (US). Stem (J).

Section TRIGONOBASIS

Leaf surface

Hairs unicellular, present on both surfaces, few along main veins on abaxial surface of *D. convolvulacea*; **glands** noted mainly on abaxial surface. **Stomata**: average size 37×24 μm, mainly confined to abaxial surface; each stoma surrounded by 3–5 epidermal cells. Adaxial anticlinal cell walls straight, abaxial walls sinuous or slightly sinuous.

Lamina T.S.

Dorsiventral. **Cuticle** thin and undulating, slightly thicker around main veins. **Epidermis**: adaxial cells mainly rectangular with thin, straight anticlinal walls; abaxial smaller than adaxial cells. **Stomata**: walls of guard cells facing pore thickened and with no projecting ledges. **Mesophyll**: palisade tissue always 1-layered. Cells of spongy tissue mainly elongated, lying parallel to surface of lamina and occupying about two-thirds of mesophyll. **Vascular bundle** of midrib much larger than remainder. Xylem groups alternating with 4 phloem units. **Bundle sheath** poorly developed. **Crystals**: idioblasts containing raphide bundles occurring in mesophyll. **Tannin** cells absent.

Petiole surface

Unicellular **hairs** and **glands** present. **Stomata** as in lamina.

Petiole T.S.

Outline somewhat crescentiform with 2 adaxial wings. **Cuticle** thin and ridged. **Epidermis** composed of thin-walled cuboidal cells with cytoplasmic contents. **Vascular bundles** varying in number from 6 (*D. galeottiana*) to 8 (*D. convolvulacea*), and embedded in thin-walled, large-celled parenchymatous tissue. Xylem consisting of tracheids, vessels, and associated parenchyma; phloem composed of small sieve-tubes, companion cells, and phloem parenchyma. **Crystals**: idioblasts containing raphide bundles few. **Tannin** cells present.

Stem T.S. Pl. VI. D, E.

Hairs, glands, and **stomata** as in lamina. **Cuticle** thick and ridged. **Epidermis** of thin-walled, rounded cells with cytoplasmic contents. **Cortex**: 4–6 layers of cells of variable size. **Endodermoid layer** separating cortex from thick-walled parenchyma cells. **Vascular bundles**: common bundles V-shaped, with 1 phloem unit at converging ends of V. Cauline bundles elliptical; 1 pair of large vessels, average diameter 231 μm. One large phloem unit on inner side of the single pair of large vessels and close to centre of pith, and another phloem unit at outer end. Average diameter of large sieve-tubes 105 μm. Phloem units sheathed with sclerenchyma. **Pith** area constituting half of central cylinder. **Crystals**: idioblasts containing raphide bundles present. **Tannin** cells noted.

Tuber T.S.

Epidermis not easily identifiable. **Cork**: first cork of primary origin; cells irregularly arranged. Storied cork of secondary origin, 5–6-layered; cells in radial rows, suberized. Cells of outer ground tissue large, spherical or irregular in outline and thin-walled; mainly radially arranged. **Vascular bundles** collateral, sporadically distributed in central ground tissue. Xylem consisting of short tracheids with scalariform to reticulate thickenings and blunt rounded ends. Phloem composed of small sieve-tubes and companion cells. **Starch grains** of variable size, mostly elliptical, hilum off-centre, evenly distributed throughout central ground tissue. **Crystals**: raphide bundles occurring at random. **Tannin** cells absent.

MATERIAL EXAMINED

Dioscorea convolvulacea Cham. & Schlechtd.; Puerto Rico; F. W. Martin, s.n. Leaf, petiole, stem, tuber.

D. galeottiana Knuth; Mexico; F. Miranda, s.n. Leaf, petiole, stem, tuber (J).

Section STENOCARPA

Stem T.S. Pl. VI. F.

Hairs absent; **glands** and **stomata** as in lamina of most species; stomata slightly sunken. **Cuticle** thin and undulating. **Epidermis** almost completely replaced by brachysclereids. **Cortex** consisting of 3–4 layers of cells of variable size. **Endodermoid layer** separating cortex from thick-walled fibres 3–5 cells thick. **Vascular bundles**: common bundles V-shaped; with 1 phloem unit at converging ends of V, and 2 phloem units terminating flanges of V. Cauline bundles somewhat elliptical; single large vessel, average diameter 210 μm. Two phloem units on inner side of vessel, and 1 phloem unit on outer side. Average diameter of large sieve-tubes 98 μm. **Pith** area constituting about one-tenth of central cylinder. **Crystals**: idioblasts containing raphide bundles absent. **Tannin** cells few.

TAXONOMIC NOTES

In *D. ternata* the epidermis is almost completely replaced by a band of brachysclereids; each cauline vascular bundle has only 1 large metaxylem vessel, thus recalling the condition in *D. sansibarensis* of section Opsophyton, subsection Macrourae, p. 86.

MATERIAL EXAMINED

Dioscorea ternata Griseb.; Brazil; A. Glaziou 14348 (US). Stem.

Section LASIOPHYTON
Leaf surface

Unicellular and bicellular **hairs** present, many on abaxial surface, mostly along main veins; **glands** present, mainly on abaxial surface. **Stomata**: average size 36×21 μm, confined to abaxial surface; each stoma surrounded by 3–5 epidermal cells. Adaxial anticlinal cell walls straight, abaxial walls sinuous.

Lamina T.S. Fig. 3.A, p. 34.

Dorsiventral. **Cuticle** thin and undulating on both surfaces, thicker around main veins. **Epidermis**: adaxial cells mainly rectangular with thin, straight anticlinal walls; abaxial smaller than adaxial cells. **Stomata**: walls of guard cells facing pore thickened and with no projecting ledges. **Mesophyll**: palisade tissue always 1-layered. Cells of spongy tissue mainly elongated, lying parallel to surface of lamina and occupying two-thirds of mesophyll. **Vascular bundle** of midrib much larger than remainder. Xylem groups alternating with 3 phloem units in *D. dregeana* and 10 in *D. dumetorum*. **Bundle sheath** around main veins poorly developed. **Crystals**: idioblasts containing raphide bundles present. **Tannin** cells absent.

Petiole surface

Unicellular and bicellular **hairs** and **glands** present. **Stomata** as in lamina.

Petiole T.S. Fig. 4H, p. 36.

Outline somewhat crescentiform, almost rounded in *D. dumetorum*. **Cuticle** thin and undulating. **Epidermis** composed of cuboidal and conical cells with cytoplasmic contents; cells lignified in *D. dumetorum*. **Cortex** separated from vascular cylinder by 2–3 layers of sclerenchyma. **Vascular bundles** 10–11, each bundle subtended by 3–5 layers of brachysclereids and lignified fibres. Lignified parenchyma in 1–2 layers occupying interfascicular regions. Xylem consisting of tracheids, vessels, and associated parenchyma; phloem composed of small sieve-tubes, companion cells, and phloem parenchyma. **Crystals**: idioblasts containing raphide bundles present. **Tannin** cells absent.

Stem T.S. Fig. 17. A–D; Pl. VII. A, B.

Hairs, glands, and **stomata** as in lamina. **Cuticle** thin and undulating. **Epidermis** of thin-walled, cuboidal or conical cells with cytoplasmic contents; cells lignified in *D. dumetorum*. **Cortex** consisting of chlorenchyma (6–10 layers) cells of variable size. **Endodermoid layer** separating cortex from vascular bundles in *D. dregeana*. Endodermoid layer consisting of 2–4 layers of brachysclereids in *D. dumetorum*. **Vascular bundles**: common bundles V-shaped (U-shaped in *D. dumetorum*), with 1 phloem unit at converging ends of V or U, and 2 phloem units terminating flanges. Cauline bundles elliptical; 1–2 pairs of large vessels, average diameter 238 μm. Two large phloem units on inner side of pair of vessels and close to centre of pith, and another

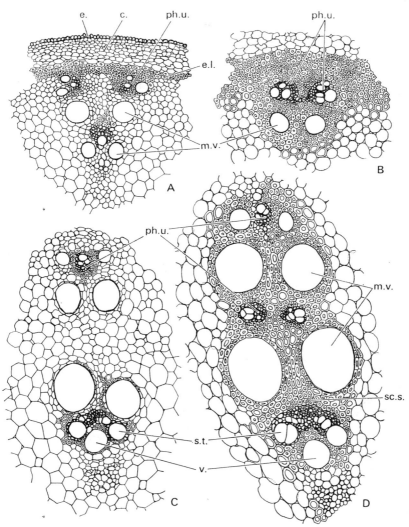

Fig. 17. Section Lasiophyton (×185). A,C, *Dioscorea dregeana*, T.S. A, common vascular bundle; C, cauline vascular bundle. B, D, *D. dumetorum*, T.S. B, common vascular bundle; D, cauline vascular bundle.

c., cortex; e., epidermis; e.l. endodermoid layer; m.v., metaxylem vessel; ph.u., phloem unit; sc.s., sclerenchyma sheath; s.t., sieve-tube; v., vessel.

phloem unit at outer end. A pair of large phloem units occurring on outer side of inner pair of large vessels of the cauline bundles and another common bundle situated on same radius as the cauline bundles in *D. dumetorum*. Average diameter of large sieve-tubes 98 μm. **Pith** area constituting about half of central cylinder. **Crystals**: idioblasts containing raphide bundles present. **Tannin** cells few.

Taxonomic Notes

The distribution of the common vascular bundles, the presence of 2 phloem units on outer side of the inner pair of large vessels of the cauline bundles, and the distribution of sclerenchyma within the vascular bundles of *D. dumetorum* separate this species from *D. dregeana*. *D. dumetorum* was described and placed in this section after Knuth's (1930) publication.

Material Examined

Dioscorea dregeana (Kunth) Th. Dur. & Sch.; Pretoria, S. Africa; B. de Winter s.n. (PRE). Leaf, petiole, stem.

D. dumetorum (Kunth) Pax: (i) Nigeria; A. W. Waitt 7 (K). (ii) Nigeria; FHI 54885 (FHI). (iii) Uganda; A. C. Tallantire 6. Leaf, petiole, stem (J).

Section TRIEUPHOROSTEMON

Leaf surface

Bicellular **hairs** present, many on abaxial surface; **glands** occurring mainly on abaxial surface. **Stomata:** average size 39×27 μm, confined to abaxial surface; each stoma surrounded by 3–5 epidermal cells. Adaxial and abaxial anticlinal cell walls straight.

Lamina T.S.

Dorsiventral. **Cuticle** thin and undulating, slightly thicker and ridged around principal veins. **Epidermis:** adaxial cells rectangular with thin, straight anticlinal walls and cytoplasmic contents; abaxial smaller than adaxial cells. **Stomata:** walls of guard cells facing pore thickened and with no projecting ledges. **Mesophyll:** palisade tissue always 1-layered. Cells of spongy tissue mainly elongated, lying parallel to surface of lamina and occupying two-thirds of mesophyll. **Vascular bundle** of midrib much larger than remainder. Xylem groups alternating with 3 phloem units. Sclerenchyma represented by 1–5 layers of fibres surrounding vascular bundle of midrib. **Crystals:** idioblasts containing raphide bundles, and styloids present. **Tannin** cells absent.

Petiole surface

Hairs, glands, and **stomata** as in lamina.

Petiole T.S.

Outline almost circular. **Cuticle** thin and undulating. **Epidermis** composed of thick-walled, rounded, or cuboidal cells. **Cortex** consisting of 8–14 layers of cells of variable size. Cortex separated from vascular cylinder by 2–4 layers of lignified parenchyma. **Vascular bundles** 7–8, each bundle subtended by 3–5 layers of fibres. Xylem consisting of tracheids, vessels, and associated parenchyma. Phloem composed of small sieve-tubes, companion cells, and phloem parenchyma. **Crystals:** idioblasts containing raphide bundles present. **Tannin** cells absent.

Stem T.S. Pl. VII. C.

Hairs, glands, and **stomata** as in lamina; few. **Cuticle** thin and undulating. **Epidermis** of thick-walled, cuboidal, or rounded cells, some retaining cytoplasm. **Cortex** consisting of 4–6 layers of cells of variable size. **Endodermoid layer** separating cortex from 4–8 layers of fibres. **Vascular bundles:** common bundles V-shaped, with 1 phloem unit at converging ends of V and 2 phloem units terminating flanges of V. Cauline bundles elliptical; 1 pair of large vessels, average diameter 308 μm. Two phloem units on inner side of the single pair of large vessels and another phloem unit at outer end. Average diameter of large sieve-tubes 133 μm. **Pith** area constituting almost half of central cylinder. **Crystals:** idioblasts containing raphide bundles present. **Tannin** cells absent.

Tuber T.S.

Epidermis partially replaced by corky layers, hence not easily identifiable. **Cork:** first cork of primary origin; cells irregularly arranged. Storied cork of secondary origin, 8–12-layered; cells in radial rows, suberized. Outer ground tissue of small, rounded or irregular, thin-walled cells, devoid of starch grains. **Vascular bundles** collateral, sporadically distributed in central ground tissue. Cells of central ground tissue larger than those of outer tissue. Xylem consisting of tracheids and associated parenchyma. Phloem composed of small sieve-tubes, companion cells, and phloem parenchyma. **Starch grains** of variable size, mostly elliptical, hilum off-centre; grains evenly distributed throughout central ground tissue. **Crystals:** raphide bundles present. **Tannin** cells absent.

Taxonomic Notes

The bicellular hairs and the general histology of the members of this section closely resemble the species of section Lasiophyton, p. 96.

Material Examined

Dioscorea pentaphylla L.: (i) China; C. O. Levine 9/28/17 (US). Stem. (ii) Philippines; G. Edano, s.n. (US). (iii) Philippines; J. V. Pancho, s.n. (LB). Leaf, petiole, stem. (iv) Madras, India; H. Santapau, s.n. Leaf, petiole, stem (J).

D. tomentosa Koenig: (i) Madras, India; H. Santapau s.n. (ii) Kerala, India, A. Abraham s.n.

Section BOTRYOSICYOS

Leaf surface

Bicellular **hairs** present along main veins of *D. cochleari-apiculata* and *D. retusa* and observed on both surfaces of *D. quartiniana*; **glands** principally on abaxial surface. **Stomata:** average size 34×23 μm, mainly confined to abaxial surface; each stoma surrounded by 3–4 epidermal cells. Adaxial anticlinal cell walls straight, abaxial walls slightly sinuous.

Lamina T.S. Fig. 18. B.

Dorsiventral. **Cuticle** thin and undulating, thicker around main veins. **Epidermis:** adaxial cells mainly rectangular with thin, straight anticlinal walls

and cytoplasmic contents; abaxial smaller than adaxial cells. **Stomata :** walls
of guard cells facing pore with upper and lower side thickened and with no
projecting ledges. **Mesophyll :** palisade tissue usually 1-layered, but sometimes
with a poorly developed second layer. Cells of spongy tissue mainly elongated

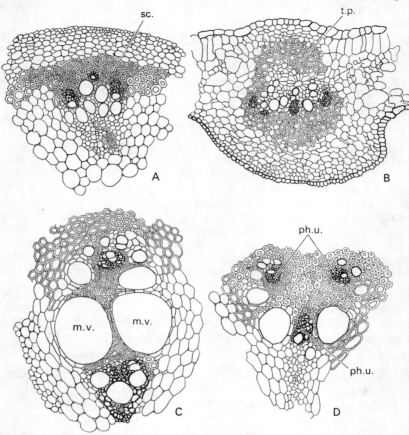

Fig. 18. Section Botryosicyos. *Dioscorea quartiniana* ($\times$185). A, T.S. portion of petiole.
B, T.S. leaf midrib. C, T.S. cauline vascular bundle. D, T.S. common vascular bundle.
m.v., metaxylem vessel; ph.u., phloem units; sc., sclerenchyma; t.p., thick-walled parenchyma.

parallel to surface of lamina and occupying half of mesophyll. **Vascular
bundle** of midrib much larger than remainder. Xylem groups alternating with
3–4 phloem units in *D. quartiniana*, 4 in *D. retusa*, and 9 in *D. cochleari-apiculata*. **Bundle sheath** poorly developed around main veins, but vascular bundle
of midrib embedded in sclerenchyma in *D. quartiniana*. **Crystals :** idioblasts
containing raphide bundles occurring in mesophyll. **Tannin** cells absent.

Petiole surface

Bicellular **hairs** present, abundant on *D. cochleari-apiculata*; **glands**
present. **Stomata** as in lamina.

Petiole T.S. Figs. 4. F, G, I, p. 36; 18. A.

Outline crescentiform in *D. retusa*, almost rounded in *D. cochleari-apiculata* and subcircular in *D. quartiniana*. **Cuticle** thin, generally wavy, but thick and ridged in places. **Epidermis** composed of thick-walled, rounded, sometimes cuboidal or conical cells with cytoplasmic contents. Sclerenchyma in many layers surrounding all vascular bundles in *D. quartiniana*; in *D. retusa* each vascular bundle subtended by 2–4 layers of fibres; in *D. cochleari-apiculata* vascular bundles embedded in thin-walled parenchymatous tissue. **Vascular bundles** varying in number from 7 (*D. cochleari-apiculata*) to 8 (*D. quartiniana*) and about 10 (*D. retusa*). Xylem consisting of tracheids, vessels, and associated parenchyma; phloem composed of small sieve-tubes, companion cells, and phloem parenchyma. **Crystals:** idioblasts containing raphide bundles present. **Tannin** cells present.

Stem T.S. Fig. 18. C, D; Pl. VII. D–F.

Hairs, glands, and **stomata** as in lamina. **Cuticle** thin and undulating. **Epidermis** of thick-walled, cuboidal cells; epidermis not easily identifiable in some specimens of *D. retusa* and apparently replaced by 4–6-layered periderm. **Cortex** consisting of several layers of chlorenchyma cells of variable size. **Endodermoid layer** separating cortex from sclerenchyma. **Vascular bundles:** common bundles V-shaped, with 1 phloem unit at converging ends of V-shaped metaxylem and 2 phloem units terminating flanges of V; in *D. cochleari-apiculata* and *D. retusa* additional phloem unit developing between flanges of V. Cauline bundles elliptical; 1–2 pairs of large vessels, average vessel diameter 219 μm. Two phloem units on inner side of innermost pair of large vessels and close to centre of pith, and another phloem unit at outer end. Average diameter of large sieve-tubes 98 μm. **Pith** area constituting about half of central cylinder in *D. cochleari-apiculata* and *D. retusa*, and about one-third in *D. quartiniana*. **Crystals:** idioblasts containing raphide bundles present. **Tannin** cells present.

Tuber T.S.

Epidermis not easily identifiable. **Cork:** first cork of primary origin, cells irregularly arranged. Storied cork of secondary origin, 4–6-layered; cells in radial rows, suberized. Outer ground tissue of large, rounded, thin-walled cells; many-layered, compressed. **Vascular bundles** collateral, sporadically distributed in central ground tissue. Xylem consisting of long tracheids with scalariform to reticulate thickenings; phloem composed of small sieve-tubes, companion cells, and phloem parenchyma. **Starch grains** of variable size, mostly rounded, hilum in centre, grains evenly distributed throughout central ground tissue. **Crystals:** raphide bundles. **Tannin** cells occurring at random.

Root T.S.

Outer tissues not seen. **Endodermis** 1-layered, cells with all walls only slightly thickened. Passage cells present. **Pericycle** 2–3-layered, inner layer interrupted by tracheal elements. **Stele** 18-arch; xylem consisting of vessels (with large vessels near central portion of vascular core), tracheids, and xylem parenchyma; phloem composed of sieve-tubes, companion cells, and phloem parenchyma; phloem alternating with xylem strands towards periphery of central cylinder. **Pith** constituting about half of central cylinder. **Crystals:** raphide bundles present. **Tannin** cells present.

TAXONOMIC NOTES

The presence of periderm in the stem of some specimens of *D. retusa* needs further study.

MATERIAL EXAMINED

Dioscorea cochleari-apiculata de Wild; Zambia; D. B. Fanshawe F8254 (K). Leaf, petiole, stem, tuber, root.

D. quartiniana A. Rich.: (i) Nigeria; A. W. Waitt 23 (K). Leaf, petiole, stem. (ii) Zambia; D. B. Fanshawe, s.n. (NDO). Leaf, petiole, stem.

D. retusa Mast.; West and East Transvaal; B. de Winter, s.n. (PRE). Leaf, petiole, stem.

SUBGENUS II. DIOSCOREA Pax

Section MACROGYNODIUM

Leaf surface

Hairs absent from both surfaces of *D. bernoulliana* and *D. urophylla*; unicellular hairs present along main veins of *D. dugesii* and *D. trifida*; **glands** noted on abaxial surface. **Stomata:** average size 30×22 μm, confined to abaxial surface; each stoma surrounded by 3–5 epidermal cells. Adaxial anticlinal cell walls straight, abaxial walls slightly sinuous.

Lamina T.S. Fig. 19. A.

Dorsiventral. **Cuticle** thin and undulating on both surfaces, thicker and ridged around main veins. **Epidermis:** adaxial cells large, rectangular with thin, straight anticlinal walls and cytoplasmic contents; abaxial mostly smaller than adaxial cells. **Stomata:** inner walls of guard cells facing pore thickened and walls with no projecting ledges. **Mesophyll:** palisade tissue always 1-layered. Cells of spongy tissue mainly elongated, lying parallel to surface of lamina and occupying about half of mesophyll. **Vascular bundle** of midrib much larger than remainder. Xylem groups often alternating with about 4–6 phloem units. **Bundle sheath:** 2–3 layers of parenchymatous cells developed around each vascular bundle. **Crystals:** idioblasts containing raphide bundles common; cuboidal and rectangular crystals present in *D. urophylla* and *D. bernoulliana* respectively. **Tannin** cells present.

Petiole surface

Hairs present or absent as indicated for leaf surface; **glands** present. **Stomata** as in lamina.

Petiole T.S. Fig. 19. B.

Outline pentagonal; heptagonal in *D. bernoulliana*. **Cuticle** thin and ridged. **Epidermis** composed of circular cells. **Cortex** 6–8-layered. **Sclerenchyma** 3–5-

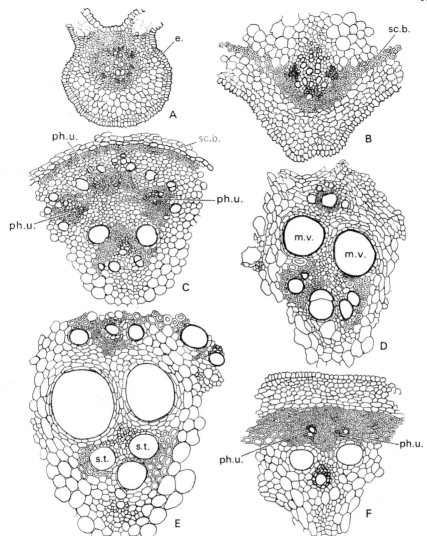

FIG. 19. Section Macrogynodium. A, *Dioscorea urophylla*, T.S. leaf midrib (×92). B, *D. bernoulliana*, T.S. portion of petiole (×185). C, *D. dugesii*, T.S. common vascular bundle (×185). D, *D. trifida*, T.S. cauline vascular bundle (×92). E, F, *D. urophylla*, T.S.: E, cauline vascular bundle (×185); F, common vascular bundle (×185).

e., epidermis; m.v., metaxylem vessel; ph.u., phloem unit; sc.b., sclerenchyma band; s.t., sieve-tubes.

layered, separating cortex from vascular cylinder in *D. bernoulliana*. **Vascular bundles:** 7 and 8 in *D. dugesii* and *D. urophylla* respectively, each bundle subtended by 2–3 layers of fibres. Xylem consisting of tracheids, vessels, and associated parenchyma; phloem composed of small sieve-tubes, companion cells, and phloem parenchyma. **Crystals:** idioblasts containing raphide bundles present. **Tannin** cells present.

Stem T.S. Fig. 19. C–F; Pl. VIII. A–D.

Hairs, glands, and **stomata** as in lamina. **Cuticle** thick and ridged. **Epidermis** of thick-walled rounded cells with cytoplasmic contents. **Cortex** consisting of 3–10 layers of cells of variable size. **Endodermoid layer** separating cortex from 2 to 4 layers of fibres. **Vascular bundles:** common bundles V-shaped, with 1 phloem unit at converging ends of V, and 2 phloem units terminating flanges of V. In *D. dugesii* 4–7 phloem units connecting flanges of V. Cauline bundles elliptical; 1 pair of large vessels, average diameter 266 μm. Two large phloem units (1 phloem unit in *D. bernoulliana*) on inner side of the single pair of large vessels and another phloem unit at outer end. Average diameter of large sieve-tubes 115 μm. Vascular bundles embedded in brachysclereids in *D. dugesii*. **Pith** area constituting one-fourth of central cylinder. **Starch grains** present in stem of *D. trifida*. **Crystals:** idioblasts of raphide bundles. **Tannin** cells present.

Tuber T.S.

Epidermis not easily identifiable. **Cork:** first cork of primary origin; cells irregularly arranged. Storied cork of secondary origin, 6–12-layered; cells in radial rows, suberized. Ground tissue of large rounded or irregular thin-walled cells, somewhat radially arranged. **Vascular bundles** collateral, sporadically distributed in ground tissue. Xylem consisting of short, blunt-ended tracheids with scalariform to reticulate thickenings; phloem composed of small sieve-tubes and companion cells. **Starch grains** of variable size, triangular and elliptical in *D. urophylla*, mostly spherical in other species. **Crystals:** raphide bundles. **Tannin** cells occurring at random.

TAXONOMIC NOTES

Cauline vascular bundles of *D. dugesii* are tightly embedded in brachysclereids. *D. bernoulliana* differs from other species in having only 1 phloem unit on inner side of the pair of large metaxylem vessels.

MATERIAL EXAMINED

Dioscorea bernoulliana Prain & Burk.; Puerto Rico; F. W. Martin, s.n. Leaf, petiole, stem, tuber.

D. dugesii Robinson; Puerto Rico; F. W. Martin, s.n. Leaf, petiole, stem, tuber.

D. trifida L.: (i) Costa Rica; H. Piltier 16323 (US). (ii) Peru; G. Klug 976 (US). Leaf, stem.

D. urophylla Hemsl.; Puerto Rico; F. W. Martin, s.n. Leaf, petiole, stem, tuber (J).

Section APODOSTEMON

Leaf surface

Hairs absent; **glands** noted, mainly on abaxial surfaces. **Stomata:** average size 30 × 24 μm, confined to abaxial surface; each stoma surrounded by 3–5 epidermal cells. Adaxial anticlinal cell walls straight, abaxial walls slightly sinuous.

Lamina T.S.

Dorsiventral. **Cuticle** thin and undulating on both surfaces, thicker and ridged around principal veins. **Epidermis:** adaxial cells large, rectangular with thin, straight, anticlinal walls and cytoplasmic contents; abaxial smaller than adaxial cells. **Stomata:** walls of guard cells facing pore thickened, especially inner walls, and with no projecting ledges. **Mesophyll:** palisade tissue always 1-layered. Cells of spongy tissue mainly elongated, lying parallel to surface of lamina and occupying two-thirds of mesophyll. **Vascular bundle** of midrib much larger than remainder. Xylem groups alternating with 6–10 phloem units. **Bundle sheath** of midrib vascular bundle replaced by 4–6 layers of sclerenchyma. **Crystals:** idioblasts containing raphide bundles. **Tannin** cells present.

Petiole surface

Hairs absent; **glands** and **stomata** as in lamina.

Petiole T.S. Fig. 20. A, D.

Outline pentagonal with 5 prominent wings. **Cuticle** thick and ridged. **Epidermis** composed of cuboidal or conical cells. **Cortex:** 4–10 layers. **Vascular bundles:** 6 in *D. spiculiflora*, 7 in *D. friedrichsthalii*, each bundle partly surrounded by 4–6 layers of fibres. Xylem consisting of tracheids, vessels, and associated parenchyma; phloem composed of small sieve-tubes, companion cells, and phloem parenchyma. **Crystals:** idioblasts containing raphide bundles. **Tannin** cells observed.

Stem T.S. Fig. 20. B, C, E, F; Pl. VIII. E, F.

Hairs absent; **glands** and **stomata** as in lamina. **Cuticle** thick and undulating. **Epidermis** of thick-walled cuboidal cells. **Cortex** consisting of 4–8 layers of cells of variable size. **Endodermoid layer** represented by 3 layers of brachysclereids, separating cortex from vascular cylinder. **Vascular bundles:** common bundles V-shaped, with 1 phloem unit at converging ends of V, and 2 phloem units terminating flanges of V. Cauline bundles elliptical; 1 pair of large vessels, average diameter 196 μm. One large phloem unit on inner side of the single pair of large vessels and close to centre of pith, and another phloem unit at outer end. Average diameter of large sieve-tubes 105 μm. **Pith** area constituting between one-third and one-fifth of central cylinder. **Crystals:** idioblasts containing raphide bundles few. **Tannin** cells absent.

Tuber T.S.

Epidermis not easily identifiable. **Cork:** first cork of primary origin, cells irregularly arranged, suberized, innermost row consisting of brachysclereids in *D. spiculiflora*. Storied cork of secondary origin, 4–10-layered, cells in radial rows, suberized. **Vascular bundles:** collateral, sporadically distributed in ground tissue. Xylem consisting of tracheids with scalariform to reticulate

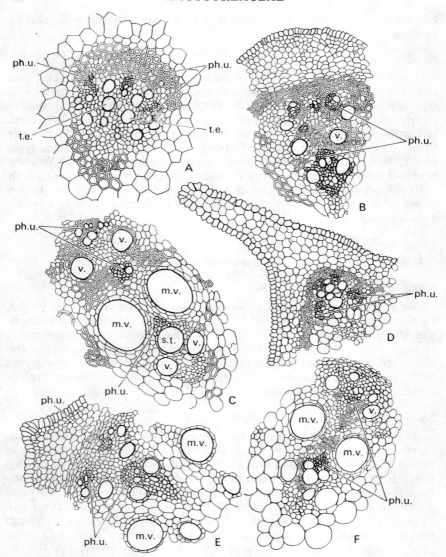

Fig. 20. Section Apodostemon (×185). A–C, *Dioscorea friedrichsthalii*: A, T.S. vascular bundle from petiole; B, T.S. common vascular bundle; C, T.S. cauline vascular bundle. D–F, *D. spiculiflora*: D, T.S. adxaial wing of petiole; E, T.S. common vascular bundle; F, T.S. cauline vascular bundle.

m.v. metaxylem vessel; ph.u., phloem unit; s.t., sieve-tube; t.e., tracheal elements; v., vessel.

thickenings; phloem composed of small sieve-tubes and companion cells. **Starch grains** of almost equal size, mostly spherical; grains evenly distributed in central ground tissue. **Crystals:** raphide bundles present. **Tannin** cells absent.

MATERIAL EXAMINED

Dioscorea friedrichsthalii Knuth; Puerto Rico; PI Acc. No. 11571. Leaf, petiole, stem, tuber.

D. spiculiflora Hemsl.: (i) Florida; PI 252684. (ii) Puerto Rico; F. W. Martin, s.n. Leaf, petiole, stem, tuber (J).

Section MACROPODA

Leaf surface. Fig. 21. A, B.

Unicellular **hairs** present on abaxial surface of *D. zingiberensis* and *D. villosa*, and multicellular hairs on *D. villosa*, hairs absent from other species; **glands** noted on abaxial surface. **Stomata**: average size 37×24 μm, confined to abaxial surface; each stoma surrounded by 2–4 epidermal cells. Adaxial anticlinal cell walls straight or curved, abaxial cell walls slightly sinuous, abaxial walls in *D. zingiberensis* straight.

Lamina T.S. Fig. 21. C.

Dorsiventral. **Cuticle** thin and undulating, slightly thicker and ridged around main veins. **Epidermis**: adaxial cells mainly rectangular with thin, straight, anticlinal walls; abaxial smaller than adaxial cells; epidermal cells generally cuboidal, with 3 large conical cells on abaxial side of main veins in *D. balcanica*. **Stomata**: walls of guard cells facing pore thickened and with no projecting ledges. **Mesophyll**: palisade tissue always 1-layered. Cells of spongy tissue mainly elongated parallel to surface of lamina and occupying about half of mesophyll. **Vascular bundle** of midrib much larger than remainder. Xylem groups alternating with 3–6 phloem units. Vascular bundles surrounded by 3–4 layers of fibres. **Crystals**: idioblasts containing raphide bundles. **Tannin** cells present.

Petiole surface

Hairs, glands, and **stomata** as in lamina.

Petiole T.S.

Outline polygonal, with 2 wings, except in *D. prazeri*, where outline almost circular. **Cuticle** thin and undulating; thick and ridged in *D. balcanica*. **Epidermis** composed of thin- to thick-walled cuboidal cells with cytoplasmic contents. **Cortex** consisting of 5–12 layers of cells of fairly uniform size. Each bundle subtended by 2–4 layers of fibres. **Vascular bundles** variable in number from 6 (*D. deltoidea*) to 7 (*D. balcanica*) and 14 (*D. villosa*), 1–2 layers of fibres occupying interfascicular regions. Xylem consisting of tracheids, vessels, and associated parenchyma; phloem composed of small sieve-tubes, companion cells, and phloem parenchyma. **Crystals**: idioblasts containing raphide bundles. **Tannin** cells present.

Stem T.S. Fig. 21. D–F; Pl. IX. A–D.

Hairs, glands, stomata as in lamina. **Cuticle** thick or thin, ridged or undulating. **Epidermis** composed of thick-walled cuboidal cells with dense cytoplasmic contents. **Cortex**: 8–12 layers of chlorenchyma cells of fairly uniform

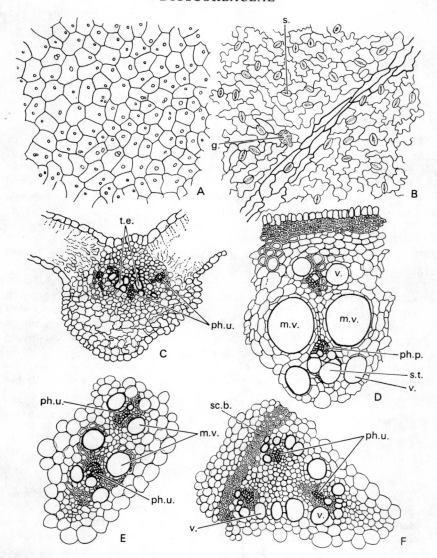

FIG. 21. Section Macropoda (×185). A, B, *Dioscorea balcanica*: A, Adaxial epidermis, surface view; B, Abaxial epidermis, surface view. C, *D. deltoidea*, T.S. leaf midrib. D, *D. zingiberensis*, T.S. portion of stem, showing cauline vascular bundle. E, F, *D. villosa*, T.S. E, cauline vascular bundle; F, common vascular bundle.

g., gland; m.v., metaxylem vessel; ph.p., phloem parenchyma; ph.u., phloem unit; s., stoma; sc.b., sclerenchyma band; s.t., sieve-tube; t.e., tracheal element; v., vessel.

size; 2–3 outer layers composed of collenchyma cells. **Endodermoid layer** separating cortex from 2–3 layers of sclerenchyma. **Vascular bundles:** common bundles V-shaped, with 1 phloem unit at converging ends of V and 2 phloem units terminating flanges of V, except *D. deltoidea* with only 1 large phloem unit within V. Cauline bundles elliptical; 1–2 pairs of large vessels, average diameter 171 μm. One phloem unit on inner side of innermost pair of vessels (2 phloem units in *D. balcanica*) and close to centre of pith, and another phloem unit at outer end. Average diameter of sieve-tubes 70 μm. **Pith** area constituting between half and two-thirds of central cylinder. **Crystals:** idioblasts containing raphide bundles; rhomboidal crystals occurring in endodermoid cells. **Tannin** cells present.

Rhizome T.S.

Epidermis composed of thick-walled cuboidal cells, compactly arranged. **Cuticle** not easily identifiable. **Cortex:** 6–10 layers of parenchyma cells of fairly uniform size. **Endodermoid layer** replaced by 2–3 layers of fibres, separating cortex from vascular cylinder. **Vascular bundles** collateral, sporadically distributed in pith parenchyma. Xylem consisting of short tracheids and xylem parenchyma; phloem composed of small sieve-tubes, companion cells, and phloem parenchyma. **Starch grains** numerous, variable in size and shape; grains filling pith parenchyma cells. Central cylinder constituting four-fifths of rhizome diameter. **Crystals:** idioblasts containing raphide bundles absent. **Tannin** cells present in cortex only.

Tuber T.S.

Epidermis not easily identifiable. **Cork:** first cork of primary origin; cells irregularly arranged. Storied cork in 8–15 layers, of secondary origin; cells in radial rows, compactly arranged, suberized. Outer ground tissue of small rounded, thin-walled cells, many-layered, compressed. Central ground tissue of large rectangular cells with somewhat storied arrangement. **Vascular bundles** collateral, sporadically distributed in central ground tissue. Xylem consisting of short tracheids with reticulate thickenings; phloem composed of small sieve-tubes, companion cells, and phloem parenchyma. **Starch grains** of variable size, mostly rectangular and rounded, grains distributed evenly throughout central ground tissue. **Crystals:** raphide bundles. **Tannin** cells present in outer ground tissue.

Root T.S.

Epidermis slightly thick-walled, cells compactly arranged. **Cortex** composed of several layers of thin-walled parenchymatous tissue, consisting of half (*D. balcanica*) to two-thirds (*D. caucasica*) of root diameter. **Endodermis** 1-layered, cells with characteristic U-shaped thickenings; all walls slightly thickened in *D. balcanica*. Passage cells present. **Pericycle** 2–3-layered, inner layer interrupted by tracheal elements. **Stele** 12-arch; 6-arch in *D. caucasica*. Xylem consisting of vessels (large vessels near central portion of vascular core), tracheids, and xylem parenchyma; phloem composed of sieve-tubes, companion cells, and phloem parenchyma. Phloem alternating with xylem strands towards periphery of central cylinder. **Pith** parenchyma replaced by fibres in *D. balcanica* and by thick-walled parenchymatous tissue in *D. caucasica*. **Crystals:** raphide bundles. **Tannin** cells present.

MATERIAL EXAMINED

Dioscorea balcanica Kosanin; Hort. Kew; E. S. Ayensu, s.n. (K). Leaf, petiole, stem, tuber, root (J).

D. caucasica Lipsky; Hort. Kew; E. S. Ayensu, s.n. (K). Leaf, petiole, stem, rhizome, root (J).

D. deltoidea Wall; Hort. Kew; E. S. Ayensu, s.n. (K). Leaf, petiole, stem (J).

D. prazeri Prain & Burk.; Hort. Kew; E. S. Ayensu, s.n. (K). Leaf, petiole, stem (J).

D. villosa L.; Hort. Kew; E. S. Ayensu, s.n. (K). Leaf, petiole, stem (J).

D. zingiberensis Wright; Hupeh, China; E. H. Wilson 2921 (US). Leaf, stem (J).

Section HETEROSTEMON

Leaf surface

Hairs absent; **glands** present on abaxial surface. **Stomata**: average size 43×30 μm, confined to abaxial surface; each stoma surrounded by 3–4 epidermal cells. Adaxial anticlinal cell walls straight, abaxial walls slightly sinuous.

Lamina T.S. Fig. 22. C; Pl. I. A, B.

Dorsiventral. **Cuticle** thin and undulating, thick and ridged around main veins. **Epidermis**: adaxial cells large, rectangular with thin, straight, anticlinal walls, and distinct cytoplasmic contents; abaxial smaller than adaxial cells. **Stomata**: wall of guard cells facing pore thickened and with no projecting ledges. **Mesophyll**: palisade tissue often indistinguishable from spongy tissue; where distinct from palisade tissue, spongy tissue occupying two-thirds of mesophyll. **Vascular bundle** of midrib much larger than remainder. Xylem groups alternating with 5–14 phloem units. Sclerenchyma represented by 4–6 layers of fibres partly surrounding vascular bundle of midrib. **Crystals**: idioblasts containing raphide bundles and rhomboidal crystals present. **Tannin** cells numerous in mesophyll.

Petiole surface

Hairs absent; **glands** and **stomata** as in lamina.

Petiole T.S. Fig. 22. E.

Outline pentagonal with 2 wings towards adaxial side. **Cuticle** thick and ridged. **Epidermis** composed of cuboidal cells. **Cortex** 4–10-layered. **Endodermoid layer** separating 2–5 layers of sclerenchyma and cortex from vascular cylinder. **Vascular bundles** 6, arranged in a circle, embedded in parenchymatous tissue. Xylem consisting of tracheids, vessels, and associated parenchyma; phloem composed of sieve-tubes, companion cells, and phloem parenchyma. **Crystals**: idioblasts containing raphide bundles and rhomboidal crystals present. **Tannin** cells noted. Extra-floral **glands** present (see p. 63).

Stem T.S. Fig. 22. F; Pl. IX. E, F; Pl. X. A.

Hairs absent; **glands** and **stomata** as in lamina. **Cuticle** thick and ridged. **Epidermis** of thick-walled circular or dome-shaped cells, and with cytoplasmic

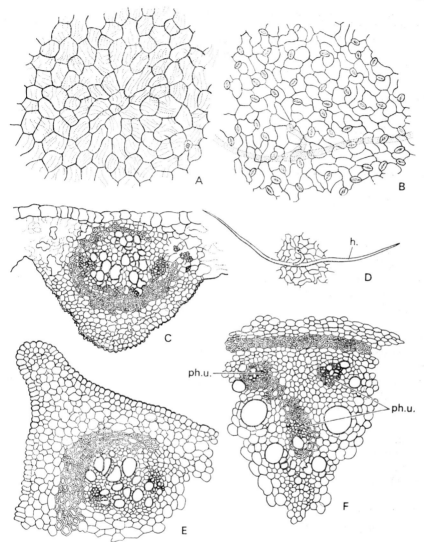

Fig. 22. Sections Heterostemon and Combilium (×185). A, B, D, *Dioscorea esculenta*: A, Adaxial epidermis, surface view; B, Abaxial epidermis, surface view; D, T-shaped hair on abaxial epidermis, surface view. C, E, *D. floribunda*: C, T.S. leaf midrib; E, T.S. portion of petiole. F, *D. composita*, T.S. portion of stem showing common vascular bundle.

h., hair, T-shaped; ph.u., phloem unit.

contents. **Cortex:** 6–10 layers of cells of variable size; 1–3 outer layers collenchymatous. **Endodermoid layer** separating cortex from 2–3 layers of fibres. **Vascular bundles:** common bundles V-shaped, with 1 phloem unit at converging ends of V, and 2 phloem units terminating flanges of V. Cauline bundles elliptical; 1 pair of large vessels, average diameter 430 μm. One large phloem unit on inner side of the single pair of large vessels and close to centre of pith and another phloem unit at outer end. Average diameter of large sieve-tubes 196 μm. **Pith** area constituting one-fourth of central cylinder. **Crystals**: idioblasts containing raphide bundles and cuboidal crystals present. **Tannin** cells observed. Extra-floral **glands** present.

MATERIAL EXAMINED

Dioscorea composita Hemsl.: (i) Mexico; F. Miranda, s.n. (ii) Florida, U.S.A.; PI 201783. (iii) Nigeria; A. W. Waitt 17 (K). (iv) Hort Kew; E.S. Ayensu, s.n. (K). (v) Mexico; J. T. Baldwin, Jr. 14368 (US). Leaf, petiole, stem (J).

D. floribunda Mart. & Gal.: (i) Puerto Rico; F. W. Martin, s.n. (ii) Florida, U.S.A.; PI 230618. (iii) Florida, U.S.A.; PI 201748. (iv) Nigeria; A. W. Waitt 15 (K). Leaf, petiole, stem (J).

Section COMBILIUM

Leaf surface Fig. 22. A, B, D.

Hairs T-shaped, observed on abaxial surface; **glands** present on abaxial surface. **Stomata**: average size 39×27 μm, confined to abaxial surface; each stoma surrounded by 2–4 epidermal cells. Adaxial anticlinal cell walls straight or curved, abaxial walls slightly sinuous.

Lamina T.S.

Dorsiventral. **Cuticle** thin and undulating, slightly thicker and ridged around main veins. **Epidermis**: adaxial cells large, rectangular, with thin, straight, anticlinal walls; abaxial smaller than adaxial cells. **Stomata**: walls of guard cells facing pore thickened and with no projecting ledges. **Mesophyll**: palisade tissue always 2-layered. Cells of spongy tissue somewhat elongated, lying parallel to surface of lamina and occupying about half of mesophyll. **Vascular bundle** of midrib much larger than remainder. Xylem groups alternating with 5 phloem units towards abaxial side of midrib. Sclerenchyma of midrib represented by 2–3 rows of fibres partly surrounding phloem units. **Crystals**: idioblasts containing raphide bundles. **Tannin** cells present.

Petiole surface

Hairs, **glands**, and **stomata** as in lamina.

Petiole T.S.

Outline polygonal or rounded. **Cuticle** thin and undulating. **Epidermis** composed of thin-walled cuboidal cells. **Cortex**: 6–8 layers of cells of variable size. Sclerenchyma represented by 3–5 layers of fibres separating cortex from vascular cylinder. **Vascular bundles** 8, arranged in a circle. Xylem consisting of tracheids, vessels, and associated parenchyma; phloem composed of sieve-tubes, companion cells, and phloem parenchyma. **Crystals**: idioblasts containing raphide bundles not observed. **Tannin** cells present. Extra-floral **glands** noted (see p. 63).

Stem T.S. Pl. X. B, C.

Hairs absent; **glands** and **stomata** as in lamina. **Cuticle** thick and ridged. **Epidermis** of thick-walled rounded cells with dense cytoplasmic contents. **Cortex**: 5–8 layers of cells of variable size; 1–3 outer layers collenchymatous. Sclerenchyma represented by 3 layers of brachyscereids separating **endodermoid layer** from vascular cylinder. **Vascular bundles**: common bundles V-shaped, with 1 phloem unit at converging ends of V, and 2 or more phloem units terminating flanges of V. Cauline bundles elliptical; 1 pair of large vessels, average diameter 420 μm. Two phloem units on inner side of the single pair of large vessels and close to centre of pith, and 2 or more phloem units at outer end. Average diameter of large sieve-tubes 196 μm. **Pith** area constituting about one-third of central cylinder. **Crystals**: idioblasts containing raphide bundles and rhomboidal crystals present. **Tannin** cells observed.

MATERIAL EXAMINED

Dioscorea esculenta (Lour.) Burk.: (i) Nigeria; A. W. Waitt 13 (K). (ii) Trinidad, W.I.; J. A. Spence, s.n. Leaf, petiole, stem (J).

D. flabellifolia Prain & Burk.: (i) N. Borneo; M. Ramos 1625 (US). (ii) Philippines; M. Ramos, s.n. (US). Stem (J).

Section OXYPETALUM

Stem T.S. Fig. 23. A–F; Pl. X. D, E.

Hairs absent; **glands** present. **Stomata** slightly sunken. **Cuticle** thick (14 μm) and undulating, ridged in places. **Epidermis** of thin-walled cuboidal cells with dense cytoplasmic contents. **Cortex**: 4–6 layers of cells of variable size; sclerenchyma represented by 1–3 layers of brachyscereids separating **endodermoid layer** from vascular cylinder. **Vascular bundles**: common bundles V-shaped, with 1 phloem unit at converging ends of V and 2 phloem units (except in *D. carionis*) terminating flanges of V. Somewhat elliptical group of metaxylem vessels and tracheids occurring in *D. carionis* with 2 phloem units radially orientated within it. Cauline bundles elliptical; 1 pair of large vessels, average diameter 455 μm. One phloem unit on inner side of the single pair of large vessels and close to centre of pith, and another phloem unit at outer end. Average diameter of large sieve-tubes 245 μm. **Pith** area constituting about one-fourth of central cylinder. **Crystals**: idioblasts containing raphide bundles. **Tannin** cells present.

MATERIAL EXAMINED

Dioscorea carionis Prain & Burk.: (i) Guatemala; P. C. Standley 68065 (US). (ii) Mexico; E. Matuda 2817 (US). Stem.

D. densiflora Hemsl.: (i) Guatemala; B. A. Krukoff D3 (US). (ii) British Honduras; P. H. Gentle 2210 (US). Stem (J).

Section BRACHYSTIGMA

Stem T.S. Fig. 23. G; Pl. X. F.

Hairs absent; **glands** present. **Stomata** observed. **Cuticle** thin and undulating. **Epidermis** of thin-walled irregular cells with dense cytoplasmic contents.

854376X   I

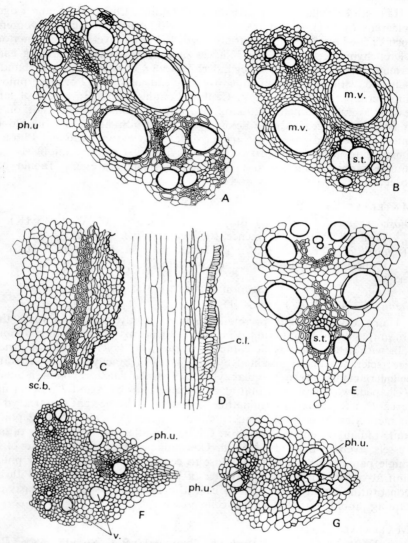

Fig. 23. Sections Oxypetalum and Brachystigma. A, E, *Dioscorea carionis*, T.S. A, cauline vascular bundle (×92); E, common vascular bundle (×185). B–D, F, *D. densiflora*: B, T.S. cauline vascular bundle (×92); C, T.S. portion of stem showing 1–3 layers of brachy-sclereids (×185); D, L.S. stem, cortical region (×185); F, T.S. common vascular bundle (×92). G, *D. sinuata*, T.S. common vascular bundle (×92).

c.l., corky layer; m.v., metaxylem vessel; ph.u., phloem unit; sc.b., sclerenchyma band; s.t., sieve-tube; v., vessel.

Cortex: 3–4 layers of cells of variable size. **Endodermoid layer** separating cortex from vascular cylinder. **Vascular bundles:** common bundles somewhat elliptical, with 2 phloem units radially orientated within the vascular bundle. Cauline bundles elliptical; 1 pair of large vessels, average diameter 224 μm. One phloem unit on inner side of the single pair of large vessels and close to centre of pith, and another phloem unit at outer end. Average diameter of large sieve-tubes 126 μm. **Pith** area constituting about one-third of central cylinder. **Crystals:** idioblasts containing raphide bundles especially numerous in pith parenchyma. **Tannin** cells present.

SPECIAL NOTE

The radial orientation of the 2 phloem units within the common vascular bundle in *D. sinuata* recalls the situation observed in *D. carionis* (section Oxypetalum, p. 113).

MATERIAL EXAMINED

Dioscorea sinuata Vell.: (i) Brazil; L. B. Smith & R. Klein 11131 (US). (ii) Argentina; A. Krapovickas 2767 (US). Stem (J).

Section LYCHNOSTEMON

Leaf surface

Hairs absent; **glands** noted on abaxial surface. **Stomata:** average size 30 × 23 μm, confined to abaxial surface; each stoma surrounded by 3–4 epidermal cells. Adaxial anticlinal cell walls straight, abaxial walls slightly sinuous.

Lamina T.S.

Dorsiventral. **Cuticle** thin and undulating, slightly thicker and ridged around main veins. **Epidermis:** adaxial cells rectangular, with thin, straight, anticlinal walls; abaxial smaller than adaxial cells. **Stomata:** walls of guard cells facing pore thickened and with no projecting ledges. **Mesophyll:** palisade tissue always 1-layered in *D. polygonoides*, 2-layered in *D. ceratandra*. Cells of spongy tissue mainly elongated, lying parallel to surface of lamina and occupying about two-thirds of mesophyll. **Vascular bundle** of midrib much larger than remainder. Xylem groups alternating with 3–4 phloem units towards abaxial side of midrib. **Crystals:** idioblasts containing raphide bundles. **Tannin** cells present.

Petiole surface

Hairs absent; **glands** and **stomata** as in lamina.

Petiole T.S. Fig. 24. A.

Outline polygonal (*D. polygonoides*) or pentagonal (*D. ceratandra*). **Cuticle** thick and ridged. **Epidermis** composed of thin-walled, conical, circular, or irregular cells, and with dense cytoplasmic contents. **Cortex:** 5–16 layers of cells of variable size. **Vascular bundles** 6, arranged in a circle, each bundle

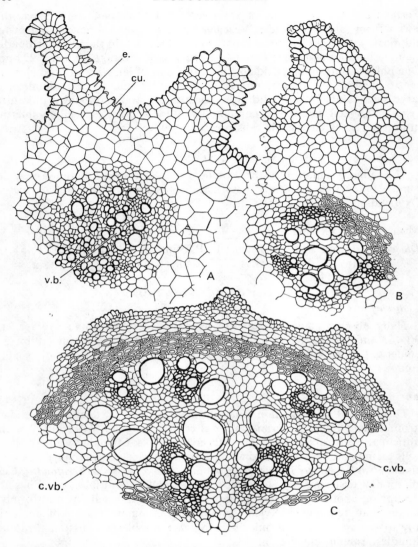

FIG. 24. Sections Lychnostemon and Macrocarpaea (×185). A, C, *Dioscorea polygonoides*: A, T.S. petiole showing portion of polygonal outline; C, T.S. portion of stem showing two common bundles lying side by side. B, *D. preussii*, T.S. petiole showing portion of pentagonal outline.

cu., cuticle; c.vb., common vascular bundle; e., epidermis; v.b., vascular bundle.

surrounded by 2–6 layers of thin-walled parenchymatous tissue. Xylem consisting of tracheids, vessels, and associated parenchyma; phloem composed of small sieve-tubes, companion cells, and phloem parenchyma. **Crystals:** idioblasts containing raphide bundles few. **Tannin** cells present.

Stem T.S. Fig. 24. C; Pl. XI. A.

Hairs absent; **glands** and **stomata** as in lamina. **Cuticle** thick and undulating. **Epidermis** of thick-walled rounded cells. **Cortex:** 5–8 layers of cells of variable size. **Endodermoid layer** separating cortex from sclerenchyma. **Vascular bundles:** common bundles V-shaped, with 1 phloem unit at converging ends of V, and 2 phloem units terminating flanges of V. Cauline bundles elliptical, 1 pair of large vessels, average diameter 217 μm. One large phloem unit on inner side of the single pair of large vessels and close to centre of pith, and another phloem unit at outer end. Average diameter of large sieve-tubes 112 μm. **Pith** area constituting about one-third of central cylinder in *D. ceratandra* and about one-tenth in *D. polygonoides.* **Crystals:** idioblasts containing raphide bundles few. **Tannin** cells present.

Tuber T.S.

Epidermis not easily identifiable. **Cork:** first cork of primary origin; cells irregularly arranged. Storied cork 4–8-layered, of secondary origin; cells in radial rows, suberized. Outer ground tissue of large, rounded, thin-walled cells; many-layered, compressed in mature tubers. Starchy parenchymatous cells separated from outer ground tissue by radial rows of cells of secondary origin. **Vascular bundles** collateral, sporadically distributed in central ground tissue. Xylem consisting of short tracheids with scalariform to reticulate thickenings; phloem composed of small sieve-tubes and companion cells. **Starch grains** of variable size, mostly truncated, hilum in centre; evenly distributed in central ground tissue. **Crystals:** raphide bundles distributed at random. **Tannin** cells absent.

Root T.S.

Outer tissues not seen. **Endodermis** 1-layered, composed of cells with all walls only slightly thickened. Passage cells present. **Pericycle** 2-layered. **Stele** 8-arch; xylem consisting of tracheids, vessels, and associated parenchyma; phloem composed of sieve-tubes, companion cells, and phloem parenchyma. Xylem sometimes abutting directly on endodermis. **Crystals:** idioblasts containing raphide bundles present. **Tannin** cells absent.

MATERIAL EXAMINED

Dioscorea ceratandra Uline; Puerto Rico; F. W. Martin, s.n. Leaf, petiole, stem, tuber, root (J).

D. polygonoides Humb. & Bonpl.: (i) Puerto Rico; F. W. Martin, s.n. (ii) Dominica, W.I.; D. Wasshausen & E. S. Ayensu 336 (US). Leaf, petiole, stem, tuber, root.

Section MACROCARPAEA

Leaf surface

T-shaped **hairs** present on abaxial surface; **glands** noted on abaxial surface. **Stomata:** average size 36×27 μm, confined to abaxial surface; each stoma surrounded by 3–4 epidermal cells. Adaxial anticlinal cell walls straight, abaxial walls slightly sinuous.

Lamina T.S.

Dorsiventral. **Cuticle** thin and undulating, slightly thicker and wavy around main veins. **Epidermis:** adaxial cells rectangular, with thin, straight, anticlinal walls and cytoplasmic contents; abaxial smaller than adaxial cells. **Stomata:** walls of guard cells facing pore thickened and with no projecting ledges. **Mesophyll:** palisade tissue always 1-layered. Cells of spongy tissue mainly elongated, lying parallel to surface of lamina and occupying about two-thirds of mesophyll. **Vascular bundle** of midrib much larger than remainder. Xylem groups alternating with 4–5 phloem units towards abaxial side of midrib. **Crystals:** idioblasts containing raphide bundles. **Tannin** cells present.

Petiole surface

Hairs, glands, and **stomata** as in lamina.

Petiole T.S. Fig. 24. B.

Outline pentagonal, with 2 wings. **Cuticle** thick and ridged. **Epidermis** composed of thick-walled cuboidal or conical cells and with dense cytoplasmic contents. **Cortex** 10–18-layered; cells of fairly uniform size. Sclerenchyma represented by 1–2 layers of fibres separating cortex from vascular cylinder. **Vascular bundles** 8, arranged in a circle, each bundle partly surrounded by 3–5 layers of fibres. Xylem consisting of tracheids, vessels, and associated parenchyma; phloem composed of sieve-tubes, companion cells, and phloem parenchyma. **Crystals:** idioblasts containing raphide bundles and rectangular crystals. **Tannin** cells present.

Stem T.S. Pl. XI. B.

Outline with 7 wings. **Hairs, glands,** and **stomata** as in lamina. **Cuticle** thick and undulating. **Epidermis** consisting of thick-walled cuboidal or conical cells with dense cytoplasmic contents. **Cortex:** 6–10 layers of cells of variable size; 1–3 outer layers collenchymatous. **Endodermoid layer** separating cortex from vascular cylinder. **Vascular bundles:** common bundles V-shaped, with 1 large phloem unit at converging ends of V and at least 5 phloem units between flanges. Cauline bundles elliptical; 1 pair of large vessels, average diameter 560 μm. Two phloem units on inner side of the single pair of vessels and close to centre of pith and 1–2 phloem units at outer end close to periphery of central cylinder. Average diameter of large sieve-tubes 182 μm. **Pith** area constituting about one-fifth of central cylinder. **Crystals:** idioblasts containing raphide bundles present. **Tannin** cells also present.

Root T.S.

Piliferous layer of irregular cells. **Exodermis** 2-layered, of slightly thick-walled, compactly arranged cells, and with dense cytoplasmic contents. **Cortex:** cells of variable size, making up about half of root diameter. **Endodermis** 1-layered, cells with characteristic U-shaped thickenings. **Pericycle** 2–4-layered. **Stele** 27-arch; xylem consisting of vessels, tracheids, and associated parenchyma; phloem composed of large sieve-tubes, companion cells, and phloem parenchyma. Xylem sometimes abutting directly on endo-dermis. **Pith** parenchyma of thick-walled cells. **Crystals**: raphide bundles and **tannin** cells observed.

SPECIAL NOTE

The T-shaped hairs in this species resemble those of section Combilium, p. 112.

MATERIAL EXAMINED

Dioscorea preussii Pax: (i) Nigeria; A. W. Waitt 24 (K). (ii) Uganda; A. C. Tallantire 5. Leaf, petiole, stem, root (J).

Section CRYPTANTHA

Leaf surface

Unicellular and bicellular **hairs** present on abaxial surface; **glands** observed on abaxial surface. **Stomata**: average size 42×28 μm, confined to abaxial surface; each stoma surrounded by 3–5 epidermal cells. Adaxial anticlinal cell walls straight, abaxial walls sinuous.

Lamina T.S.

Dorsiventral. **Cuticle** thin and undulating, ridged around main veins. **Epidermis**: adaxial cells mainly rectangular, compressed in material examined; abaxial smaller than adaxial cells. **Stomata**: walls of guard cells facing pore thickened and with no projecting ledges. **Mesophyll**: palisade tissue always 1-layered. Cells of spongy tissue mainly elongated, lying parallel to surface of lamina, and occupying two-thirds of mesophyll. **Vascular bundle** of mid-rib much larger than remainder. Xylem groups alternating with 3 phloem units; fibres in 3–5 layers partly surrounding vascular bundle. **Crystals**: idioblasts containing raphide bundles. **Tannin** cells numerous.

Petiole surface

Hairs, **glands**, and **stomata** as in lamina.

Petiole T.S.

Outline pentagonal. **Cuticle** thick and ridged. **Epidermis** composed of thick-walled cells. **Cortex**: 6–12-layered; cells of variable size. **Endodermoid layer** separating cortex from 3 to 6 layers of sclerenchyma represented by fibres. **Vascular bundles** 8, each bundle partly surrounded by fibres. Xylem consisting of tracheids, vessels, and associated parenchyma; phloem com-posed of sieve-tubes, companion cells, and phloem parenchyma. **Crystals**: idioblasts containing raphide bundles. **Tannin** cells present.

Stem T.S. Fig. 25. A, B; Pl. XI. C.

Hairs absent; **glands** and **stomata** present. **Cuticle** thick and ridged. **Epidermis** of thin-walled rectangular cells. **Cortex**: 4–8 layers of cells of variable size. **Endodermoid layer** separating cortex from a distinct layer of brachy-sclereids, and 3–6 layers of thick-walled parenchyma cells. **Vascular bundles**: common bundles V-shaped, with 1 phloem unit at converging ends of V and

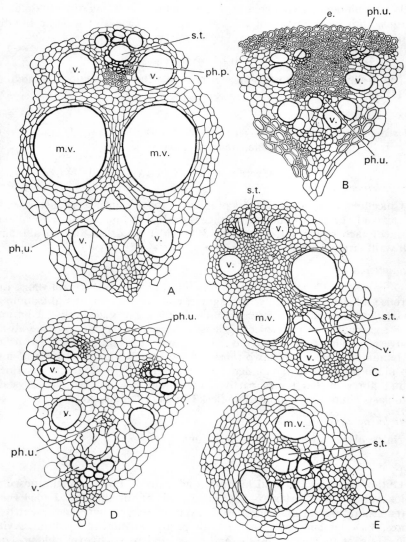

FIG. 25. Sections Cryptantha, Sarcantha, and Lasiogyne. A, B, *Dioscorea hastata*, T.S. A, cauline vascular bundle (×185); B, common vascular bundle (×185). C, D, *D. amazonum*, T.S. C, cauline vascular bundle (×92); D, common vascular bundle (×185). E, *D. discolor*, T.S. common vascular bundle (×185).

e., epidermis; m.v., metaxylem vessel; ph.p., phloem parenchyma; ph.u., phloem unit; s.t., sieve-tube; v. vessel.

2 other phloem units terminating flanges of V. Cauline bundles elliptical; 1 pair of large vessels, average diameter 306 μm. One large phloem unit on inner side of the single pair of large vessels and another phloem unit at outer end. Average diameter of large sieve-tubes 126 μm. **Pith** area constituting

about one-third of central cylinder. **Crystals**: idioblasts containing raphide bundles. **Tannin** cells present.

TAXONOMIC NOTES

The unicellular hairs, and the anatomy of the stem show a close resemblance to section Stenophora, p. 133.

MATERIAL EXAMINED

Dioscorea glauca Mühl.; Hort. Kew; E. S. Ayensu, s.n. Leaf, petiole.
D. hastata Vell.; S. America; E. Warming, s.n. (US 290135). Leaf, stem (J).

Section SARCANTHA

Stem T.S. Fig. 25. C, D; Pl. XI D.

Hairs absent; **glands** few. **Stomata** present, slightly sunken. **Cuticle** thick and ridged. **Epidermis** of thick-walled irregular cells with dense cytoplasmic contents. **Cortex**: 4–8 layers of cells of variable size. **Endodermoid layer** separating cortex from sclerenchyma represented by 2–3 layers of brachysclereids. **Vascular bundles**: common bundles V-shaped, with 1 phloem unit at converging ends of V and 2 phloem units terminating flanges of V. Cauline bundles elliptical; 1 pair of large vessels, average diameter 392 μm. One large phloem unit on inner side of the single pair of large vessels, frequently with small phloem units on outer side of same pair of large vessels, and another phloem unit at outer end close to periphery of central cylinder. Average diameter of large sieve-tubes 294 μm. **Pith** constituting about one-fourth of central cylinder. **Crystals**: idioblasts containing raphide bundles. **Tannin** cells few.

MATERIAL EXAMINED

Dioscorea amazonum Mart.: (i) Guyana; J. S. de la Cruz 4458 (US). (ii) Brazil; R. de la Froes 21190 (US). Stem (J).

Section LASIOGYNE

Leaf surface

Hairs absent; **glands** present. **Stomata**: average size 18×18 μm, mainly confined to abaxial surface; each stoma surrounded by 3–4 epidermal cells. Adaxial and abaxial anticlinal cell walls straight.

Lamina T.S.

Dorsiventral. **Cuticle** thin and undulating. **Epidermis**: adaxial cells mainly cuboidal with thin, slightly wavy anticlinal walls; abaxial smaller than adaxial cells. **Stomata**: walls of guard cells facing pore thickened and with no projecting ledges. **Mesophyll**: palisade tissue always 1-layered. Cells of spongy tissue mainly elongated, lying parallel to surface of lamina, and occupying two-thirds of mesophyll. **Vascular bundle** of midrib much larger than remainder. Xylem groups alternating with 3 phloem units towards abaxial side of midrib. **Crystals**: idioblasts containing raphide bundles present. **Tannin** cells absent.

Petiole surface

Hairs absent; **glands** and **stomata** as in lamina.

Petiole T.S.

Outline pentagonal. **Cuticle** thin and undulating. **Epidermis** composed of thin-walled cuboidal cells with dense cytoplasmic contents. **Cortex**: 6–8 layers of cells of variable size. **Vascular bundles** 6, arranged in a circle; each bundle surrounded by 3–4 layers of fibres. Xylem consisting of tracheids, vessels, and associated parenchyma; phloem composed of sieve-tubes, companion cells, and phloem parenchyma. Lignified parenchyma in 2–3 layers occupying interfascicular regions. **Crystals**: idioblasts containing raphide bundles present. **Tannin** cells absent.

Stem T.S. Fig. 25. E; Pl. XI. E.

Hairs absent; **glands** and **stomata** as in lamina. **Cuticle** thin and undulating, ridged in places. **Epidermis** of thick-walled cuboidal cells. Outer tangential walls ridged. **Cortex**: 8–12 layers of cells of variable size; 1–4 outer layers collenchymatous. Sclerenchyma represented by 4–6 layers of fibres separating cortex from vascular cylinder. **Vascular bundles**: common bundles V-shaped, with 1 large phloem unit in centre of V. Cauline bundles elliptical; 1 pair of large vessels, average diameter 378 μm. One phloem unit on inner side of pair of large vessels and another phloem unit at outer end close to periphery of central cylinder. Average diameter of large sieve-tubes 224 μm. **Pith** area constituting about one-third of central cylinder. **Crystals**: idioblasts containing raphide bundles present. **Tannin** cells absent.

MATERIAL EXAMINED

Dioscorea discolor Kunth: (i) Hort. Kew; E. S. Ayensu, s.n. (K). (ii) Peru; F. Woytkowski 6188 (US). Leaf, petiole, stem (J).

Section ORIENTALI-ASIATICAE

Petiole surface

Hairs absent; **glands** and **stomata** noted.

Petiole T.S.

Outline pentagonal. **Cuticle** thin and undulating. **Epidermis** composed of thin-walled cuboidal cells with dense cytoplasmic contents. **Vascular bundles** 5, arranged in a circle; each bundle partly surrounded by 5–8 layers of fibres and embedded in thin-walled parenchyma. Xylem consisting of tracheids, vessels, and associated parenchyma; phloem composed of small sieve-tubes, companion cells, and phloem parenchyma. **Crystals**: idioblasts containing raphide bundles present. **Tannin** cells absent.

Stem T.S. Fig. 26. A, B; Pl. XI. F; Pl. XII. A.

Hairs absent; **glands** and **stomata** as on petiole. **Cuticle** thin and undulating. **Epidermis** of thick-walled cuboidal cells with dense cytoplasmic contents. **Cortex**: 3–6 layers of cells of variable size. Sclerenchyma represented by 3–4 layers of brachysclereids, separated from cortex by **endodermoid layer.** **Vascular bundles:** common bundles V-shaped, with 1 phloem unit at converging ends of V and 2 phloem units terminating flanges of V. Cauline bundles elliptical; 1 pair of large vessels, average diameter 224 μm. One phloem unit on inner side of pair of vessels and another phloem unit at outer end close to periphery of central cylinder. Average diameter of large sieve-tubes 77 μm. **Pith** area constituting about half of central cylinder. **Crystals:** idioblasts containing raphide bundles few. **Tannin** cells absent.

MATERIAL EXAMINED

Dioscorea collettii Hook. f.: (i) Kweichow, China; Y. Tsiang 9197 (US). (ii) China; A. Henry 12338 (US). Petiole, stem (J).

D. gracillima Miq.: (i) Chekiang, China; R. C. Ching 1459 (US). (ii) Japan; M. Togosi 1060 (US). Stem (J).

Section ASTEROTRICHA

Leaf surface Fig. 26. D.

Hairs stellate, present on abaxial surface; **glands** observed. **Stomata:** average size 37 $\times$ 24 μm, confined to abaxial surface; each stoma surrounded by 3–4 epidermal cells. Adaxial anticlinal cell walls straight, abaxial walls sinuous.

Lamina T.S. Fig. 26. C.

Dorsiventral. **Cuticle** thin and undulating, slightly thicker and ridged around main veins. **Epidermis:** adaxial cells rectangular, with thin anticlinal walls, and with dense cytoplasmic contents; abaxial smaller than adaxial cells. **Stomata:** walls of guard cells facing pore thickened and with short outer projecting ledges. **Mesophyll:** palisade tissue always 1-layered. Cells of spongy tissue mainly elongated, lying parallel to surface of lamina and occupying about half of mesophyll. **Vascular bundle** of midrib much larger than remainder. Xylem groups alternating with about 6 phloem units towards abaxial side of midrib. Sclerenchyma represented by 3–5 layers of fibres partly surrounding vascular bundle of midrib. **Crystals:** idioblasts containing raphide bundles. **Tannin** cells present.

Petiole surface

Hairs, glands, and **stomata** as in lamina.

Petiole T.S.

Outline almost circular. **Cuticle** thin and undulating. **Epidermis** composed of thin-walled cuboidal or circular cells. **Cortex:** 4–8 layers of cells of variable size. **Vascular bundles** 8, arranged in a circle, each bundle partly surrounded by 3–5 layers of fibres except for an incipient vascular bundle. Lignified parenchyma cells, 1–2-layered, occupying interfascicular regions. Xylem consisting of tracheids, vessels, and associated parenchyma; phloem composed of sieve-tubes, companion cells, and phloem parenchyma. **Crystals:** idioblasts containing raphide bundles. **Tannin** cells present.

Stem T.S. Fig. 26. F; Pl. XII. B.

Hairs very few; **glands** and **stomata** as in lamina. **Cuticle** thick and undulating. **Epidermis** of thick-walled circular cells, with dense cytoplasmic contents. **Cortex:** 10–16 layers of chlorenchyma cells of variable size; 1–3 outer layers collenchymatous. **Endodermoid layer** separating cortex from sclerenchyma. **Vascular bundles:** common bundles V-shaped, with 1 phloem unit at converging ends of V and 3–5 phloem units terminating wide ends of V. Cauline bundles elliptical; 1 pair of large vessels, average diameter 434 μm. Two phloem units on inner side of pair of large vessels and close to centre of pith, and another phloem unit at outer end close to periphery of central cylinder; other phloem units appearing within bundles. Average diameter of large sieve-tubes 196 μm. Vascular bundles embedded in sclerenchyma. **Pith** area constituting about one-sixth of central cylinder. **Crystals:** idioblasts containing raphide bundles. **Tannin** cells present.

Tuber T.S.

Epidermis not easily identifiable. **Cork:** first cork of primary origin; cells loosely arranged. Storied cork of secondary origin, cells many-layered, slightly suberized. **Cortex** separated from inner ground tissue by 6–8 layers of storied cells. Inner ground tissue composed of thin-walled parenchymatous cells. **Vascular bundles** collateral, sporadically distributed in inner ground tissue. Xylem consisting of long tracheids and associated parenchyma; phloem composed of sieve-tubes, companion cells, and phloem parenchyma. **Starch grains** of variable size, mostly truncated, hilum in centre; grains generally distributed around vascular bundles. **Crystals:** raphide bundles. **Tannin** cells present.

Root T.S. Fig. 26. E.

Piliferous layer composed of irregular cells with root-hairs. **Exodermis** 1-layered, of thin-walled cells, compactly arranged. **Cortex:** cells of irregular size, constituting about one-third of root diameter; innermost cells, 2–3-layered, flattened, smaller than rest of cortical cells. **Endodermis** 1-layered, cells with characteristic U-shaped thickenings. Passage cells present. **Pericycle** 2-layered, inner layer interrupted by vascular elements. **Stele** 20-arch; xylem consisting of vessels (large vessels near centre of vascular core), tracheids and xylem parenchyma; phloem composed of sieve-tubes, companion cells and phloem parenchyma. Each phloem unit partly surrounded by fibres. Phloem alternating with xylem towards periphery of central cylinder. **Pith** constituting about half of central cylinder. **Crystals:** idioblasts containing raphide bundles. **Tannin** cells present.

TAXONOMIC NOTES

The stellate hairs of this section show a relationship to those of section Syntepaleia, p. 130.

MATERIAL EXAMINED

Dioscorea schimperiana Hochst.: (i) Singapore; I. H. Burkill, s.n. (ii) Pretoria, S. Africa; B. de Winter, s.n. (PRE). (iii) Uganda; A. C. Tallantire 2.

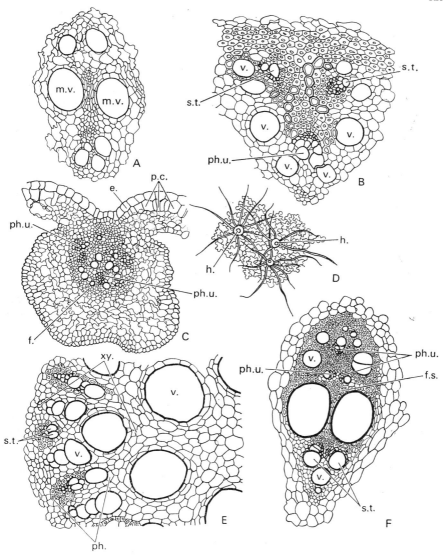

Fig. 26. Sections Orientali-asiaticae and Asterotricha. A, *Dioscorea collettii*, T.S. cauline vascular bundle (×92). B, *D. gracillima*, T.S. common vascular bundle (×185). C–F, *D. schimperiana*: C, T.S. leaf midrib (×92); D, Stellate hairs on abaxial surface of leaf (×92); E, T.S. minor portion of root (×185); F, T.S. cauline vascular bundle (×92).

e., epidermis; f., fibres; f.s., fibrous sheath; h., hair, stellate; m.v., metaxylem vessel; p.c., palisade cell; ph., phloem; ph.u., phloem unit; s.t., sieve-tube; v., vessel; xy., xylem

(iv) Zambia; D. B. Fanshawe 8189 (K). Leaf, petiole, stem, tuber, root (J).

Section ENANTIOPHYLLUM

Leaf surface. Fig. 27. A, B.

Hairs absent; **glands** present mainly on abaxial surface. **Stomata**: average size 39×26 μm, confined to abaxial surface; each stoma surrounded by 3–4 epidermal cells. Adaxial anticlinal cell walls straight or curved, abaxial walls slightly sinuous; adaxial and abaxial walls slightly sinuous in *D. cayenensis*, *D. rotundata*, and *D. wattii*.

Lamina T.S. Fig. 27. C.

Dorsiventral. Cuticle thin and undulating, thick and ridged in some species. **Epidermis**: adaxial cells mainly rectangular with thin, straight, anticlinal walls and with cytoplasmic contents; multiple adaxial epidermis in *D. luzonensis*. **Stomata**: walls of guard cells facing pore thickened and with no projecting ledges. **Mesophyll**: palisade tissue mostly 1-, sometimes 2-layered. Cells of spongy tissue mainly elongated, lying parallel to surface of lamina and occupying half to two-thirds of mesophyll; palisade and spongy tissue less distinguishable in *D. wattii*. **Vascular bundle** of midrib much larger than remainder. Xylem groups alternating with 3–7 phloem units. Sclerenchyma represented by 2–9 layers of fibres partially surrounding vascular bundle of midrib. **Crystals**: idioblasts containing raphide bundles noted. **Tannin** cells present, numerous in *D. luzonensis*, *D. minutiflora*, *D. praehensilis*, and *D. rotundata*.

Petiole T.S. Fig. 4. D, p. 36.

Outline pentagonal, with 5 wings in *D. alata*. **Cuticle** thin and undulating, ridged in places. **Epidermis** of thin-walled cuboidal cells with dense cytoplasmic contents. **Cortex**: 3–9 layers of cells of variable size; 1–2 outer layers collenchymatous. Cortex separated from vascular cylinder by 1–3 layers of fibres and lignified parenchyma. **Vascular bundles** 3–8, arranged in a circle, each bundle partly surrounded by 3-5 layers of fibres. Xylem consisting of tracheids, vessels, and associated parenchyma; phloem composed of sieve-tubes, companion cells, and phloem parenchyma. **Crystals**: idioblasts containing raphide bundles. **Tannin** cells present.

Stem T.S. Figs. 27. D, E; 28. A–C, E; Pl. XII. C–F; Pl. XIII. A.

Hairs absent; **glands** and **stomata** as in lamina. **Cuticle** thin, ridged or undulating. **Epidermis** of thin- or thick-walled cuboidal, conical or circular cells, and with dense cytoplasmic contents. **Cortex** of 3–7 layers of cells of variable size; 1–3 outer layers collenchymatous. **Endodermoid layer** separating cortex from either lignified parenchyma or 2–5 layers of fibres or brachysclereids. **Vascular bundles**: common bundles V-shaped, with 1 phloem unit at converging ends of V and 2 or more phloem units terminating flanges of V. Cauline bundles elliptical; 1 or 2 pairs of large vessels, average diameter 454 μm. Two phloem units on inner side of innermost pair of large vessels,

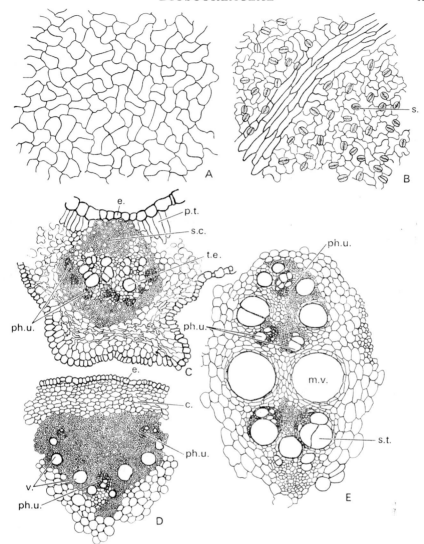

FIG. 27. Section Enantiophyllum. *Dioscorea rotundata* (×185). A, Adaxial epidermis, surface view. B, Abaxial epidermis, surface view. C, T.S. leaf midrib. D, T.S. common vascular bundle. E, T.S. cauline vascular bundle.

e., epidermis; c., cortex; m.v., metaxylem vessel; ph.u., phloem unit; p.t., palisade tissue; s., stoma; s.c., sclerenchyma; s.t., sieve-tube; t.e., tracheal element; v., vessels.

1 phloem unit or more at outer end, sometimes 2 phloem units between pairs of vessels. Average diameter of large sieve-tubes 185 μm. **Pith** constituting one-third to half of central cylinder. **Starch grains** occurring in pith of some species. **Crystals**: idioblasts containing raphide bundles present; rhomboidal crystals occurring in *D. cayenensis*. **Tannin** cells present.

Tuber T.S.

Epidermis not easily identifiable. **Cork :** first cork of primary origin; cells irregularly arranged, suberized. Storied cork of secondary origin, many-layered; cells in radial rows, suberized. Outer ground tissue many-layered, cells of variable size, storied in places as in *D. luzonensis.* Inner ground tissue composed of thick-walled cells, filled with starch, and tannin cells in some species. **Vascular bundles** collateral, sporadically distributed in central ground tissue. Xylem consisting of tracheids and associated parenchyma; vessels observed in *D. luzonensis;* phloem composed of sieve-tubes, companion cells, and phloem parenchyma. **Starch grains** of variable size and shape, mostly elliptical or rounded, hilum off-centre; grains generally concentrated around vascular bundles. **Crystals :** raphide bundles. **Tannin** cells present.

Root T.S. Fig. 28. D.

Piliferous layer of irregular cells. **Exodermis** 1-layered, of thick-walled, compactly arranged cells. **Cortex :** cells of variable size, constituting about half of root diameter. **Endodermis** 1-layered, cells with characteristic U-shaped thickenings. Passage cells present. **Pericycle** 3–4-layered, inner layer interrupted by tracheal elements. **Stele** variable, e.g. 12-arch in *D. alata* and 32-arch in *D. luzonensis.* Xylem consisting of vessels, tracheids, and associated parenchyma; phloem composed of sieve-tubes, companion cells, and phloem parenchyma. Xylem alternating with phloem towards periphery of central cylinder. **Pith** parenchyma of thick-walled cells. **Crystals :** raphide bundles. **Tannin** cells present.

Special Note

This section contains the largest number of species, including the most important of the edible species, and exhibits a wide range of variation in some aspects of its anatomy.

Material Examined

Dioscorea alata L.: (i) Ghana; E. S. Ayensu, s.n. (ii) Philippines; J. V. Pancho, s.n. (LB). (iii) Nigeria; A. W. Waitt 9 (K). (iv) Trinidad, W.I.; J. A. Spence, s.n. (v) Philippines; W. L. Stern 2338 (US). (vi) Uganda; A. C. Tallantire 10. Leaf, petiole, stem, tuber, root (J).

D. batatas Decne.; Chelsea Physic Gard.; J. G. Vaughan, s.n. (QEC). Leaf, petiole, stem.

D. cayenensis Lamk.: (i) Ghana; E. S. Ayensu, s.n. (ii) Nigeria; A. W. Waitt 4 (K). (iii) Trinidad, W.I.; J. A. Spence, s.n. (iv) Uganda; A. C. Tallantire, s.n. Leaf, petiole, stem (J).

D. divaricata Blanco; Philippines; J. V. Pancho, s.n. (LB). Stem.

D. lecardii de Wild; Uganda; A. C. Tallantire, s.n. Leaf, petiole, stem, tuber, root.

D. luzonensis Schauer; Philippines; W. L. Stern 2339 (US). Leaf, petiole, stem, tuber, root (J).

D. minutiflora Engl.: (i) Hort. Kew; E. S. Ayensu, s.n. (K). (ii) Uganda; A. C. Tallantire, s.n. Leaf, petiole, stem.

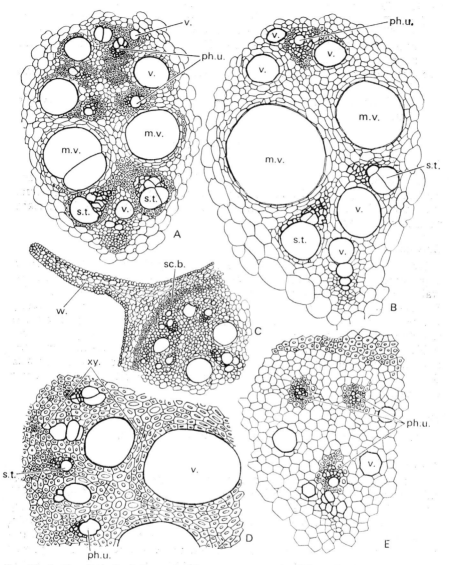

FIG. 28. Section Enantiophyllum. A, *Dioscorea cayenensis*, T.S. cauline vascular bundle (×92). B, D, *D. luzonensis*: B, T.S. cauline vascular bundle (×185); D, T.S. portion of inner part of root (×185). C, *D. alata*, T.S. stem showing one of five wings (×92). E, *D. wattii*, T.S. portion of stem, showing common vascular bundle (×185).

m.v., metaxylem vessel; ph.u., phloem unit; sc.b., sclerenchyma band; s.t., sieve-tube; v., vessel; w., wing; xy., xylem.

D. oppositifolia L.; Madras, India; H. Santapau, s.n. Stem, tuber (J).

D. praehensilis Benth.: (i) Nigeria; A. W. Waitt 27 (K). (ii) Nigeria; FHI 54897 (FHI). (iii) Uganda; A. C. Tallantire 7. (iv) Zambia; D. B. Fanshawe F8269 (K). (v) Zambia; D. B. Fanshawe F8338 (K). Leaf, petiole, stem (J).

D. rotundata Poir.: (i) Ghana; E. S. Ayensu, s.n. (ii) Nigeria; A. W. Waitt 2 (K). Leaf, petiole, stem (J).

D. wattii Prain & Burk.; Hort. Kew; E. S. Ayensu, s.n. (K). Leaf, petiole, stem.

Section SYNTEPALEIA

Leaf surface

Stellate **hairs** present on abaxial surface; **glands** noted on abaxial surface. **Stomata**: average size 30×21 μm, confined to abaxial surface; each stoma surrounded by 3–5 epidermal cells. Adaxial anticlinal cell walls straight, abaxial walls sinuous.

Lamina T.S.

Dorsiventral. **Cuticle** thin and undulating, slightly thicker around main veins. **Epidermis**: adaxial cells mainly rectangular, with thin, straight, anticlinal walls, and dense cytoplasmic contents; abaxial smaller than adaxial cells. **Stomata**: walls of guard cells facing pore thickened and with no projecting ledges. **Mesophyll**: palisade tissue always 1-layered. Cells of spongy tissue mainly elongated, lying parallel to surface of lamina and occupying about half of mesophyll. **Vascular bundle** of midrib much larger than the remainder and partly surrounded by 3–5 layers of fibres; xylem groups alternating with 5 phloem units. **Crystals**: idioblasts containing raphide bundles. **Tannin** cells present.

Petiole surface

Stellate **hairs** present; **glands** and **stomata** as in lamina.

Petiole T.S.

Outline pentagonal. **Cuticle** thin and undulating. **Epidermis** composed of thin-walled rounded cells with dense cytoplasmic contents. **Cortex**: 5–11 layers of cells of variable size. Sclerenchyma fibres 4–5-layered, separating cortex from vascular cylinder. **Vascular bundles** 6, arranged in a circle. Xylem consisting of tracheids, vessels, and associated parenchyma; phloem composed of sieve-tubes, companion cells, and phloem parenchyma. **Crystals**: idioblasts containing raphide bundles. **Tannin** cells present. Extra-floral **glands** noted (see p. 63).

Stem T.S. Fig. 29. A; Pl. XIII. B.

Hairs, glands, and **stomata** as in lamina. **Cuticle** thin and undulating. **Epidermis** of thin-walled cuboidal cells with dense cytoplasmic contents. **Cortex**: 6–10 layers of cells of variable size, storied in places. **Endodermoid layer** separating cortex from vascular cylinder. **Vascular bundles**: common bundles

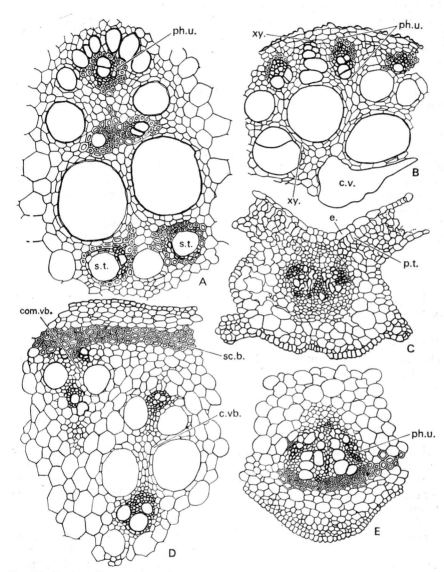

FIG. 29. Sections Syntepaleia and Stenophora (×185). A, B, *Dioscorea hirtiflora*: A, T.S. cauline vascular bundle; B, T.S. small portion of inner part of root. C–E, *D. nipponica*: C, T.S. leaf midrib; D, T.S. part of stem showing common and cauline vascular bundles; E, T.S. portion of petiole.

com.vb., common vascular bundle; c.v., compressed vessel; c.vb., cauline vascular bundle; e., epidermis; ph.u., phloem unit; p.t., palisade tissue; sc.b., sclerenchyma band; s.t., sieve-tube; xy., xylem.

V-shaped, with one phloem unit at converging ends of V and two phloem units terminating flanges of V. Cauline bundles elliptical; 2 pairs of large vessels, average diameter 266 μm. Two phloem units on inner side of pair of largest vessels, 1–2 phloem units immediately external to pair of largest vessels, and another phloem unit at outer end close to periphery of central cylinder. Average diameter of large sieve-tubes 98 μm. **Pith** area constituting about one-fourth of central cylinder. **Crystals**: idioblasts containing raphide bundles. **Tannin** cells present.

Root T.S. Fig. 29. B.

Outer tissues not seen. **Endodermis** 1-layered, cells compactly arranged; all cell walls only slightly thickened. Passage cells present. **Pericycle** 1–2-layered, inner layer interrupted by tracheal elements. **Stele** 13-arch, xylem consisting of large vessels, few tracheids and associated parenchyma; phloem composed of large sieve-tubes, companion cells, phloem parenchyma and fibres. **Pith** parenchyma thin-walled, partly obliterated in material examined. **Crystals**: idioblasts containing raphide bundles few. **Tannin** cells present.

TAXONOMIC NOTES

The presence of stellate hairs in this section suggests its relationship with section Asterotricha, p. 123.

MATERIAL EXAMINED

Dioscorea hirtiflora Benth.: (i) Hort. Kew; E. S. Ayensu, s.n. (K). (ii) Zambia; D. B. Fanshawe, s.n. (NDO). Leaf, petiole, stem, root (J).·

Section STENOCOREA

Stem T.S. Pl. XIII. C.

Hairs absent; **glands** noted. **Stomata** present, slightly sunken. **Cuticle** thick and ridged. **Epidermis** of thin-walled irregular cells with dense cytoplasmic contents. **Cortex**: 3–5 layers of cells of variable size. **Endodermoid layer** separating cortex from 1–2 layers of thick-walled parenchyma cells. **Vascular bundles**; common bundles V-shaped, with 1 phloem unit at converging ends of V and another phloem unit between flanges of V. Cauline bundles elliptical; 1 pair of large vessels, average diameter 322 μm. Two phloem units on inner side of pair of large vessels and close to centre of pith, and another phloem unit at outer end close to periphery of central cylinder. Average diameter of large sieve-tubes 126 μm. **Pith** area constituting about one-fifth of central cylinder. **Crystals**: idioblasts containing raphide bundles. **Tannin** cells present.

MATERIAL EXAMINED

Dioscorea stenomeriflora Prain & Burk.; Malaya; Herb. Calcuttensis 5152 (US).

SUBGENUS III. STENOPHORA (Uline) Knuth

Section STENOPHORA

Leaf surface

Hairs unicellular, present on both surfaces; **glands** noted. **Stomata**: average size 36×27 μm, mainly confined to abaxial surface; each stoma surrounded by 3–5 epidermal cells. Adaxial anticlinal cell walls slightly sinuous, abaxial walls sinuous.

Lamina T.S. Fig. 29. C.

Dorsiventral. **Cuticle** thin and undulating, slightly thicker and ridged around principal veins. **Epidermis**: adaxial cells mainly rectangular with thin walls; abaxial smaller than adaxial cells. **Stomata**: walls of guard cells facing pore thickened, especially at corners, and with no projecting ledges. **Mesophyll**: palisade tissue always 2-layered, inner layer less distinguishable from spongy tissue. Cells of spongy tissue mainly elongated, lying parallel to surface of lamina and occupying about half of mesophyll. **Vascular bundle** of midrib much larger than remainder. Xylem groups alternating with 4–5 phloem units. Sclerenchyma represented by 3–5 layers of fibres partly surrounding vascular bundle of midrib. **Crystals**: idioblasts containing raphide bundles. **Tannin** cells present.

Petiole surface

Hairs few, **glands** and **stomata** as in lamina.

Petiole T.S. Fig. 29. E.

Outline pentagonal. **Cuticle** thin and undulating, slightly thicker and ridged in places. **Epidermis** composed of thick-walled rounded cells with dense cytoplasmic contents. **Vascular bundles** 8, arranged in a circle, each bundle bounded externally by 2–3 layers of fibres. Lignified parenchyma of 2–3 layers occupying interfascicular regions. Xylem consisting of tracheids, vessels, and associated parenchyma; phloem composed of large sieve-tubes, companion cells, and phloem parenchyma. **Crystals**: idioblasts containing raphide bundles. **Tannin** cells present.

Stem T.S. Fig. 29. D; Pl. XIII. D.

Hairs, glands, and **stomata** as in lamina. **Cuticle** thick and undulating. **Epidermis** of thick-walled circular or cuboidal cells with dense cytoplasmic contents. **Cortex**: 3–12 layers of cells of variable size. **Endodermoid layer** separating cortex from 4 to 6 layers of fibres. **Vascular bundles**: common bundles V-shaped, with 1 phloem unit at converging ends of V and 2 phloem units terminating flanges of V. Cauline bundles elliptical; 2 pairs of large vessels, average diameter 210 μm. One large phloem unit on inner side of pair of largest vessels and another phloem unit at outer end close to periphery of central cylinder. Average diameter of sieve-tubes 70 μm. **Pith** area constituting about half of central cylinder. **Crystals**: idioblasts containing raphide bundles. **Tannin** cells present.

TAXONOMIC NOTES

The unicellular hairs and the general anatomy of this section show a close resemblance to section Cryptantha, p. 119.

MATERIAL EXAMINED

Dioscorea nipponica Makino; Hort. Kew; E. S. Ayensu, s.n. (K). Leaf, petiole, stem (J).

SUBGENUS IV. TESTUDINARIA (Salisb.) Uline s. em.

Leaf surface

Hairs absent; **glands** present. **Stomata:** average size 35×21 μm, mainly confined to abaxial surface; each stoma surrounded by 3–4 epidermal cells. Adaxial anticlinal cell walls slightly sinuous, but straight in *D. sylvatica*; abaxial walls slightly sinuous.

Lamina T.S.

Dorsiventral. **Cuticle** thin and undulating, thick and ridged around principal veins. **Epidermis:** adaxial cells mainly rectangular with thin walls, and with dense cytoplasmic contents; abaxial smaller than adaxial cells. **Stomata:** walls of guard cells facing pore thickened and with no projecting ledges. **Mesophyll:** palisade tissue always 1-layered. Cells of spongy tissue mainly irregularly shaped, and occupying half of mesophyll. **Vascular bundle** of midrib much larger than remainder. Xylem alternating with 2–4 phloem units. **Crystals:** idioblasts containing raphide bundles present. **Tannin** cells numerous, shaped like pieces of jigsaw.

Petiole surface

Hairs absent; **glands** and **stomata** as in lamina.

Petiole T.S.

Outline circular, pentagonal, and crescentiform in *D. elephantipes*, *D. sylvatica*, and *D. hemicrypta* respectively. **Cuticle** thin and ridged. **Epidermis** composed of thin-walled cuboidal or rectangular cells with cytoplasmic contents. **Cortex:** 4–8 layers of cells of variable size. **Vascular bundles** 6, arranged in a circle, except in *D. hemicrypta*, where 5, arranged in a crescent; each bundle partly surrounded by 2–3 layers of fibres. Xylem consisting of tracheids, vessels, and associated parenchyma; phloem composed of large sieve-tubes, companion cells, and phloem parenchyma. Lignified parenchyma of 1–2 layers occupying interfascicular regions. **Crystals:** idioblasts containing raphide bundles. **Tannin** cells present. Extra-floral **glands** present in *D. hemicrypta* and *D. sylvatica* (see p. 63).

Stem T.S. Fig. 30. A–D; Pl. XIII. E, F; Pl. XIV. A.

Hairs absent; **glands** and **stomata** as in lamina. **Cuticle** thin and undulating, sometimes ridged. **Epidermis** of thin-walled cuboidal or conical cells with dense cytoplasmic contents. **Cortex:** 6–8 layers of cells of variable size; in

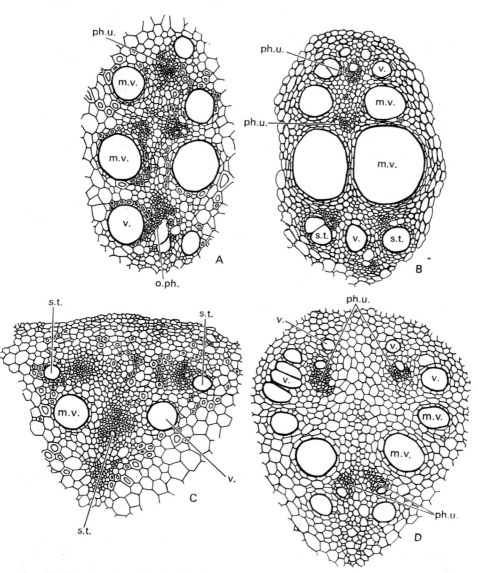

Fig. 30. Subgenus Testudinaria. A, C, *Dioscorea elephantipes*, T.S.: A, cauline vascular bundle (×62); C, common vascular bundle (×62). B, D, *D. sylvatica*, T.S.: B, cauline vascular bundle (×124); D, common vascular bundle (×124).

m.v., metaxylem vessel; o.ph., obliterated phloem; ph.u., phloem unit; s.t., sieve-tube; v., vessel.

D. elephantipes and *D. hemicrypta* 1–3 layers of cortical cells appearing much larger than remainder and containing tannin. **Endodermoid layer** separating cortex from sclerenchyma represented by 4–6 layers of fibres. **Vascular bundles**: common bundles V-shaped; with 1 large phloem unit at converging ends of V and with 2 phloem units terminating flanges of V. Cauline bundles elliptical; 1–2 pairs of large vessels, average diameter 191 μm. One large phloem unit on inner side of innermost pair of vessels (2 phloem units in *D. sylvatica*), and another on outer side close to periphery of central cylinder, sometimes phloem units present between pairs of vessels. Average diameter of large sieve-tubes 88 μm. **Pith** area varying from less than one-third to half of central cylinder. **Crystals**: idioblasts containing raphide bundles present. **Tannin** cells also present.

SPECIAL NOTE

D. hemicrypta and *D. sylvatica* were described and assigned to this sub-genus after Knuth's (1924) publication. Burkill (1952) suggested that this section should be considered as a section of *Dioscorea*.

MATERIAL EXAMINED

Dioscorea elephantipes Spreng.: (i) Hort. Kew; E. S. Ayensu, s.n. (K). (ii) Hort. Amsterdam; E. S. Ayensu, s.n. (AMD). Leaf, petiole, stem.
D. hemicrypta Burk.; Hort. Kew; E. S. Ayensu, s.n. (K). Leaf, petiole, stem.
D. sylvatica Ecklon: (i) Nigeria; A. W. Waitt, 20 (K). (ii) Pretoria, S. Africa; B. de Winter, s.n. (PRE). (iii) Hort. Kew; E. S. Ayensu, s.n. Leaf, petiole, stem (J). (iv) Swaziland.

RAJANIA L.

Leaf surface

Hairs absent, except for unicellular hairs in *R. mucronta* and *R. hastata* on abaxial surfaces; **glands** present mainly on abaxial surfaces. **Stomata**: average size 39 × 26 μm, mainly confined to abaxial surface; each stoma surrounded by 3–5 epidermal cells. Adaxial anticlinal cell walls straight; abaxial walls slightly sinuous, but sinuous in *R. hastata* and straight in *R. tenuiflora*.

Lamina T.S.

Dorsiventral. **Cuticle** thin and undulating, ridged around main veins. **Epidermis**: adaxial cells mainly rectangular with thin, wavy, anticlinal walls; abaxial smaller than adaxial cells. **Stomata**: walls of guard cells facing pore thickened and with no projecting ledges. **Mesophyll**: palisade tissue mostly 1-layered, sometimes 2-layered in *R. cordata*. Cells of spongy tissue mainly elongated, lying parallel to surface of lamina and occupying about half of mesophyll. **Vascular bundle** of midrib much larger than remainder. Sclerenchyma represented by thick-walled fibres surrounding vascular bundle of midrib except in *R. cordata*. Xylem groups alternating with 3–7 phloem units. **Crystals**: idioblasts containing raphide bundles present. **Tannin** cells few.

Stem T.S. Pl. XIV. B.

Hairs absent, **glands** and **stomata** as in lamina. **Cuticle** thin and undulating, ridged in places. **Epidermis** of thick-walled cuboidal or rounded cells and with dense cytoplasmic contents. **Cortex**: 5–10-layered, cells of variable size; 2–3 outer layers collenchymatous. **Endodermoid layer** separated from cortex by a distinct layer of brachysclereids. **Vascular bundles**: common bundles V-shaped, with 1 phloem unit in centre of V. Cauline bundles elliptical; 1 pair of large vessels, average diameter 144 μm. Two phloem units on inner side of pair of vessels and close to centre of pith and another phloem unit at outer end close to periphery of central cylinder. Average diameter of sieve-tubes 53 μm. **Pith** area constituting about half of central cylinder. **Crystals**; idioblasts containing raphide bundles present. **Tannin** cells few.

Rhizome T.S.

Piliferous layer with hairs present. **Exodermis** 3–4-layered, cells compactly arranged, with dense cytoplasmic contents. **Cortex**: 10–12 layers of cells of variable size. **Endodermoid layer** separating cortex from vascular cylinder. **Vascular bundles** collateral, sporadically distributed in central cylinder. Xylem consisting of tracheids and associated parenchyma; phloem composed of large sieve-tubes, companion cells, and phloem parenchyma. **Starch grains** rounded or elliptical, sometimes truncated, hilum off-centre; grains filling pith parenchyma cells. **Pith** constituting four-fifths of central cylinder. **Crystals**: idioblasts containing raphide bundles present. **Tannin** cells few.

Tuber T.S.

Epidermis not easily identifiable. **Cork**: first cork of primary origin; cells irregularly arranged. Storied cork of secondary origin, 3–4-layered and in radial rows. Ground tissue composed of rounded, thin-walled cells, irregularly arranged. **Vascular bundles** collateral, sporadically distributed in ground tissue. Xylem consisting of tracheids and associated parenchyma; phloem composed of small sieve-tubes, companion cells, and phloem parenchyma. **Starch grains** rounded, hilum off-centre; grains generally distributed around vascular bundles. **Crystals**: raphide bundles. **Tannin** cells present.

Root T.S.

Piliferous layer composed of somewhat rectangular cells with numerous root-hairs. **Exodermis** 1-layered, of thick-walled cells and compactly arranged. **Cortex**: 8–12-layered, cells of irregular size, innermost cells smaller than rest of cortical cells and somewhat flattened. **Endodermis** 1-layered, cells with characteristic U-shaped thickenings. Passage cells present. **Pericycle** 1–2-layered, inner layer interrupted by vascular elements. **Stele** 7-arch; xylem consisting of vessels (with large vessels near centre of vascular core), tracheids and xylem parenchyma; phloem composed of large sieve-tubes, companion cells, and phloem parenchyma. Centre of pith having 1 large vessel element. **Crystals**: raphide bundles few. **Tannin** cells few.

SPECIAL NOTE

General anatomy resembles that of species of *Dioscorea*.

MATERIAL EXAMINED

Rajania cordata L.; Puerto Rico; F. W. Martin, s.n. Leaf, petiole, stem, rhizome, tuber, root.

R. hastata L.: (i) Isla de Pinos, W.I.; A. H. Curtiss 506 (K). (ii) Haiti; E. K. Ekman 2910 (K). Leaf, petiole, stem.

R. mucronata Willd.; Dominican Rep.; E. J. Valeur 905 (K). Leaf, petiole, stem.

R. tenuiflora Knuth; Cuba; C. V. Morton & J. Acuna 3020 (K). Leaf, petiole, stem.

TAMUS L.

Leaf surface

Hairs absent; **glands** present on abaxial surface. **Stomata**: average size 36×29 μm, mainly confined to abaxial surface; each stoma surrounded by 3–4 epidermal cells. Adaxial anticlinal cell walls slightly sinuous, abaxial walls sinuous.

Lamina T.S.

Dorsiventral. **Cuticle** slightly thickened and undulating, thicker and ridged around main veins. **Epidermis**: adaxial cells mainly rectangular or cuboidal with straight anticlinal walls and dense cytoplasmic contents; abaxial smaller than adaxial cells. **Stomata**: walls of guard cells facing pore thickened and with no projecting ledges. **Mesophyll**: palisade tissue mostly 1-layered, sometimes 2-layered in *T. communis*. Cells of spongy tissue mainly elongated or irregularly shaped, and occupying about half of mesophyll. **Vascular bundle** of midrib much larger than remainder. Xylem groups alternating with 3 phloem units. **Crystals**: idioblasts containing raphide bundles present. **Tannin** cells also present.

Petiole surface

Hairs absent; **glands** and **stomata** as in lamina.

Petiole T.S.

Outline pentagonal, with 2 wings towards adaxial side. **Cuticle** thin and ridged. **Epidermis** composed of thin-walled circular or cuboidal cells and with dense cytoplasmic contents. **Vascular bundles** varying in number from 6 (*T. edulis*) to 7 (*T. communis*), arranged in a circle; each bundle partly surrounded by 2–4 layers of fibres. Xylem consisting of tracheids, vessels, and associated parenchyma; phloem composed of small sieve-tubes, companion cells, and phloem parenchyma. Lignified fibres in 1–2 layers occupying interfascicular regions. **Crystals**: idioblasts containing raphide bundles few. **Tannin** cells present.

Stem T.S. Pl. XIV. D, E.

Hairs absent; **glands** and **stomata** as in lamina. **Cuticle** thick and ridged. **Epidermis** of thick-walled circular or cuboidal cells with dense cytoplasmic contents. **Cortex**: cells of variable size, 3–4-layered and 8–15-layered in *T.*

edulis and *T. communis* respectively. **Endodermoid layer** separating cortex from sclerenchyma. **Vascular bundles**: common bundles V-shaped, with 1 phloem unit at centre of V. Cauline bundles elliptical; 1 pair of large vessels, average diameter 196 μm. One large phloem unit on inner side of the single pair of large vessels and close to centre of pith, and another phloem unit at outer end close to periphery of central cylinder. Average diameter of large sieve-tubes 84 μm. **Pith** area variable, about one-third to half of central cylinder in *T. edulis* and about four-fifths in *T. communis*. **Crystals**: idioblasts containing raphide bundles present. **Tannin** cells also present.

Tuber T.S.

Epidermis not easily identifiable. **Cork**: first cork of primary origin; cells irregularly arranged, suberized. Storied cork of secondary origin, 6–8-layered; cells in radial rows, suberized. **Cambial cells** in 4–6 layers separating outer ground tissue from central ground tissue. **Vascular bundles** collateral, somewhat radially arranged in central ground tissue. Xylem consisting of tracheids and associated parenchyma; phloem composed of small sieve-tubes and companion cells. **Starch grains** of variable size, mostly rounded, hilum off-centre; grains distributed throughout central ground tissue. **Crystals**: raphide bundles. **Tannin** cells present.

Root T.S.

Outer tissues not seen. **Endodermis** 1-layered, cells with characteristic U-shaped thickenings and pits. Passage cells present. Innermost layer of cortex exhibiting structure similar to that of endodermis. **Pericycle** 3–4-layered, inner layer interrupted by tracheary elements. **Stele** 7-arch; xylem consisting of vessels (with large vessels orientated towards centre of vascular core), tracheids, and xylem parenchyma; phloem composed of small sieve-tubes, companion cells, and phloem parenchyma. **Pith** constituting about one-fifth of central cylinder. **Crystals**: raphide bundles. **Tannin** cells few.

MATERIAL EXAMINED

Tamus communis L.: (i) Surrey, U.K.; C. R. Metcalfe, s.n. (K). (ii) Surrey, U.K.; E. S. Ayensu, s.n. (iii) Devon, U.K.; S. Rogers, s.n. Leaf, petiole, stem, tuber, root (J).

T. edulis Lowe; Tenerife, Canary Is.; A. G. Cabezon, s.n. (TENE). Leaf, petiole, stem, tuber, root (J).

DIOSCOREACEAE

GENERA AND SPECIES REPORTED ON IN THE LITERATURE

ABROL, KAPOOR, and CHOPRA (1962) *Dioscorea deltoidea* Wall.; rhizome.
AYENSU (1965) *Dioscorea* spp.; stem vascular bundles.
——(1969) *Dioscorea, Tamus*; nodal anatomy.
——(1970a) *Dioscorea composita* Hemsl.; stem vascular bundles.
——(1970b) *Dioscorea cayenensis* Lamk., *D. rotundata* Poir.; all parts.
BEAUVISAGE (1888) *Dioscorea batatas*; stem vascular bundles.
BEHNKE (1965a) *Dioscorea reticulata* Gay; phloem-glomerulus. Notes on *D. bulbifera* L., *D. macroura* Harms.

BEHNKE (1965c) *Dioscorea macroura* Harms., *D. reticulata* Gay; phloem-glomerulus.
BERGMANN (1913) *Dioscorea daemona, D. discolor, D. pentaphylla, D. sativa*; glands.
BLUNDEN, HARDMAN, and TREASE (1963) *Dioscorea belizensis* Lundell; root, tuber.
BRAUN (1957) *Dioscorea batatas* Desne, *Tamus communis* L.; nodal anatomy.
BUCHERER (1889) *Dioscorea batatas, D. sinuata, Tamus communis*; leaf, stem, root, tuber.
BURKILL (1937) *Dioscorea sansibarensis* Pax; tuber.
—— (1939, 1940) *Tamus communis* L.; leaf.
—— (1949) *Tamus communis* L.; stem.
—— (1960) *Dioscorea alata* L., *D. bulbifera* L. and var. *anthropophagorum, D. caucasica* Lipsky, *D. cayenensis* Lamk., *D. dodecaneura* Vell. (also tuber), *D. dregeana* Th. Dur., *D. gillettii* Milne-Redh., *D. glauca* Mühl., *D. hemicrypta* Burk., *D. opposita* Thunb. (= *D. batatas*), *D. pentaphylla* L., *D. pyrenaica* Bubani, *D. sansibarensis* Pax, *D. tsaratanensis* Perr.; stem. Also miscellaneous information on tubers, hairs, glands, etc.
CORDEMOY (1894) *Dioscorea sativa*; rhizome.
CORRENS (1888) *Dioscorea* spp.; glands (original not seen).
DALE (1901) *Dioscorea sativa* L.; tuber.
DEINEGA (1898) *Dioscorea brasiliensis* Willd.; leaf.
DUCHARTRE (1885) *Dioscorea batatas* Desne; leaf, stem.
FALKENBERG (1876) *Dioscorea villosa*; course of vascular bundles.
GAUSSEN (1966) *Borderea chouardii* (Gaussen) Heslot (*Dioscorea chouardii*), *B. pyrenaica* (Bub.) Mieg. (*D. pyrenaica*), *Tamus communis* L.; petiole, stem.
GENTNER (1904) *Dioscorea macroura*; leaf glands.
—— (1905) Notes on several *Dioscorea* spp.; leaf glands.
GRAVIS (1934) *Dioscorea, Tamus, Testudinaria*; leaf traces.
GUÉDÈS (1967) *Dioscorea bulbifera, Tamus communis*; leaf.
GUILLAUD (1878) *Tamus communis* L.; rhizome.
HILL and FREEMAN (1903) *Dioscorea praehensilis* Benth.; root.
HOLM (1913) *Dioscorea villosa* L.; all parts.
JUNGNER (1888) *Dioscorea alata* L., *D. batatas* Desne, *D. bonariensis* Ten., *D. bulbifera* L., *D. convolvulacea* Klotzsch, *D. discolor* Hort. Ber., *D. japonica* Thunb., *D. punctata* Brown, *D. quinqueloba* Thunb., *D. retusa* Wight, *D. sativa* L., *D. septemloba* Hort. Ber. (nec. Thunb.), *D. triphylla* L., *D. villosa* L., *Dioscorea* spp., *Tamus communis* L., *Testudinaria elephantipes* Burch., *T. rupicola* Ecklon; leaf, stem.
KIRCHNER, LOEW, and SCHRÖTER (1934) *Tamus communis* L.; all parts.
KNUTH (1924) Anatomical information from other workers summarized.
KNY (1881) *Dioscorea batatas, D. sinuata* Arrab., *D. villosa* L., *Rajania brasiliensis* Griseb. (*D. teretiuscula* Klotzsch), *Tamus conicus, Testudinaria elephantipes* Hérit., *T. silvatica* Hort.; stem vascular bundles.
—— (1886) *Dioscorea convolvulacea* Cham. et Schlecht.; tracheids in tuber.
KOCH and BRUHN (1962) *Dioscorea floribunda* Mart. et Gal.; tuber.
LECLERC DU SABLON (1902) *Tamus communis*; tuber.
LINDINGER (1907) *Dioscorea discolor*; root, tuber.
MACDOUGAL (1912) *Dioscorea alata*; stem.
MARTIN and ORTIZ (1963) *Dioscorea floribunda* Mart. et Gal., *D. spiculiflora* Hemsl.; tuber.
MASON (1926) *Dioscorea alata* L.; phloem.
MESSERI (1925) *Tamus communis* L.; seedling anatomy.
MIÈGE (1958) *Dioscorea burkilliana* J. Miège, *D. mangenotiana* J. Miège; stem, leaf, tuber.
MOHL (1845) *Tamus elephantipes* L.; stem.
MOROT (1882) *Dioscorea batatas*; root.
NÄGELI (1858) *Dioscorea batatas* Desne, *Tamus communis* L.; course of vascular bundles in stem.
ORR (1923) *Dioscorea macroura* Harms.; leaf glands.
—— (1926) *Dioscorea alata* L., *D. bulbifera* L., *D. cayenensis* Lam., *D. convolvulacea* Cham. et Schlecht., *D. discolor* Kunth, *D. elephantopus* Spreng. (*Testudinaria elephantipes* Burch.), *D. esculenta* (Lour.) Burk., *D. glabra* Roxb., *D. laurifolia* Wall., *D. macroura* Harms., *D. multicolor* Lind. et And., *D. opposita* Thunb., *D. orbiculata* Hook. f., *D. pentaphylla* L., *D. piscatorum* Prain et Burk., *D. polyclades* Hook. f., *D. porteri* Prain et Burk., *D. pyrifolia* Kunth, *D. scortechinii* Prain et Burk., *D. triphylla* L., leaf glands.

PIROTTA and BUSCALIONI (1898*a*, *b*) *Dioscorea alata, D. batatas, D. bulbifera, D. hirsuta, D. villosa, Tamus communis, Testudinaria elephantipes*; vascular tissue.

PREUSS (1885) *Tamus communis*; petiole.

QUEVA (1893*b*) *Dioscorea batatas* Desne, *Helmia bulbifera* Kunth; bulbil.

——[1] (1894*b*) *Dioscorea aculeata* L.; all parts. *D. altissima*; stem, tuber. *D. anguina* Roxb.; stem. *D. batatas* Desne; all parts. *D. discolor* Hort. Ber.; stem. *D. illustrata* Hort.; all parts. *D. javanica* Hort.; stem, root, tuber. *D. kita*; tuber. *D. multicolor* Lind. et André; all parts. *D. pentaphylla* L.; leaf, root, tuber. *D. pyrenaica* Bub. et Bord.; leaf, stem. *D. quinqueloba* Thunb.; all parts. *D. repanda* Blume; leaf, stem, tuber. *D. salicifolia* Blume; stem. *D. sinuata* Vell.; all parts. *D. spiculata* Blume; leaf, stem, root. *D. spinosa* Roxb.; root (spinous). *D. variifolia* Kunze; leaf, stem. *D. villosa* L.; all parts. *Helmia bulbifera* Kunth; leaf, root, tuber, bulbil. *H. hirsuta* Kunth; leaf, root, tuber. *Rajania angustifolia* Sw.; leaf, stem. *R. cordata* L.; leaf, stem. *R. pleioneura* Griseb.; stem. *Tamus communis* L.; all parts. *T. cretica* L.; leaf, stem. *T. edulis*; leaf, stem. *Testudinaria elephantipes* Burch.; all parts.

—— (1894*c*) *Tamus communis* L.; tuber.

RAGHAVAN (1960) Brief notes on hairs and epidermis of several spp. of *Dioscorea*.

SCHAEDE (1939) *Dioscorea macroura* Harms.; leaf glands.

SCHLICKUM (1896) *Dioscorea bulbifera* L.; seedling anatomy.

SCOTT (1897) *Dioscorea praehensilis* Benth.; root (spinous).

SHAH (1963) *Dioscorea alata* L.; stem vessel elements.

—— et al. (1966, 1967) *Dioscorea alata* L.; stem vessel elements.

SIEDLER (1892) *Dioscorea bonariensis*; root.

SMITH (1916) *Dioscorea villosa* L.; seedling anatomy.

SPARSHOTT (1935) *Testudinaria elephantipes*; seedling anatomy, tuber.

STAUDERMANN (1924) *Dioscorea cumingii* Burk., *D. fasciculata* Roxb., *D. oppositifolia* L., *D. pyrifolia* Kunth, *D. spinosa* Roxb., *D. tomentosa* Koenig; hairs.

TROLL and MEYER (1955) *Dioscorea macroura*; petiole meristem.

ULINE (1898) Anatomical information mostly taken from other works.

WINKLER (1925) *Testudinaria elephantipes*; stem glands.

ZIMMERMANN (1932) *Dioscorea sativa*; glands. Report of Correns's work.

[1] See Burkill (1960, p. 348, footnote) for information on the correct names for Queva's material.

STENOMERIDACEAE

STENOMERIS Planch.

Leaf surface Fig. 5 B, p. 40.

Hairs absent; bicellular **glands** present. **Stomata** anomocytic, average size 45×31 μm, mainly confined to abaxial surface; each stoma surrounded by 4 epidermal cells. Adaxial and abaxial anticlinal cell walls slightly sinuous.

Lamina T.S.

Dorsiventral. **Cuticle** thin and undulating. **Epidermis**: adaxial cells rectangular, with thin wavy anticlinal walls; abaxial slightly smaller than adaxial cells. **Stomata**: walls of guard cells facing pore thickened and with no projecting ledges. **Mesophyll**: palisade and spongy tissues scarcely distinguishable, cells somewhat elongated and lying parallel to surface of lamina. **Vascular bundle** of midrib much larger than remainder. Xylem groups alternating with 3 phloem units towards abaxial side of midrib. Sclerenchyma represented by 6–8 layers of fibres partly surrounding main vascular bundles. **Crystals**: idioblasts containing raphide bundles present; substance resembling crystal sand occurring in epidermal cells. **Tannin** cells absent.

Petiole surface

Hairs absent; **glands** and **stomata** as in lamina.

Petiole T.S.

Outline crescentiform. **Cuticle** thick and undulating, ridged in places. **Epidermis** composed of thin-walled, irregular cells with dense cytoplasmic contents. **Vascular bundles** 7–9, arranged in a crescent; each bundle surrounded by 4–8 layers of fibres and embedded in thin-walled parenchymatous tissue. Xylem consisting mainly of tracheids and associated parenchyma; phloem composed of sieve-tubes, companion cells, and phloem parenchyma. **Crystals**: idioblasts containing raphide bundles few. **Tannin** cells absent.

Stem T.S. Pl. XIV. C.

Hairs absent; **glands** and **stomata** as in lamina. **Cuticle** thick and ridged. **Epidermis** of thin-walled cuboidal or rectangular cells with dense cytoplasmic contents. **Cortex**: 6–8-layered, cells of variable size. Sclerenchyma represented by 4–5 layers of fibres, separating cortex from vascular cylinder. **Vascular bundles** partly common and partly cauline. Common bundles V-shaped, with 1 large phloem unit at converging ends of V. Cauline bundles elliptical; 2 pairs of large vessels, average diameter 301 μm. One large phloem unit on inner side of pair of largest vessels and close to centre of pith, and another phloem unit at outer end close to periphery of central cylinder. Average diameter of large sieve-tubes 126 μm. **Pith** constituting about half of central cylinder. **Crystals:** idioblasts containing raphide bundles present, mostly in cortex. **Tannin** cells absent.

SPECIAL NOTE

The anatomy of this genus can hardly be separated from that of the Dioscoreaceae. Hutchinson's (1959) elevation of this genus to familial rank (Stenomeridaceae) is therefore not wholly supported. It is suggested that this family should be reduced to generic rank and placed under the Dioscoreaceae.

MATERIAL EXAMINED

Stenomeris borneensis Oliver; Philippines; E. D. Merrill 7301 (K). Leaf, petiole, stem.

S. dioscoreifolia Planch.; Philippines; G. E. Edano 11116 (K). Leaf, petiole, stem.

STENOMERIDACEAE

GENERA AND SPECIES REPORTED ON IN THE LITERATURE

ORR (1926) *Stenomeris dioscoreifolia* Planch.; leaf glands.
QUEVA (1894*b*) *Stenomeris dioscoreifolia* Planch.; leaf, stem.

TRICHOPODACEAE

A DETAILED investigation of *Trichopus zeylanicus* was conducted by Watson (1936), who concluded that the anatomy of this genus supports its inclusion in the Dioscoreaceae. Further studies of this genus (Ayensu 1966) together with *Avetra* and other genera of the Dioscoreales have shown conclusively that *Trichopus* should be kept as a monotypic genus of Trichopodaceae and that *Avetra* should be included in the Dioscoreaceae.

AVETRA H. Perrier

Leaf surface

Hairs absent from both surfaces; bulb-like multicellular **glands** on short unicellular stalks absent. **Stomata** anomocytic, average size $45 \times 45 \ \mu$m, mainly confined to abaxial surface; each stoma surrounded by 3–5 epidermal cells. Adaxial anticlinal cell walls straight, abaxial walls sinuous.

Lamina T.S.

Dorsiventral. **Cuticle** thick and undulating. **Epidermis:** adaxial cells cuboidal, with thick, straight anticlinal walls, and cytoplasmic contents; abaxial same size as adaxial cells. **Stomata:** walls of guard cells facing pore thickened and with no projecting ledges. **Mesophyll:** palisade and spongy tissues indistinguishable; cells somewhat elongated and lying parallel to surface of lamina. **Vascular bundle** of midrib much larger than remainder. Xylem consisting mainly of tracheids and associated parenchyma; phloem composed of sieve-tubes, companion cells, and phloem parenchyma. Xylem groups alternating with 5–6 phloem units towards abaxial side of midrib. Sclerenchyma represented mainly by brachysclereids in 8–12 layers surrounding vascular bundle of midrib. **Crystals:** idioblasts containing raphide bundles present. **Tannin** cells absent.

Petiole surface

Hairs and **glands** absent; **stomata** as in lamina.

Petiole T.S.

Outline crescentiform. **Cuticle** thick and undulating, slightly ridged in places. **Epidermis** composed of thick-walled cuboidal cells with dense cytoplasmic contents. **Vascular bundles** 5, arranged in a crescent; each bundle surrounded by sclerenchyma represented by 5–10 layers of fibres and embedded in thick-walled parenchyma cells. Xylem consisting of tracheids, vessels, and associated parenchyma; phloem composed of sieve-tubes, companion cells, and phloem parenchyma. **Crystals:** idioblasts containing raphide bundles present. **Tannin** cells absent.

Stem T.S. Pl. XV. A.

Hairs and **glands** absent. **Stomata** as in lamina. **Cuticle** thick and undulating, ridged in places. **Epidermis** of thick-walled cuboidal cells with dense cytoplasmic contents. **Cortex:** 5–10 layers of cells of variable size. Sclerenchyma represented by 4–8 layers of brachysclereids separating cortex from vascular cylinder. **Vascular bundles** partly common and partly cauline, embedded in thick-walled fibres. Common bundles having V-shaped arrangement of metaxylem vessels and tracheids together with one large phloem unit in centre of V. Cauline bundles having elliptical arrangement of metaxylem vessels (at least 2 pairs of large vessels, average diameter 238 μm) and tracheids, with 1 large phloem unit on inner side of innermost pair of large vessels, 1–3 phloem units external to same pair of vessels, and another phloem unit at end close to periphery of central cylinder (Pl. XV. A). Xylem consisting of tracheids, vessels, and associated parenchyma. Average diameter of large sieve-tubes 84 μm. Companion cells, phloem fibres, and parenchyma present. **Pith** area constituting about one-fourth of central cylinder. **Crystals:** idioblasts containing raphide bundles few. **Tannin** cells absent.

MATERIAL EXAMINED

Avetra sempervirens Perrier: (i) Malagasy Republic; G. F. S. Elliot 2745 (K).
   (ii) Malagasy Republic; M. H. Humber 28966 (P). Leaf, petiole, stem.

TRICHOPUS Gaertn.

Leaf surface Figs. 5. C, p. 40, 31. A, B.

   Hairs absent from both surfaces; crescent-shaped multicellular **glands** on short unicellular stalks present mainly on abaxial surface. **Stomata** anomocytic, average size 33 × 30 μm, mainly confined to abaxial surface; each stoma surrounded by 3–4 epidermal cells. Adaxial and abaxial anticlinal cell walls deeply sinuous.

Lamina T.S. Fig. 31. C.

   Dorsiventral. **Cuticle** thin and undulating on both surfaces, slightly thicker around main veins. **Epidermis:** adaxial cells large, cuboidal with thin, straight anticlinal walls and cytoplasmic contents; abaxial smaller than adaxial cells. **Stomata:** walls of guard cells facing pore thickened and with no projecting ledges. **Mesophyll:** palisade tissue confined to adaxial surface, always 1-layered. Cells of spongy tissue mainly elongated, lying parallel to surface of lamina and occupying about two-thirds of mesophyll. **Vascular bundle** of midrib conspicuously larger than remainder. Xylem groups alternating with 7–9 phloem units towards abaxial side of midrib. Xylem consisting of tracheids and associated parenchyma. Phloem composed of small sieve-tubes, companion cells, and phloem parenchyma. Sclerenchyma represented by many rows of fibres completely surrounding vascular bundles. **Crystals:** idioblasts containing raphide bundles present. **Tannin** cells absent.

Petiole surface

   Hairs absent; **glands** and **stomata** as in lamina.

Petiole T.S. Fig. 31. D.

Outline seven-sided with an adaxial groove. **Cuticle** slightly thickened and ridged. **Epidermis** composed of thin-walled cuboidal cells with cytoplasmic contents. **Vascular bundles** 5, arranged in a circle or an arc, each surrounded by many layers of sclerenchyma; 7 small bundles also appearing between the large bundles. All vascular bundles embedded in thin-walled parenchymatous tissue with intercellular spaces. Xylem consisting of tracheids and associated parenchyma. Phloem composed of small sieve-tubes, companion cells, and phloem parenchyma; 5–7 phloem units occurring in a vascular bundle. **Crystals:** idioblasts containing raphide bundles present. **Tannin** cells absent.

Stem T.S. Fig. 31. E; Pl. XIV, F; Pl. XV. B.

Outline conspicuously winged at various points. **Hairs** absent; **glands** and **stomata** as in lamina. **Cuticle** thin and ridged. **Epidermis** of thin-walled, rectangular or cuboidal cells with cytoplasmic contents. **Cortex:** 4–6 layers of cells of variable size, up to 12 layers in wings. **Endodermoid layer** represented by 6–8 layers of fibres, separating cortex from vascular cylinder. **Vascular bundles** and general plan of course of vascular strands contrasting strongly with those of the genera of the Dioscoreaceae. Vascular bundles in 2 rings; outer ring consisting of 8 collateral bundles, each exhibiting a U-shaped arrangement of tracheal elements with 1–3 phloem patches. Inner ring consisting of 8 amphivasal bundles, outlines of bundles triangular with 3–6 phloem patches. All bundles embedded in thick-walled parenchymatous tissue towards periphery of vascular cylinder. Xylem consisting mainly of tracheids and associated parenchyma; phloem composed of small sieve-tubes, companion cells, and phloem parenchyma. **Pith** of thin-walled, large-celled parenchymatous tissue occupying two-thirds of central cylinder. **Crystals:** idioblasts containing raphide bundles present. **Tannin** cells absent.

Rhizome T.S.

Epidermis composed of thick-walled cuboidal cells, compactly arranged, with cytoplasmic contents. **Cuticle** thin and ridged. **Cortex:** 10 layers of cells of fairly uniform size. **Endodermoid layer** consisting of cells with characteristic U-shaped thickenings, separating cortex from vascular cylinder. **Pericycle** consisting of many layers of cells. **Stele** with many separate concentric amphivasal bundles. Xylem consisting of tracheids; phloem composed of small sieve-tubes, companion cells, and phloem parenchyma. **Starch grains** numerous in pith parenchyma. **Crystals:** idioblasts containing raphide bundles present. **Tannin** cells absent.

Root T.S.

Epidermis of thick-walled cells, somewhat compactly arranged, with cytoplasmic contents. **Exodermis** 1-layered; cells compactly arranged, walls slightly thickened, suberized. **Cortex:** several layers of parenchymatous tissue. Outer 2–3 layers of small, evenly arranged cells. Inner cortex of large cells. **Endodermis** 1-layered, discontinuous; cells with characteristic U-shaped thickenings. **Pericycle** 1–2-layered. **Stele** 10-arch. Xylem consisting of

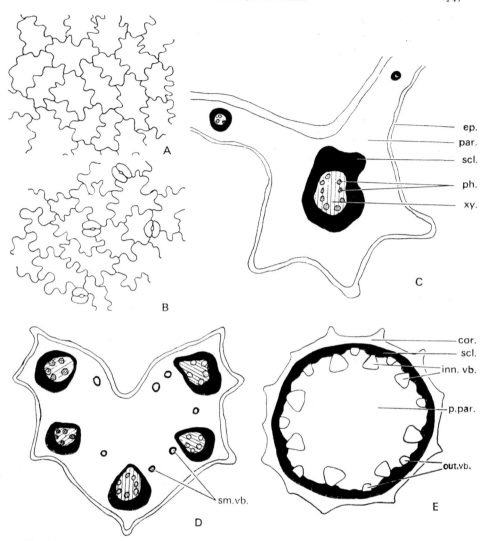

FIG. 31. Trichopodaceae. *Trichopus zeylanicus* (after Ayensu 1966). A, Adaxial epidermis, surface view (×330). B, Abaxial epidermis, surface view (×330). C, T.S. leaf midrib (×82). D, T.S. petiole, showing general vascular plan (×32). E, T.S. stem, general vascular plan (×82).

cor., cortex; ep., epidermis; inn.vb., inner vascular bundle; out.vb., outer vascular bundle; par., parenchyma; p.par., pith parenchyma; ph., phloem; scl., sclerenchyma; sm.vb., small vascular bundle; xy., xylem.

tracheids, vessels, and associated parenchyma; phloem composed of small sieve-tubes, companion cells, and phloem parenchyma. **Pith** parenchyma of thick-walled cells. **Crystals:** idioblasts containing raphide bundles present. **Tannin** cells absent.

MATERIAL EXAMINED

Trichopus zeylanicus Gaertn.; Kerala, India; A. Abraham, s.n. Leaf, petiole, stem, rhizome, root (J).

TRICHOPODACEAE

GENERA AND SPECIES REPORTED ON IN THE LITERATURE

AYENSU (1966) *Trichopus zeylanicus* Gaertn.; all parts.
BECCARI (1870*a*) *Trichopus zeylanicus* (as *Trichopodium zeylanicum* Thw.); stem.
QUEVA (1894*b*) *Trichopus zeylanicus* Gaertn.; all parts.
SOLEREDER (1888–9) *Trichopus zeylanicus*; leaf.
WATSON (1936) *Trichopus zeylanicus* Gaertn.; all parts.

STEMONACEAE

(Roxburghiaceae)

THE anatomy of the vegetative organs of the genera in this family has been described in two articles (Tomlinson and Ayensu 1968, Ayensu 1968*a*). The morphology of the genus *Croomia* was studied in some detail because ample material was available. For the most part the account under this family will represent those described in the publications cited above.

CROOMIA Torr. ex Torr. et A. Gray

Leaf surface. Fig. 32. A, B, H–J.

Hairs and **glands** absent. **Stomata** anomocytic, average size 45×31 μm, mainly confined to abaxial surface; each stoma surrounded by 4–5 epidermal cells. Adaxial and abaxial anticlinal cell walls sinuous.

Lamina T.S. Fig. 32. C–G, K (C and E are paradermal views).

Dorsiventral. **Cuticle** thin and undulating on both surfaces, slightly thicker around principal veins. **Epidermis**: adaxial cells mainly rectangular with thin, straight anticlinal walls and cytoplasmic contents; abaxial same size as adaxial cells. Marginal epidermal cells papillose, outer walls distinctly striate. **Stomata**: walls of guard cells facing pore somewhat thickened and with projecting ledges. **Mesophyll** uniformly chlorenchymatous, 3–5-layered; mostly 3-layered at margin and becoming several-layered towards midrib and principal veins; cells much-lobed, adaxial layer relatively compact (Fig. 32. C) but cells not anticlinally extended to form a distinct palisade; abaxial layer of loosely arranged cells, much-lobed (Fig. 32. E). **Vascular bundles** all alike apart from range in size, from small blind-ending veins to midrib; all separated from each epidermis by at least 1 layer of chlorenchyma. Largest veins resembling those of petiole and with inconspicuously collenchymatous abaxial subepidermal layers; small veins with reduced vascular tissues. Tracheids without definite end walls and with annular or spiral, rarely scalariform-reticulate wall thickenings. Sieve-tubes mostly with simple plates on transverse to oblique indistinct end walls. **Bundle sheath** inconspicuously sheathed by a single layer of longitudinally elongated chlorenchymatous cells, without thick-walled sheathing layers except for cells with slightly thickened walls next to phloem. **Crystals** present. **Tannin** cells absent.

Petiole surface

Hairs and **glands** absent. **Stomata** numerous and as in lamina.

Petiole T.S. Fig. 33. A, C.

Outline crescentiform. **Cuticle** thin, conspicuously striate. **Epidermis** composed of somewhat thicker-walled cells than epidermis of lamina. **Vascular**

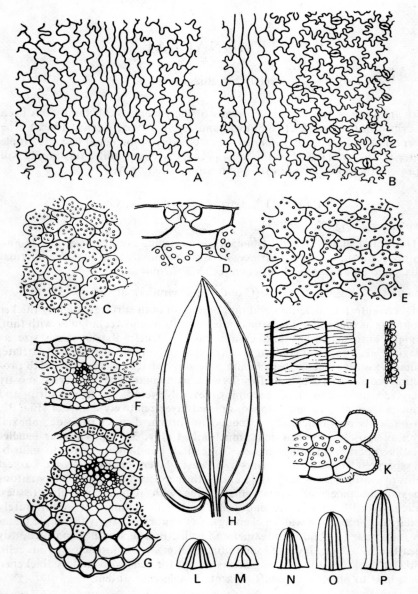

FIG. 32. *Croomia pauciflora* (after Tomlinson and Ayensu 1968). A, Adaxial epidermis, surface view (×100). B, Abaxial epidermis, surface view (×100). C, Adaxial paradermal view of lamina (×180). D, T.S. stoma (×470). E, Abaxial paradermal view of lamina (×180). F, T.S. minor vein of lamina (×180). G, T.S. midrib (×180). H, Outline of leaf showing distribution of major longitudinal veins (×1). I, Details of venation, midrib to left (×3). J, Details of leaf margin showing papillae (×30). K, T.S. leaf margin (×290). L–P, Series of flattened scales from rhizome (×1).

bundles 5; each vascular bundle with many narrow adaxial tracheal elements, adaxial protoxylem elements often partly occluded. Phloem with irregularly arranged, narrow sieve-tubes. **Bundle sheath** cells usually distinctly collenchymatous. **Crystals**: idioblasts containing raphide bundles present. **Tannin** cells absent.

Scale leaf. Fig. 32. L–P.

Epidermis: cells thin-walled, more or less rectangular in surface view. **Mesophyll** of uniform colourless parenchyma. Veins resembling major longitudinal veins of foliage leaf.

Stem T.S. Fig. 33. B, D–F; Pl. XVI. A.

Hairs and **glands** absent. **Cuticle** thin. **Epidermis**: cells somewhat thick-walled, longitudinally extended, more or less rectangular in surface view but commonly with oblique end walls, normally colourless but basal cells with red vacuoles. **Cortex**: outermost 2–3 layers small-celled and distinctly collenchymatous; ground parenchyma otherwise uniformly large-celled, thin-walled, and colourless except for chloroplasts in outermost cells distally. Medullary ground parenchyma cells widest and with some tendency to collapse. **Vascular bundles** 8–11, mostly amphivasal, arranged in a ring; narrower vascular bundles collateral, xylem discontinuous on outer side and without conspicuous protoxylem. Phloem with inconspicuous sieve-tubes surrounded by xylem and in turn surrounding a central strand of somewhat inflated cells with apparent wall thickenings which may represent obliterated protophloem. **Bundle sheath**: 2–3 layers of narrow, slightly thick-walled fibres or prosenchymatous cells; sheath in large bundles usually incomplete next to protoxylem. **Starch grains** present.

Rhizome T.S. Fig. 34. A–E.

Epidermis: cells thin- to thick-walled, uniform, and resembling those of aerial stem. **Cortex** wide, uniformly parenchymatous and with abundant starch except for somewhat narrower but scarcely collenchymatous peripheral cells. **Stele** angular in outline, delimited from cortex by a more or less continuous but indistinct endodermoid layer of cells with suberized walls but without obvious Casparian thickenings. Endodermoid layer separated from vascular tissues by an indistinct 1–3-layered pericycle. Stele including an irregular cylinder of 9–10 indistinct and anastomosing vascular bundles, forming a more or less continuous cylinder except for 2 somewhat more isolated and opposed lateral bundles. Additional small isolated phloem strands common next to pericycle. Larger vascular bundles somewhat amphivasal. Vascular cylinder enclosing a continuous but irregular cylinder of fibres; fibres often penetrating deeply between vascular bundles. Sclerenchyma delimited internally by a further suberized layer resembling the peripheral endodermoid layer, 2 layers sometimes continuous via gaps in vascular system. Medulla of thin-walled starch-filled tissue resembling cortical ground tissue. **Starch grains** abundant in ground parenchyma; grains up to 18 μm wide, ellipsoidal, flattened; hilum inconspicuous but obviously eccentric.

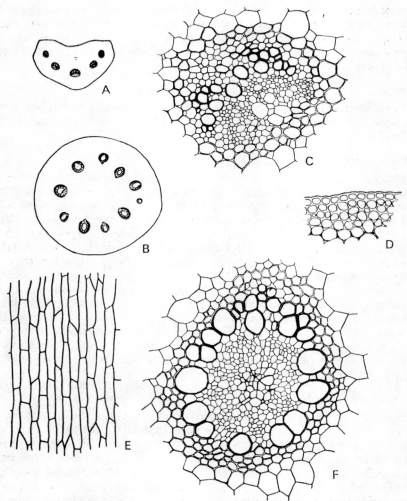

Fig. 33. *Croomia pauciflora* (after Tomlinson and Ayensu 1968). A, T.S. showing vascular plan of petiole (×10). B, T.S. showing vascular plan of stem (×10). C, T.S. collateral vascular bundle of petiole (×180). D, T.S. surface layers of stem (×100). E, Epidermis of stem, surface view (×100). F, T.S. amphivasal vascular bundle of stem (×180).

Root T.S. Fig. 34. F–L.

Epidermis persistent but often collapsing somewhat. Root-hairs uncommon, arising as outgrowths of otherwise unmodified cells. **Exodermis** a compact layer of narrow, suberized but scarcely thick-walled cells. **Cortex** very wide, of uniformly starch-filled parenchyma with well-developed intercellular spaces; innermost cells somewhat wider than outermost. **Endodermis** inconspicuously differentiated from innermost cortical layer but small-celled, thin-walled, and with conspicuous Casparian strips. **Pericycle** 1-layered,

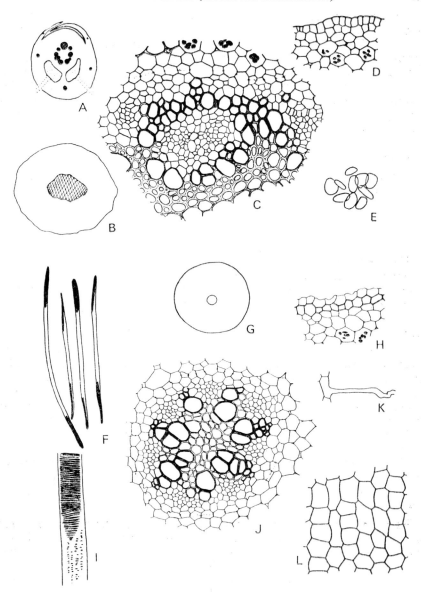

FIG. 34. *Croomia pauciflora* (after Tomlinson and Ayensu 1968). A, Diagram showing insertion of vascular tissues of lateral organs and rhizome. B, T.S. rhizome, stele cross-hatched (×10). C, T.S. periphery of rhizome stele to show one large amphivasal bundle (×180). D, T.S. rhizome, surface layers (×100). E, Starch grains (×400). F, Root vessel elements, extent of perforation shown as solid black (×25). G, T.S. root, general plan. (×10). H, T.S. root, surface layers (×100). I, Details of vessel element lower limit of a perforation plate (×180). J, T.S. root stele (×180). K, L.S. root-hair (×100). L, Epidermis from branch root, surface view (×100).

thin-walled, inconspicuous but usually distinguished from tissues within by its larger cells. **Stele** narrow, hexarch to heptarch (6–7) xylem poles; xylem arms irregular. Tracheal elements consisting of vessels (average length 2 mm and width 33 μm), each with long scalariform perforation plates on very oblique end walls up to 300 μm long. Thickening bars between perforations scarcely thinner than those on very similar imperforate end walls of tracheids in other organs. Tracheal elements together with central thick-walled medulla forming a fairly regular stellate core; narrow, thin-walled phloem strands occupying angles between protoxylem poles.

MATERIAL EXAMINED

Croomia pauciflora Torr.; Miami, Florida, U.S.A.; P. B. Tomlinson, s.n. Leaf, petiole, stem, rhizome, root (J).

STEMONA Lour.

Leaf surface

Hairs and **glands** absent. **Stomata** anomocytic, average size 48×33 μm, mainly confined to abaxial surface; each stoma surrounded by 3–4 epidermal cells. Adaxial and abaxial anticlinal cell walls slightly sinuous.

Lamina T.S.

Dorsiventral. **Cuticle** thin and slightly undulating on both surfaces. **Epidermis**: adaxial cells mainly rectangular with thin, straight anticlinal walls; abaxial slightly smaller than adaxial cells. **Stomata**: walls of guard cells facing pore thickened and with no projecting ledges. **Mesophyll** crushed in material examined. **Vascular bundles** collateral, that of midrib larger than remainder. Xylem consisting mainly of tracheids and associated parenchyma. Phloem composed of small sieve-tubes, companion cells, and phloem parenchyma. Ground parenchyma extending to interfascicular regions. **Crystals**: idioblasts containing raphide bundles few, styloids many. **Tannin** cells present mainly in cortex.

Stem T.S. Pl. XVI. B.

Hairs and **glands** absent. **Stomata** not detected. **Cuticle** rather thick and ridged. **Epidermis** of thick-walled circular cells. **Cortex** consisting of 8–12 layers of cells of uniform size. Sclerenchyma in 6–8 layers separating cortex from vascular cylinder. **Vascular bundles** partly common and partly cauline. Common bundles 13, collateral, with characteristic V-shaped arrangement; cauline bundles 13, strictly amphivasal with elliptically shaped arrangement of metaxylem vessels, large vessels orientated toward periphery of central cylinder. Xylem consisting of vessels, tracheids, and associated parenchyma; phloem composed of small sieve-tubes, companion cells, and phloem parenchyma. **Pith** area constituting about half of central cylinder, parenchyma cells larger in centre of area. **Crystals**: idioblasts containing raphide bundles and styloids present. **Tannin** cells randomly distributed in cortex.

SPECIAL NOTE

Of the 3 genera in the Stemonaceae the genus *Stemona* possesses anatomical characters that show the closest affinity to those of the genera of the Dioscoreaceae. The V-shaped and the elliptical shaped arrangement of the common and cauline bundles in the stem of this genus is not exhibited by either *Croomia* or *Stichoneuron*.

MATERIAL EXAMINED

Stemona curtisii Hook. f.: Siam; Haniffi and Nurr 4368 (K). Leaf, petiole, stem.

STICHONEURON Hook. f.

Stem T.S. Pl. XVI. C.

Hairs and **glands** absent. **Stomata** not observed. **Cuticle** thin and undulating. **Epidermis** of thick-walled rectangular cells. **Cortex** 8–10-layered, cells of variable size. **Endodermoid layer** separating cortex from vascular cylinder. **Vascular bundles** in 2 rings; outer ring consisting of 20 collateral bundles, each surrounded by 4–6 layers of fibres and embedded in thick-walled, parenchymatous tissue; inner ring consisting of 5 amphivasal bundles, evenly spaced and close to outer bundles, each bundle surrounded by 3–4 layers of fibres and embedded in thin-walled, parenchymatous tissue. Xylem consisting of tracheids, vessels, and associated parenchyma; phloem composed of small sieve-tubes, companion cells, and phloem parenchyma. **Starch grains** of variable size and shape present in inner, thin-walled, parenchyma cells. **Crystals**: idioblasts containing raphide bundles. **Tannin** cells present.

MATERIAL EXAMINED

Stichoneuron caudatum Ridley: (i) Malaya; E. J. Corner 28716 (K). (ii) Malaya; E. J. Corner 37056 (K). Stem.

STEMONACEAE

GENERA AND SPECIES REPORTED ON IN THE LITERATURE

AYENSU (1968) *Croomia pauciflora* Torr.; all parts. *Stemona curtisii* Hook. f.; leaf, stem. *S. kerrii* Craib; stem. *Stichoneuron caudatum* Ridley; stem.
HOLM (1905) *Croomia pauciflora* Torr.; all parts.
—— (1927) *Croomia pauciflora* Torr.; leaf (repetition of part of 1905 paper).
JUNGNER (1888) *Roxburghia* sp.; leaf, stem.
LACHNER-SANDOVAL (1892) *Roxburghia javanica*, with notes on *R. gloriosa* and *R. viridiflora*; stem vascular bundles.
TOMLINSON and AYENSU (1968) *Croomia pauciflora* Torr.; all parts.

APPENDIX I

KEY TO THE SUBGENERA OF DIOSCOREA
(Knuth 1924)

A. Seeds provided with elongate wing below   I. Helmia
B. Seeds surrounded on all sides by a membranous wing   II Dioscorea
C. Seeds winged above; tubers hypogeal   III Stenophora
D. Seeds winged above; tubers epigeal, very large, externally corky-woody   IV Testudinaria

SUBGENUS I. HELMIA (Kunth) Benth.

A. Leaves entire or somewhat sinuate:

   a. Male flowers fasciculate on the rachis of the spike, ±pedicellate:

      Fertile stamens 6:

      I. Stem twining to the right; anthers extrorse (*D. tubulosa* Griseb. excl.). America   Sect. 1 Dematostemon

      II. Stem twining to the left; anthers introrse (species often xerophytic). Madagascar   Sect. 2 Brachyandra

      Fertile stamens 3. Madagascar   Sect. 3 Madagascariensia

   b. Male flowers verticillate—capitulate on the rachis of the spike, rarely solitary, ±sessile; stem twining to the left:

      Stamens 6; column of the style fairly long; capsule oblong, sessile. South America   Sect. 4 Sphaerantha

      Stamens 3; column of the style none or almost none; capsule oblanceolate. South America   Sect. 5 Hyperocarpa

   c. Male flowers solitary on the rachis of the spike, rarely two together; sessile; stamens 6, inserted on the base of the perianth; stem twining to the left or to the right:

      Suffruticose; stems ±lignified and thickened; capsule oblong, coriaceous. America   Sect. 6 Chondrocarpa

      Herbaceous or suffruticose, stem not thickened. Tropical Africa, S. Africa, Madagascar   Sect. 7 Opsophyton

      I. Leaves opposite, very long-mucronate   (Subsec. Macrourae)

      II. Leaves alternate; inflorescence paniculate-congested   (Subsec. Euopsophyton)

      III. Leaves alternate; spike scarcely or very little branched   (Subsec. Isocantha)

   d. Male flowers solitary on the rachis of a ±narrow raceme, pedicellate; stamens 6 or 3; styles separate; stigmas undivided;
stem twining to the right:

      Stamens 3, inserted on the perianth lobes. Mexico, Central
America   Sect. 8 Trigonobasis

      Stamens 6 or 3, central or inserted on the base of the
perianth:

        I. Stamens 6; anthers opening at the apex; filaments very
short. South America   Sect. 9 Centrostemon

       II. Stamens 3; separate, often inserted on a fleshy disc.
South America   Sect. 10 Cycladenium

       III. Stamens 3; filaments fleshy, ±connate. South America
                                         Sect. 11 Monadelpha

   e. Male flowers in short, solitary cymes; stamens 6; stem twining
to the left. Argentina   Sect. 12. Trigonocarpa

B. Leaves with 3–5 leaflets:

   a. Male flowers in spike, distantly arranged; leaves trifoliate:

      Stamens 6. South America   Sect. 13 Stenocarpa
      Stamens 3. South America   Sect. 14 Trifoliatae

   b. Spikes of male flowers laxer, united into compound racemes;
in spikelets, stylar column very short:

      Fertile stamens 6; leaves often 3-foliate. Tropical Africa and
Asia   Sect. 15 Lasiophyton
      Fertile stamens 3, alternating with 3 sterile ones; leaves often
5-foliate. Tropical Asia   Sect. 16 Trieuphorostemon

   c. Male flowers spicate, congested in a dense spike; stylar column
very short; fertile stamens 3, alternating with 3 sterile ones;
leaves 5-foliate. Tropical Africa   Sect. 17 Botryosicyos

SUBGENUS II. DIOSCOREA Pax

A. Capsule obovate, elliptic or almost orbicular; leaves undivided,
sometimes lobed:

   a. Fertile stamens 6 (*D. rupicola* of Sect. 23 Rhacodophyllum
excl.):

      Capsule large:

        I. Male flowers arranged in cymose fascicles; rudimentary
style large. Mexico, Central and South America
                                  Sect. 18 Macrogynodium

       II. Male flowers fasciculate-capitulate or rarely solitary,
sessile; rudimentary style none or almost none:

         1. Stamens equally long:

           (i) Capsule longer than broad. Mexico, South
America   Sect. 19 Apodostemon

           (ii) Capsule as long as broad. North America,
Eurasia   Sect. 20 Macropoda

         2. 3 stamens longer than the rest. Mexico
                                  Sect. 21 Heterostemon

III. Male flowers solitary, fairly long pedicellate. Brazil
                                             Sect. 22 Hoehnea

IV. Male flowers solitary; stem without prickles; leaves ±
lobed. South Africa   Sect. 23 Rhacodophyllum

V. Male flowers solitary, very rarely fasciculate (*D. birmanica*). Stem ±armed with prickles; leaves entire.
Asia, Tropical Pacific Islands   Sect. 24 Combilium

Capsule small. Species of Chile; one of Peru (*D. weberbaueri*
Sect. 26, Microdioscorea); one from Brazil (*D. microcephala*
of the same sect.):

I. Flowers long pedicellate; leaves entire   Sect. 25 Parallelostemon

II. Flowers capitulate or fasciculate, sessile or subsessile:
    1. Leaves entire, or sagittiform at the base:
       (i) Procumbent or ascending, caulescent, slightly or
          scarcely branched; perianth lobes often unequal
                           Sect. 26 Microdioscorea
       (ii) Low growing, dwarf   Sect. 27 Pygmaeophyton
    2. Leaves coarsely 5–9-lobed   Sect. 28 Chirophyllum

b. Fertile stamens 3, alternating with 3 staminodes:
Glabrous. America:
   I. Male flowers single:
     1. Inflorescence axis zigzag-cincinniform. Mexico,
Brazil   Sect. 29 Cincinnorachis
     2. Inflorescence axis not zigzag. Mexico   Sect. 30 Oxypetalum
   II. Male flowers pedicellate, fasciculate:
     1. Stamens long, curved inwards; staminodes dilated;
stigmas elongated; capsule fleshy at least when young.
Mexico   Sect. 31 Sarcocapsa
     2. Stamens short; staminodes filiform; stigmas short.
Central America, Brazil   Sect. 32 Brachystigma
   III. Male flowers sessile, capitulate, rarely scorpioid.
Mexico to Argentina   Sect. 33 Lychnostemon
   Pilose. Africa   Sect. 34 Macrocarpaea

c. Fertile stamens 3; staminodes none:
Flowers capitulate or fasciculate, pedicellate; flowers rarely
sessile, and then stamens long:
   I. Stamens long:
     1. Filaments and anthers separate. Flowers ±fasciculate:
       (i) Flower companulate or scarcely crateriform;
tube short. Mexico   Sect. 35 Polyneuron
       (ii) Flower cylindrical; tube long. Mexico
                         Sect. 36 Siphonantha
     2. Filaments above and anthers connate. Flowers ±
capitulate. Bolivia   Sect. 37 Symphyostemon

II. Stamens short. Ecuador   Sect. 38 Pseudodematostemon

Flowers capitulate or solitary, sessile; stamens short:

 I. Flowers capitulate. Brazil Sect. 39 Hemidematostemon

 II. Flowers solitary. Brazil   Sect. 40 Triapodandra

Flowers solitary, pedicellate; filaments short:

 (i) Stamens free. Brazil   Sect. 41 Pedicellatae

 (ii) Anthers inserted on the disc or staminal column. Brazil,
  Bolivia   Sect. 42 Disciferae

B. Capsule broader than long; leaves undivided, at most lobed:

 a. Leaves alternate; male inflorescence branched; stamens inserted on the perianth-tube. America:

 Male flowers sessile, membranous:

  I. Stamens 6   Sect. 43 Cryptantha

  II. Stamens 3:

   1. Filaments very short Sect. 44 Strutantha

   2. Filaments elongate Sect. 45 Macrothyrsa

 Male flowers pedicellate, very slightly fleshy:

  I. Stamens 6:

   1. Stylar column very short Sect. 46 Sarcantha

   2. Stylar column elongate Sect. 47 Lasiogyne

  II. Stamens 3, alternating with 3 staminodes Sect. 48 Periandrium

 b. Leaves alternate; stamens 6, 3 fertile. E. Asia Sect. 49 Orientali-asiaticae

 c. Leaves alternate; stamens 3 only. Central E. Asia Sect. 50 Japonicae

 d. Leaves opposite, rarely alternate; spikes simple or compound,
 mostly verticillate—congested in the axils of leaves. Stamens
 central, short. Asia, Africa, America:

 Stamens 6, very rarely 3 abortive:

  I. Stellate-pilose; perianth-segments almost equal. Africa
      Sect. 51 Asterotricha

  II. Simply pilose (one species excluded); perianth segments
   unequal. Asia, Africa, America Sect. 52 Enantiophyllum

 Stamens 3, alternating with 3 staminodes; perianth segments
  unequal; stellate-pilose. W. Africa Sect. 53 Syntepaleia

 e. Leaves alternate; otherwise as *d.* Sect. 54 Stenophyllidium

 f. Leaves alternate; anthers of male flowers horned. Tube of the
 female flower externally 6-keeled Sect. 55 Stenocorea

C. Leaves deeply 3-lobed. Madagascar Sect. 56 Cardiocapsa

SUBGENUS III. STENOPHORA (Uline) R. Knuth

A. Leaves ±lobed; ±glabrous. N. China, Korea, Japan Sect. 57 Stenophora

B. Leaves cordate, ±tomentose beneath. S. China Sect. 58 Shannicorea

SUBGENUS IV. TESTUDINARIA (Salisb.) Uline s.em.

APPENDIX II

KEY TO THE OLD WORLD SECTIONS
OF THE GENUS DIOSCOREA
(Burkill 1960)

1. Storage in a rhizome — Stenophora
1'. Storage in a tuber:
  2. Annual increment within the tuber from a continuous-growth zone which increases the size of the tuber without altering its shape:
    3. Dwarfed plants of rocky places; wingless seeds. (Tuber with a rather thin layer of cork) — Borderea
    3'. Rather small, but not dwarfed, climbing; seeds winged. (Tuber with a very thick coat of cork, so hard that above the soil no other protection is needed) — Testudinaria
  2'. Annual increment to the tuber not covering the surface of the previous year:
    4. Annually new storage swelling crowns that of the previous year. (A high climber with intensely poisonous tubers which are at the surface of the soil, and have no corky coat) — Macroura
    4'. Annually storage lobes are directed downwards, depleted for the growth of the next year and replaced:
      5. Perennial bud on the tuber so close to the surface of the soil that the annual stem comes above the soil in its first internode:
        6. Torus of the male flower virtually absent. (Annual lobe thick-necked, single, broadly attached to the corm) — Opsophyton
        6'. Torus of the male flower enlarged as the top of the pedicel. (Lobes of various forms):
          7. Seeds winged for gliding, i.e. the wing is disposed to balance the seed in flight:
            8. Male inflorescence a simple spike or, if the flowers are pedicellate, the pedicels so short that it is spiciform; sometimes a second flower is present on the pedicel of a few of the lowest flowers:
              9. Stem twining to the right:
                10. Male flowers as little water-stores, all as a rule closely packed: hairs stiletto or dendroid, but not stellate — Enantiophyllum
                10'. Male flowers herbaceous; hairs stellate. (Anthers sometimes apiculate) — Asterotricha
              9'. Stem twining to the left; male flowers strictly racemose:
                11. Seeds evenly winged all round — Stenocorea
                11'. Seeds with equal wings extended from either end. (Laminae very generally lobed) — Rhacodophyllum

8′. Male flowers in small cymes along a racemose axis:
    12. Seeds as in the last section with even wings extended from either end of the seed. (Strangely hooked hairs)
        Macrocarpaea
    12′. Seeds evenly winged all round:
        13. Leaves very variable, if large lobed or compounded; fertile stamens 6   Cardiocapsa
        13′. Leaves entire; fertile stamens 3   Madagascarienses
7′. Seeds winged for whirling before a puff of wind, incapable of gliding, the wing being entirely or almost entirely from one end of the seed:
    14. Wing directed towards the distal end of the loculus; laminae simple, entire:
        15. Stem twining to the left:
            16. Capsule 4–6 times as long as broad; seeds with wings as in the genus *Stenomeris*, being fan-like. (Tuber may carry thorny roots)   Paramecocarpa
            16′. Capsule about twice as long as broad; seeds with or without the wing extended down the margin:
                17. Corm giving origin to numerous clavate lobes lying under a fierce armature of thorny roots; or in cultivated races unarmed; male inflorescence spicate; ability to fruit almost lost   Combilium
                17′. Corm giving origin to a single annual tuber; male inflorescence with little cymes of flowers along its axis   Shannicorea
        15′. Stem twining to the right. (Male flowers on a raceme on very short pedicels; capsules with high shoulders)   Cotinifoliae
    14′. Wing directed towards the base of the loculus; laminae compounded:
        18. Male flowers with no pedicel, but if not sessile then raised on a pediment which lifts the bract of the flower with the flower; capsules sometimes too large and heavy to become reflexed completely; fertile stamens often reduced to 3
            Lasiophyton
        18′. Male flowers at the base of the inflorescence in small cymes, but there only; stamens of two sizes   Illigerastrum
5′. Corm deep enough in the soil for 2–3 internodes to be within the soil. (The margins of the seed usually carry traces of the wing, which is directed towards the base of the capsule):
    19. Capsule-wall woody   Xylinocapsa
    19′. Capsule-wall parchmenty at the end of the season's growth:
        20. Male flower-bud globose:
            21. Torus of the male flower making a bell at the mouth of which the 6 anthers stand, their filaments inserted at the very base
            Campanuliflorae

21'. Torus of the male flower cup- or saucer-
shaped; stamens inserted just above the
base   Brachyandra

20'. Male flower-bud pyriform (inflorescence
a raceme)   Seriflorae

19''. Capsule-walls retain their fleshiness as in
Tamus beyond seed-ripening for upwards
of 6 months   Pachycapsa

APPENDIX III

KEY TO AND SECTIONAL REGROUPING OF
DIOSCOREA (Matuda 1954)

Male flowers with 6 fertile stamens:
Short filaments   Section A
Long filaments   Section B
Male flowers with 3 fertile stamens:
3 central or semi-central stamens, erect, free, inserted in the base
of the perianth tube   Section C
3 stamens (semi-central), long or short, curved towards the
centre, generally united at the perianth base   Section D
Male flowers with 3 fertile stamens and 3 staminodes   Section E

SECTION A

Section Apodostemon	Subgenus	II
„ Sphaerantha	„	I
„ Dematostemon	„	I
„ Enantiophyllum	„	II

SECTION B

Section Macrogynodium	Subgenus	II
„ Combilium	„	II
„ Heterostemon	„	II
Subsection Euopsophyton	„	I

SECTION C

Section Polyneuron	Subgenus	II
„ Napaephyton	„	II
„ Siphonantha	„	II

SECTION D

Section Trigonobasis	Subgenus	I
„ Polyneuron	„	II

SECTION E

Section Lychnostemon	Subgenus	II
„ Cincinnorachis	„	II
„ Oxypetalum	„	II
„ Sarcocapsa	„	II
„ Higinbothamia	„	II

APPENDIX IV

LISTS OF SELECTED DIAGNOSTIC CHARACTERS

THE lists under this appendix refer only to materials that I have personally examined. They are therefore not complete.

HABIT

LEAVES

Simple leaves occur in most species of the Dioscoreales. There are, however, a few sections of *Dioscorea* which have compound leaves.

Compound leaves

Cardiocapsa
Illigerastrum
Lasiophyton

Stenocarpa
Trifoliatae

Lobed leaves

Dioscorea
  Sections Macroura
      Rhacodophyllum
      Stenophora

Tamus

PETIOLE LENGTH

Most genera in the order have relatively long petioles.

Relatively short petioles

Dioscorea
  Sections Brachyandra
      Dematostemon
      Enantiophyllum

DIRECTION OF TWINING

Generally, species of some sections of *Dioscorea* twine to the left while others twine to the right.

Twining to the right

Dioscorea
  Sections Asterotricha
      Centrostemon
      Choristogyne
      Cotinifoliae
      Cryptantha
      Cycladenium
      Dematostemon
      Enantiophyllum
      Hyperocarpa
      Macrothyrsa

  Sections Periandrium
      Sarcantha
      Strutantha
      Trigonobasis

Avetra

Stenomeris

Twining to the left

Stemona

Stem erect

Stichoneuron

Croomia
Trichopus

HAIRS (on leaf except where stated)

Hairs are not abundant in the Dioscoreales except in a few sections of *Dioscorea*. The various hair types encountered are largely confined to species from the Old World. There is hardly any variation of hair type in the New World species except in length.

Unicellular hairs
Dioscorea subgenus I, *Helmia*
  Sections Lasiophyton (+uni-
    cellular
      Trigonobasis
Dioscorea subgenus II, *Dioscorea*
  Sections Cryptantha (+bicellular)
    Macrogynodium (some spp.)
    Macropoda (+multi-
      cellular; some spp.)
Dioscorea subgenus III, *Stenophora*
  Section Stenophora
Rajania hastata
R. mucronata

Bicellular hairs
Dioscorea subgenus I, *Helmia*
  Sections Botryosicyos
    Lasiophyton (+uni-
      cellular)
    Trieuphorostemon
Dioscorea subgenus II, *Dioscorea*
  Section Cryptantha (+unicellular)

T-shaped hairs
Dioscorea subgenus II, *Dioscorea*
  Sections Combilium
    Macrocarpaea

Stellate hairs
Dioscorea subgenus II, *Dioscorea*

Sections Asterotricha
  Syntepaleia

Hairs absent
Avetra
Dioscorea subgenus I, *Helmia*
  Sections Brachyandra
    Chondrocarpa
    Dematostemon
    Opsophyton
    Sphaerantha (stem)
    Stenocarpa (stem)
Dioscorea subgenus II, *Dioscorea*
  Sections Apodostemon
    Brachystigma (stem)
    Enantiophyllum
    Heterostemon
    Lasiogyne
    Lychnostemon
    Macrogynodium(some spp.)
    Macropoda (some spp.)
    Orientali-asiaticae
    Oxypetalum (stem)
    Sarcantha (stem)
    Stenocorea (stem)
Dioscorea subgenus IV, *Testudinaria*
Stemonaceae
Stenomeris
Tamus
Trichopus

GLANDS

Bicellular glands
Stenomeris

Crescentiform glands
Trichopus

Bulb-like multicellular glands on short unicellular stalks
Dioscorea   *Tamus*
Rajania

Glands not observed
Stemonaceae   *Avetra*

TANNINS

Tannins present
Dioscoreaceae (most spp.)
Stemonaceae (most spp.)

Tannins conspicuously absent
Stenomeridaceae
Trichopodaceae

CRYSTALS

Idioblasts containing raphides of calcium oxalate have been observed in all spp. of the families in Dioscoreales.

Styloids

Stemona (numerous in leaves; also a few raphide bundles).
Dioscorea tomentosa (leaf)

BIBLIOGRAPHY

ABROL, B. K., KAPOOR, L. D., and CHOPRA, I. C. (1962) Pharmacognostic study of the rhizome of *Dioscorea deltoidea* Wall. *Planta med.* **10**, 335–40.

AKAHORI, A. (1965) Studies of the steroidal compounds of domestic plants. XLIV. Steroidal sapogenins contained in Japanese *Dioscorea* species. *Phytochemistry* **4**, 97–106.

ALLARD, H. A. (1945) Some behaviors of the yams (*Dioscorea*) of the family Dioscoreaceae. *Castanea* **10**, 8–13.

—— (1947) The direction of twist of the corolla in bud, and twining of the stems in Convolvulaceae and Dioscoreaceae. Ibid. **12**, 88–94.

ANKERMAÑN, B. (1905) Kulturkreise und Kulturschichten in Afrika. *Z. Ethnol.* **36**, 62–90.

ANZALDO, F. E., MARAÑON, J., and ANCHETA, S. (1956) [1957] Screening of Philippine plants for steroidal sapogenins, I. *Philipp. J. Sci.* **85**, 305–14.

ARBER, A. (1918) Further notes on intrafascicular cambium in monocotyledons. *Ann. Bot.* **32**, 87–9.

—— (1925) *Monocotyledons: a morphological study*. Cambridge University Press.

ARCHIBALD, E. E. A. (1967) The genus *Dioscorea* in the Cape Province west of East London. *Jl. S. Afr. Bot.* **33**, 1–46.

ARISZ, W. H. (1952) Transport of organic compounds. *A. Rev. Pl. Physiol.* **3**, 109–30.

ARNOTT, H. J. (1959) Leaf clearings. *Turtox News* **37**, 192–4.

AYENSU, E. S. (1965) Notes on the anatomy of the Dioscoreaceae. *Ghana J. Sci.* **5** (1), 19–23.

—— (1966) Taxonomic status of *Trichopus*: anatomical evidence. *J. Linn. Soc.* (Bot.) **59**, 425–30.

—— (1967) Aerosol OT solution—an effective softener of herbarium specimens for anatomical study. *Stain Technol.* **42**, 155–6.

—— (1968a) Comparative vegetative anatomy of the Stemonaceae (Roxburghiaceae). *Bot. Gaz.* **129**, 160–5.

—— (1968b) The anatomy of *Barbaceniopsis*, a new genus recently described in the Velloziaceae. *Am. J. Bot.* **55**, 399–405.

—— (1969) Aspects of the complex nodal anatomy of the Dioscoreaceae. *J. Arnold Arbor.* **50**, 124–37.

BAILEY, I. W. (1956) Nodal anatomy in retrospect. Ibid. **37**, 269–87.

—— and TUPPER, W. W. (1918) Size variations in tracheary cells: I. A comparison between the secondary xylems of vascular cryptogams, gymnosperms and angiosperms. *Proc. Am. Acad. Arts Sci.* **54**, 149–204.

BARUA, A. K., CHAKRAVARTI, D., and CHAKRAVARTI, R. N. (1954) Saponins from Indian *Dioscorea* plants. *J. Indian chem. Soc.* **31**, 173–8.

——, ——, and —— (1956) Steroid sapogenins from Indian *Dioscorea* plants II. Ibid. **33**, 798–803.

BARY, A. DE (1884) *Comparative anatomy of the vegetative organs of the phanerogams and ferns*. Clarendon Press: Oxford.

BEAUVISAGE, G. (1888) La course des faisceaux dans la tige du *Dioscorea batatas*. *Bull. Soc. bot. Lyon* **6**, 78–88.

BECCARI, O. (1870a) Nota sul *Trichopodium zeylanicum* Thw. *Nuovo G. bot. ital.* **2**, 13–19.

—— (1870b) Nota sull'embrione delle Dioscoreacee. Ibid. **2**, 149–55.

BEHNKE, H.-D. (1965a) Über das Phloem der Dioscoreaceen unter besonderer Berücksichtigung ihrer Phloembecken. I. *Z. Pflanzenphysiol.* **53**, 97–125.

—— (1965b) Über den Feinbau 'gitterartig' aufgebauter Plasmaeinschlüsse in den Siebelementen von *Dioscorea reticulata*. *Planta* **66**, 106–12.

—— (1965c) Über das Phloem der Dioscoreaceen unter besonderer Berücksichtigung ihrer Phloembecken. II. *Z. Pflanzenphysiol.* **53**, 214–44.

BENTHAM, G. and HOOKER, J. D. (1883) Dioscoreaceae and Roxburghiaceae. In *Genera Plantarum* **3**, 741–7. L. Reeve & Co.: London.

BERGMANN, E. (1913) *Die Entwicklungsgeschichte der extranuptialen Nektarien von Dios-*

corea discolor. Diss. Münster. 30 pp. (Seen in *Just's bot. Jber*. **41** (2), Sec. 20, No. 59 (1913).)

BLUNDEN, G. and HARDMAN, R. (1963) *Dioscorea belizensis* Lundell as a source of diosgenin. *J. Pharm. Pharmac*. **15**, 273–80.

——, ——, and TREASE, G. E. (1963). The anatomy of *Dioscorea belizensis* Lundell. *J. Pharm. Pharmac*. **15**, 394–405.

——, ——, and —— (1966) Some observations on the propagation of *Dioscorea belizensis* Lundell and other steroid-yielding yams. *Planta med*. **14**, 84–9.

BOYD, L. (1932) Monocotyledonous seedlings. *Trans. bot. Soc. Edinb*. **31**, 1–224.

BRAUN, H. J. (1957) Die Leitbündelbecken in den Nodien der Dioscoreaceae, mit besonderer Berücksichtigung eines neuartigen Typs assimilate-leitender Zellen. *Ber. dt. bot. Ges*. **70**, 305–22.

BROUWER, R. (1953) The arrangement of the vascular bundles in the nodes of the Dioscoreaceae. *Acta bot. néerl*. **2**, 66–73.

BROWN, R. (1810) Dioscoreae. *Prodromus Florae Novae Hollandiae*, pp. 294–5. London.

BUCHERER, E. (1889) Beiträge zur Morphologie und Anatomie der Dioscoreaceen. *Biblthca bot*. **3** (16), 1–35.

BURCHELL, W. J. (1824) *Travels in the interior of Southern Africa*, Vol. II. London.

BURKILL, I. H. (1935) *A dictionary of economic products of the Malay Peninsula*. Crown Agents: London.

—— (1937) The development of the tuber of *Dioscorea sansibarensis* Pax. *Blumea* Suppl. 1, 232–7.

—— (1939) Growth and tensions between the nerves in the leaf-blade of *Tamus communis* Linn. *J. Bot., Lond*. **77**, 325–33.

—— (1940) The distribution of raphides in the leaves of *Tamus communis* Linn. Ibid. **78**, 17–19.

—— (1949) The ontogeny of the stem of the Common Bryony, *Tamus communis* Linn. *J. Linn. Soc*. (Bot.) **53**, 313–82.

—— (1952) Testudinaria as a section of the genus *Dioscorea*. *Jl S. Afr. Bot*. **18**, 177–91.

—— (1960) The organography and the evolution of Dioscoreaceae, the family of the yams. *J. Linn. Soc*. (Bot.) **56**, 319–412.

CHEADLE, V. I. (1942) The occurrence and types of vessels in the various organs of the plant in the Monocotyledoneae. *Am. J. Bot*. **29**, 441–50.

—— (1943a) The origin and certain trends of specialization of the vessel in the Monocotyledoneae. Ibid. **30**, 11–17.

—— (1943b) Vessel specialization in the late metaxylem of the various organs in the Monocotyledoneae. Ibid. 484–90.

—— (1944) Specialization of vessels within the xylem of each organ in the Monocotyledoneae. Ibid. **31**, 81–92.

—— and UHL, N. W. (1948a) Types of vascular bundles in the Monocotyledoneae and their relation to the late metaxylem conducting elements. Ibid. **35**, 486–96.

—— and —— (1948b) The relation of metaphloem to the types of vascular bundles in the Monocotyledoneae. Ibid. 578–83.

—— and WHITFORD, N. B. (1941) Observations on the phloem in the Monocotyledoneae. I. The occurrence and phylogenetic specialization in structure of the sieve tubes in the metaphloem. Ibid. **28**, 623–7.

COPELAND, E. B. (1916) Growth phenomena of *Dioscorea*. *Philipp. J. Sci*. C, Bot. **11**, 227–41.

CORDEMOY, H.-J. DE (1893) Sur le rôle des tissus secondaires à réserves des Monocotylédones arborescentes. *C.r. hebd. Séanc. Acad. Sci., Paris* **117**, 132–4.

—— (1894) *Recherches sur les Monocotylédones à accroissement secondaire*. Thesis, University of Paris. 108 pp. Lille. (See *Beih. bot. Zbl*. **5**, 89–91 (1895).)

CORRELL, D. S., SCHUBERT, B. G., GENTRY, H. S., and HAWLEY, W. O. (1955) The search for plant precursors of cortisone. *Econ. Bot*. **9**, 307–75.

CORRENS, C. E. (1888) Zur Anatomie und Entwicklungsgeschichte der extranuptialen Nectarien von *Dioscorea*. *Sber. Akad. Wiss. Wien* **97**, 651–74.

COURSEY, D. G. (1967) *Yams*. Longmans: London. 230 pp.

CRÉÉT, P. (1953) A propos de l'embryogénie du *Dioscorea oppositifolia* L. *Bull. Soc. bot. Fr*. **100**, 306–7.

168 BIBLIOGRAPHY

CRUZADO, H. J., DELPIN, H., and ROARK, B. A. (1965) Sapogenin production in relation to age of tuber in two *Dioscorea* species. *Turrialba* 15, 25–8.

DALE, E. (1901) On the origin, development, and morphological nature of the aerial tubers in *Dioscorea sativa* Linn. *Ann. Bot.* 15, 491–501.

DARLINGTON, C. D. and WYLIE, A. P. (1955) *Chromosome atlas of cultivated plants*, 2nd edn. George Allen & Unwin: London.

DAVIS, G. L. (1966) *Systematic embryology of the angiosperms*. Wiley: New York, London, Sydney. 528 pp.

DECROCK, E. (1908) Contribution à l'étude des fécules de l'Indochine. *Annls. Mus. colon. Marseille* sér. 2, 6, 67–129.

DEINEGA, V. (1898) Beiträge zur Kenntniss der Entwickelungsgeschichte des Blattes und der Anlage der Gefässbündel. *Flora* 85, 439–98.

DUCHARTRE, P. (1885) Influence de la sécheresse sur la végétation et la structure de l'igname de Chine (*Dioscorea batatas* Dcne). *Bull. Soc. bot. Fr.* 32, 156–67.

DUTROCHET, H. (1835) Observations sur la forme et la structure primitives des embryons végétaux. *Nouv. Annls Mus. Hist. nat.* 4, 165–211.

ENDLICHER, S. L. (1837) Roxburghiaceae. *Genera Plantarum*, pp. 157, 1197. Vindobonae.

ENGLER, A. (1892) *Syllabus der Vorlesungen über specielle und medicinisch-pharmaceutische Botanik*, pp. 86–7. Borntraeger: Berlin.

ERDTMAN, G. (1952) *Pollen morphology and plant taxonomy. Angiosperms*. Chronica Botanica Co.: Waltham, Mass.

ESAU, K. (1943) Ontogeny of the vascular bundle in *Zea mays*. *Hilgardia* 15, 327–68.

—— (1953) *Plant Anatomy*. Wiley: New York (2nd edn. 1965).

—— (1965) *Vascular differentiation in plants*. Holt, Rinehart & Winston: New York.

——, CURRIER, H. B., and CHEADLE, V. I. (1957) Physiology of phloem. *A. Rev. Pl. Physiol.* 8, 349–74.

EUNUS, A. M. (1952) Contribution to the morphology of the *Dioscorea*. I. Embryology of *D. glabra* Roxb. *Proc. Pakist. sci. Conf.*, pp. 81–2.

FALKENBERG, P. (1876) *Vergleichende Untersuchungen über den Bau der Vegetationsorgane der Monocotyledonen*, pp. 202. Stuttgart.

GAERTNER, J. (1788) *De fructibus et seminibus plantarum*, Vol. I, p. 44, t. 14. Stuttgart.

GAUSSEN, H. (1966) Flore des Pyrénées. Famille des Dioscoreaceae. *Docums Cartes Prod. vég. Toulouse*, sér. Pyrénées, 4 (3), 23 pp.

GENTNER, G. (1904) Über den Bau und die Funktionen der Vorläuferspitze von *Dioscorea macroura*. *Ber. dt. bot. Ges.* 22, 144–8.

—— (1905) Über die Vorläuferspitzen der Monokotylen. *Flora* 95, 327–83.

GOEBEL, K. (1905) Morphologische und biologische Bemerkungen. 16. Die Knollen der Dioscoreen und die Wurzelträger der Selaginellen, Organe, welche zwischen Wurzeln und Sprossen stehen. Ibid. 167–212.

GOOD, R. (1964) *The geography of the flowering plants*. Wiley: New York.

GOODWIN, A. J. H. (1939) The origins of certain African food-plants. *S. Afr. J. Sci.* 36, 445–63.

GRAVIS, A. (1934) Théorie des traces foliaires. *Mém. Acad. r. Belg. Cl. Sci.*, sér. 2, 12, 59 pp. (Also in: *Recueil de quelques travaux d'anatomie végétale exécutés à Liége de 1929 à 1935*. Bruxelles (1936).)

GREENWOOD-BARTON, L. H. (1961). Yam starches from Nigeria. Report No. 51 of the Tropical Products Institute, London.

GUÉDÈS, M. (1967) Sur la morphologie de la feuille de deux Dioscoréacées. *Phyton, Horn* 12, 216–27.

GUILLAUD, A. (1878) Recherches sur l'anatomie comparée et le développement des tissus de la tige dans les Monocotylédones. *Annls Sci. nat.*, Bot., sér. 6, 5, 5–176.

HAPP, H. (1950) Die Dioscoreaceen-Knoten. Staatsexamensarbeit, München (unpublished).

HAUMAN, L. (1916) Les Dioscoréacées de l'Argentine. *An. Mus. nac. Hist. nat. B. Aires* 27, 441–513.

HEGNAUER, R. (1963) *Chemotaxonomie der Pflanzen*. II. *Monocotyledoneae*. Birkhäuser Verlag: Basel and Stuttgart, 540 pp.

HILL, A. W. (1960) The morphology and seedling structure of the geophilous species of *Peperomia*, together with some views on the origin of monocotyledons. *Ann. Bot.* 20, 395–427.

—— (1938) The monocotylous seedlings of certain dicotyledons with special reference to the Gesneriaceae. *Ann. Bot.* (N.S.) **2**, 127–43.

HILL, T. G. and FREEMAN, W. G. (1903) The root structure of *Dioscorea prehensilis*. *Ann. Bot.* **17**, 413–24.

HOLLÓ, J. (1964). L'utilisation industrielle de l'igname. Paper presented to the 1er Congrès Internationale des Industries Agricoles et Alimentaires des Zones Tropicales et Sub-Tropicales, Abidjan.

HOLM, T. (1905) *Croomia pauciflora* Torr. An anatomical study. *Am. J. Sci.*, ser. 4, **20**, 50–4.

—— (1913) Medicinal plants of North America. 79. *Dioscorea villosa* L. *Merck's Rep.* **22**, 311–14. (Seen in *Bot. Zbl.* **126** (1914), 61.)

—— (1927) Sciaphilous plant-types. *Beih. bot. Zbl.* **44**, 1–89.

HOLTTUM, R. E. (1955) Growth habits of monocotyledons—variations on a theme. *Phytomorphology* **5**, 399–413.

HORNELL, J. (1934) Indonesian influence on East African culture. *Jl R. anthrop. Inst.* **64**, 305–32.

HUBER, H. (1969) Die Samenmerkmale und Verwandtschaftsverhältnisse der Liliifloren. *Mitt. bot. StSamml.*, Münch. **8**, 219–538.

HUTCHINSON, J. (1934) *The families of flowering plants*. II. *Monocotyledons*, 1st edn. Macmillan: London.

—— (1959) *The families of flowering plants*. II. *Monocotyledons*, 2nd edn. Clarendon Press: Oxford.

JOHANSEN, D. A. (1950) *Plant embryology*. Chronica Botanica Co.: Waltham, Mass.

JOHNSTON, H. H. (1908) *George Grenfell and the Congo*, pp. 600–2.

JUNGNER, J. R. (1888) Bidrag till kännedomen om anatomien hos familjen Dioscoreae. (Beiträge zur Kenntnis der Anatomie der Familie Dioscoreae.) *Bih. K. Svenska Vetensk Akad. Handl.* **13** (7), 1–84.

JUSSIEU, A. L. DE (1789) *Genera Plantarum*, pp. 40–3. Paris.

—— (1839) Mémoire sur les embryons monocotylédonés. *Annls Sci. nat.*, Bot., sér. 2, **11**, 341–61.

KIRCHNER, O. VON, LOEW, E., and SCHRÖTER, C. (1934) *Lebensgeschichte der Blütenpflanzen Mitteleuropas*, Vol. 1 (3), pp. 686–719. Stuttgart.

KLOTZSCH, F. (1859) Die Aristolochiaceae des Berliner Herbariums. *Mber. K. Akad. Wiss. Berl.*, pp. 571–626.

KNUTH, R. (1924) Dioscoreaceae. *In* Engler, *Das Pflanzenreich*, **87** (IV. 43), pp. 1–387.

—— (1930) Dioscoreaceae. *In* Engler and Prantl, *Die natürlichen Pflanzenfamilien*, 2nd edn., Vol. 15a, pp. 438–62.

KNY, L. (1881) Ueber einige Abweichungen im Bau des Leitbündels der Monokotyledonen. *Verh. bot. Ver. Prov. Brandenb.* **23**, 94–109.

—— (1886) Ein Beitrag zur Entwickelungsgeschichte der Tracheïden. *Ber. dt. bot. Ges.* **4**, 267–76.

KOCH, W. and BRUHN, C. (1962) Über die Morphologie der Speicherorgane einiger mittelamerikanischer Dioscoreen. *Flora, Jena* **152**, 670–8.

LABAT, J. (1959) Sapogeninas en Dioscoreas argentinas. *An. Asoc. quim. argent.* **47**, 5–7.

LACHNER-SANDOVAL, V. (1892) Beitrag zur Kenntniss der Gattung *Roxburghia*. *Bot. Zbl.* **50**, 65–70, 97–104, 129–35.

LAWTON, J. R. S. and LAWTON, J. R. (1967) The morphology of the dormant embryo and young seedling of five species of *Dioscorea* from Nigeria. *Proc. Linn. Soc. Lond.* **178**, 153–9.

LECLERC DU SABLON (1902) Sur le tubercule du *Tamus communis*. *Revue gén. Bot.* **14**, 145–50.

LINDINGER, L. (1907) Über den morphologischen Wert der an Wurzeln entstehenden Knollen einiger *Dioscorea*-Arten. *Beih. bot. Zbl.* **21** (1), 311–24.

LINDLEY, J. (1832) *Aristolochia. Botanical register*, vol. 18, pl. 1543. London.

—— (1853) *The vegetable kingdom*, 3rd edn. London.

LINNAEUS, C. (1737) *Genera Plantarum*, 1st edn, pp. 305–6. Lugduni Batavorum.

—— (1753) *Species Plantarum*. 1st edn, pp. 1028–34. Holmiae.

LOUREIRO, J. DE (1790) Tetrandria. Genus III. *Stemona. Flora cochinchinensis*, vol. 1 p. 404. Ulyssipone.

MACDOUGAL, D. T. (1912) The water balance of desert plants. *Ann. Bot.* **26**, 71–93.

MAHESHWARI, P. (1950) *An introduction to the embryology of angiosperms.* McGraw-Hill: New York.

MAKER, R. E. and APPLEZWEIG, N. (1949) Steroidal sapogenins as a source of cortical steroids. *Chem. Engng News* **46** (27), 3348.

——, WAGNER, R. B., ULSHAFER, P. R., WHITTBECKER, E., GOLDSMITH, D. P., and RUOF, C. H. (1947) Steroidal sapogenins. *J. Am. chem. Soc.* **69**, 2167, 2373.

MARTIN, F. W., CABANILLAS, E., and GASKINS, M. H. (1966) Economics of the sapogenin-bearing yam as a crop plant in Puerto Rico. *J. Agric. Univ. P. Rico* **50**, 53–64.

——, DELFEL, N. E., and CRUZADO, H. J. (1963) *Dioscorea friedrichsthalii*, another sapogenin-bearing species. *Turrialba* **13**, 159–63.

—— and DELPIN, H. (1965) Sapogenin production and agronomic potential of *Dioscorea spiculiflora*. Ibid. **15**, 296–9.

—— and ORTIZ, S. (1963) Origin and anatomy of tubers of *Dioscorea floribunda* and *D. spiculiflora*. *Bot. Gaz.* **124**, 416–21.

MASON, T. G. (1926) Preliminary note on the physiological aspects of certain undescribed structures in the phloem of the great yam *Dioscorea alata* Linn. *Scient. Proc. R. Dub. Soc.* **18**, 195–8.

MATUDA, E. (1954) Las Dioscoreas de México. *An. Inst. Biol. Univ. Méx.* **24**, 279–390.

MESSERI, E. (1925) Ricerche sullo sviluppo del sistema vascolare in alcune monocotiledoni. *Nuovo G. bot. ital.* **32**, 317–62.

METCALFE, C. R. (1936) An interpretation of the morphology of the single cotyledon of *Ranunculus ficaria* based on embryology and seedling anatomy. *Ann. Bot.* **50**, 103–20.

—— (1938) The morphology and mode of development of the axillary tubercles and root tubers of *Ranunculus ficaria*. *Ann. Bot.* (N.S.) **2**, 145–57.

—— (1960) *Anatomy of the monocotyledons. I. Gramineae.* Clarendon Press: Oxford.

—— (1963) Comparative anatomy as a modern botanical discipline. *Adv. bot. Res.* **1**, 101–47.

MIÈGE, J. (1948) Le *Dioscorea esculenta* Burkill en Côte d'Ivoire. *Revue int. Bot. appl. Agric. trop.* **28**, 509–14.

—— (1957) Influence de quelques caractères des tubercules semences sur la levée et le rendement des ignames cultivées. *J. Agric. trop. Bot. appl.* **4**, 315–42.

—— (1958) Deux ignames ouest-africaines à tubercules vivaces. *Bull. Inst. fr. Afr. noire,* sér. A, **20**, 39–59.

MIÉGEVILLE, L'ABBÉ (1866) Essai de détermination d'une Dioscorinée récemment découverte dans les Pyrénées. *Bull. Soc. bot. Fr.* **13**, 373–9.

MOHL, H. VON (1845) Untersuchungen über den Mittelstock von *Tamus elephantipes* L. *Vermischte Schriften*, pp. 186–94. Tübingen.

MOROT, L. (1882) Note sur les prétendus faisceaux collatéraux de certaines racines. *Bull. Soc. bot. Fr.* **29**, 115–16.

MORTON, C. V. (1936) Notes on *Dioscorea* with special reference to the species of the Yucatan Peninsula. *Carnegie Inst. Wash., Publ. No. 461*, pp. 239–53.

MUELLER, F. VON (1860) *Petermannia*. In *Fragmenta phytographiae Australiae,* Vol. 2. Melbourne.

NÄGELI, C. (1858) Über das Wachsthum des Stammes und der Wurzel bei den Gefässpflanzen. *Beitr. wiss. Bot.* **1**, 1–156.

NAKAJIMA, G. (1933) Chromosome numbers in some angiosperms. *Jap. J. Genet.* **9**, 1–5.

ORR, M. Y. (1923) The leaf glands of *Dioscorea macroura* Harms. *Notes R. bot. Gdn Edinb.* **14**, 57–72.

—— (1926) On the secretory organs of the Dioscoreaceae. Ibid. **15**, 133–46.

PEAL, W. J. (1961) Some steroids of Uganda Dioscoreaceae. *Proc. Symp. Phytochemistry,* pp. 93–5. Hong Kong University Press.

PERRIER DE LA BATHIE, H. (1924) Un nouveau genre de Dioscoréacées. *Bull. Soc. bot. Fr.* **71**, 25–7.

PHILIPPI, R. A. (1862) Descripción de las especies nuevas de plantas y insectos hallodos en este viage. *An. Univ. Chile,* no. 46, pp. 62–3.

PIROTTA, R. and BUSCALIONI, L. (1898*a*) Sulla presenza di elementi vascolari plurinucleati nelle Dioscoreacee. *Atti R. Accad. Naz. Lincei Rc. Sed. solen.,* ser. 5, **7**, 141–5.

—— and —— (1898*b*) Sulla presenza di elementi vascolari multinucleati nelle Dioscoreacee. *Annali R. Ist. Bot. Roma* **7**, 237–54.

PLANCHON, J.-E. (1852) Description d'un genre nouveau du groupe des Thismiées (1). *Annls Sci. nat.*, Bot., sér. 3, **18**, 319–20.

PRAIN, D. and BURKILL, I. H. (1936, 1939) An account of the genus *Dioscorea* in the East. *Ann. R. Bot. Gdns Calcutta* **14** (1, 2), 1–210, 211–528.

PREUSS, P. (1885) *Die Beziehungen zwischen dem anatomischen Bau und der physiologischen Function der Blattstiele und Gelenkpolster*. Diss. Berlin. 58 pp. (Seen in *Just's bot. Jber.* **13** (1), Sec. IIB, No. 89 (1885).)

QUEVA, C. (1893*a*) Caractères anatomiques de la tige des Dioscorées. *C.r. hebd. Séanc. Acad. Sci.*, Paris **117**, 295–7.

—— (1893*b*) Les bulbilles des Dioscorées. Ibid. 316–18.

—— (1894*a*) Caractères anatomiques de la feuille des Dioscorées. *C.r. Ass. fr. avanc. sci.* 502–4. (Original not seen.)

—— (1894*b*) Recherches sur l'anatomie de l'appareil végétatif des Taccacées et des Dioscorées. *Mém. Soc. Sci. agric.* Lille, sér. 4, **20**, 1–457.

—— (1894*c*) Le tubercule de *Tamus communis* L. *C.r. Ass. fr. avanc. sci.* 551–9. (Original not seen.)

RAGHAVAN, R. S. (1958) A chromosome survey of Indian Dioscoreas. *Proc. Indian Acad. Sci.* **48**, 59.

—— (1960) Studies on the genus *Dioscorea* L. *Bull. bot. Surv. India* **2**, 379–86.

RAO, A. N. (1953) Embryology of *Dioscorea oppositifolia* L. *Phytomorphology* **3**, 121–6.

—— (1955) Embryology of *Trichopus zeylanicus* Gaertn. *J. Indian bot. Soc.* **34**, 213–21.

RAO, P. S. and BERI, R. M. (1952) Starch from *Dioscorea hispida* Dent. *Sci. Cult.* **17**, 482–3.

—— and —— (1955). *Dioscorea* starches. *Sci. Cult.* **20**, 397–8.

REICHENBACH, H. G. (1828) *Conspectus regni vegetabilis*, p. 44. Lipsiae.

SALISBURY, R. A. (1866) *The genera of plants*, pp. 10–14. London.

SAMPSON, H. C. (1936) List of cultivated crop plants. *Kew Bull.*, addit. ser. 12, pp. 68–9.

SARGANT, E. (1903) A theory of the origin of monocotyledons, founded on the structure of their seedlings. *Ann. Bot.* **17**, 1–92.

SASS, J. E. (1958) *Botanical microtechnique*, 3rd edn. Iowa State College Press: Ames.

SCHAEDE, R. (1939) Die Bakteriensymbiose von *Dioscorea macroura. Jb. wiss. Bot.* **88**, 1–21.

SCHLICKUM, A. (1896) Morphologischer und anatomischer Vergleich der Kotyledonen und ersten Laubblätter der Keimpflanzen der Monokotylen. *Biblthca bot.* **6** (35), 88 pp.

SCHLITTLER, J. (1949) Die systematische Stellung der Gattung *Petermannia* F. v. Muell. und ihrer phylogenetischen Beziehungen zu den Luzuriagoideae Engl. und den Dioscoreaceae Lindl. *Vjschr. Naturf. Ges. Zürich* **94**, Beih. 1, 1–28. (Also in: *Mitt. bot. Mus. Univ. Zürich* **183**, ser. Bot. Nr. 31.)

SCHUBERT, B. (1966) Studies in *Dioscorea*, 1: A collection from British Honduras. *J. Arnold Arbor.* **47**, 147–59.

SCOTT, D. H. (1897) On two new instances of spinous roots. *Ann. Bot.* **11**, 327–32.

SEIDEMANN, J. (1964) Mikroskopische Untersuchung verschiedener *Dioscorea* Stärken. *Stärke* **16**, 246–53.

SHAH, J. J. (1963) Coenocytic vessel elements in *Dioscorea alata* L. *Nature, Lond.* **197**, 1125.

——, POULOSE, K. V., and UNNIKRISHNAN, K. (1966) Nodal vessels in *Dioscorea alata* L. *Curr. Sci.* **35**, 183–4.

——, UNNIKRISHNAN, K., and POULOSE, K. V. (1966) Vessel member length–diameter and perforation plate–vessel member length relations in *Dioscorea alata* L. *Biologia Pl.* **8**, 421–6.

——, ——, and —— (1967) Vessel members in the stem of *Dioscorea alata* L. *Can. J. Bot.* **45**, 155–67.

SHARMA, A. K. and DE, D. N. (1956) Polyploidy in *Dioscorea. Genetica* **28**, 112–20.

SIEDLER, P. (1892) Ueber den radialen Saftstrom in den Wurzeln. *Beitr. Biol. Pfl.* **5**, 407–42. (See p. 428.)

SIMS, J. (1812) *Roxburghia gloriosa*. Green-flowered Roxburghia. *Curtis's bot. Mag.* **35**, pl. 1500. London.

SMITH, B. W. (1937) Notes on the cytology and distribution of the Dioscoreaceae. *Bull. Torrey bot. Club* **64**, 189–97.

SMITH, J. E. (1807) *Roxburghia viridiflora*. Green-flowered Roxburghia. *Exotic botany*, Vol. 1, pp. 111–12, pl. 57. London.

SMITH, P. M. (1916) The development of the embryo and seedling of *Dioscorea villosa*. *Bull. Torrey bot. Club* **43**, 545–58.

SOLEREDER, H. (1888–9) Beiträge zur vergleichenden Anatomie der Aristolochiaceen. *Bot. Jb.* **10**, 410–524. (See pp. 507–9.)

—— and MEYER, F. J. (1928–33) *Systematische Anatomie der Monokotyledonen*. Borntraeger: Berlin.

SOLMS-LAUBACH, H. (1878) Ueber monocotyle Embryonen mit scheitelbürtigem Vegetationspunkt. *Bot. Ztg.* **36**, 65–74, 81–91.

SPARSHOTT, E. N. (1935) Observations on the formation, development and structure of the tuber of *Testudinaria elephantipes*, and on the origin of the vegetative shoot. *J. Linn. Soc.* **49**, 593–610.

STAUDERMANN, W. (1924) Die Haare der Monokotylen. *Bot. Arch.* **8**, 105–84. (See pp. 142–3.)

STEBBINS, G. L. and KHUSH, G. S. (1961) Variation in the organization of the stomatal complex in the leaf epidermis of monocotyledons and its bearing on their phylogeny. *Am. J. Bot.* **48**, 51–9.

STRASBURGER, E. (1872) *Die Coniferen und die Gnetaceen*, pp. 317–18. Jena.

SUESSENGUTH, K. (1921) Beiträge zur Frage des systematischen Anschlusses der Monokotylen. *Beih. bot. Zbl.* **38** (2), 1–79.

SWAIN, T. (1963) *Chemical plant taxonomy*. Academic Press: London.

TING, Y. and CHI, C. W. (1948) The Chinese sweet potato, *Dioscorea esculenta* (Lour.) Burk. *J. agric. Ass. China* no. 186, pp. 23–33.

TOMLINSON, P. B. and AYENSU, E. S. (1968) Morphology and anatomy of *Croomia pauciflora* (Stemonaceae). *J. Arnold Arbor.* **49**, 260–75.

—— and —— (1969) Notes on the vegetative morphology and anatomy of Petermanniaceae (Monocotyledones). *Bot. J. Linn. Soc.* **62**, 17–26.

TROLL, W. and MEYER, H.-J. (1955) Entwicklungsgeschichtliche Untersuchungen über das Zustandekommen unifazialer Blattstrukturen. *Planta* **46**, 286–360.

ULINE, E. B. (1898) Eine Monographie der Dioscoreaceen. *Bot. Jb.* **25**, 126–65.

—— (1899) *Higinbothamia*, a new genus, and other new Dioscoreaceae. *Publs Field Mus. nat. Hist.*, Bot. ser., **1** (5), 413–18.

VAVILOV, N. I. (1951) *The origin, variations, immunity and breeding of cultivated plants* (Trans. K. Starr Chester). Ronald Press: New York.

WALL, M. E., EDDY, C. R., WILLAMAN, J. J., CORRELL, D. S., SCHUBERT, B. G., and GENTRY, H. S. (1954a) Survey of plants for steroidal sapogenins and other constituents. *J. Am. pharm. Ass.* **44**, 503.

——, ——, ——, ——, ——, and —— (1954b) *Steroidal sapogenins*, XV. Supp. table of data for steroidal sapogenins XII. U.S. Dept. Agric., Agricultural Research Service, Eastern Utilization Research Branch, Philadelphia 18, Pennsylvania.

——, FENSKE, C. S., WILLAMAN, J. J., CORRELL, D. S., SCHUBERT, B. G., and GENTRY, H. S. (1955a) *Steroidal sapogenins*, XXVI. Supp. table of steroidal sapogenins XXI. U.S. Dept. Agric., Eastern Utilization Research Branch, Philadelphia 18, Pennsylvania.

——, ——, ——, ——, ——, and —— (1955b) Survey of plants for steroidal sapogenins and constituents. *J. Am. pharm. Ass.* **44**, 438.

——, KRIDER, M. M., KREWSON, C. F., EDDY, C. R., WILLAMAN, J. J., CORRELL, D. S., and GENTRY, H. S. (1954) *Steroidal sapogenins*, XIII. Supp. table of data for steroidal sapogenins VII. U.S. Dept. Agric., Agricultural Research Service, Eastern Utilization Research Branch, Philadelphia 18, Pennsylvania.

WATSON, E. V. (1936) A study of the anatomy of *Trichopus zeylanicus* Gaertn. *Notes R. bot. Gdn Edinb.* **19**, 135–56.

WILLAMAN, J. J., FENSKE, C. S., and CORRELL, D. S. (1953) Occurrence of alkaloids in *Dioscorea*. *Science, N.Y.* **118**, 329–30.

WINKLER, H. (1925) Massenhafte Nektarabsonderung bei *Testudinaria elephantipes*. *Ber. dt. bot. Ges.* **43**, 590–2.

ZIMMERMANN, J. G. (1932) Über die extrafloralen Nektarien der Angiospermen. *Beih. bot. Zbl.* **49** (1), 99–196. (See pp. 148, 152.)

ZIMMERMANN, M. H. and TOMLINSON, P. B. (1966) Analysis of complex vascular systems in plants: optical shuttle method. *Science, N.Y.* **152**, 72–3.

SUPPLEMENTARY LITERATURE

AYENSU, E. I. (1970a) Analysis of the complex vascularity in stems of *Dioscorea composita*. *J. Arnold Arbor.* **51**, 228–40.

—— (1970b) Comparative anatomy of *Dioscorea rotundata* and *Dioscorea cavenensis*. *Bot. J. Linn. Soc.*, Suppl. **1**, 127–36.

RAMACHANDRAN, K. (1968) Cytological studies in Dioscoreaceae. *Cytologia* **33**, 401–10.

AUTHOR INDEX

SUBJECT INDEX

NOTE: *Where genera and families have been specially studied, the page numbers are given in bold type. Italic page numbers refer to illustrations.*

PLATES

PLATE I

A, *Dioscorea composita*, T.S. part of leaf showing the abundance of tannin (×40).

B, *D. floribunda*, T.S. midrib of leaf showing seven phloem units abaxial to xylem strands in midrib (×60).

ph.u., phloem unit; p.t., palisade tissue; t., tannin; t.e., tracheal element; xy., xylem.

PLATE I

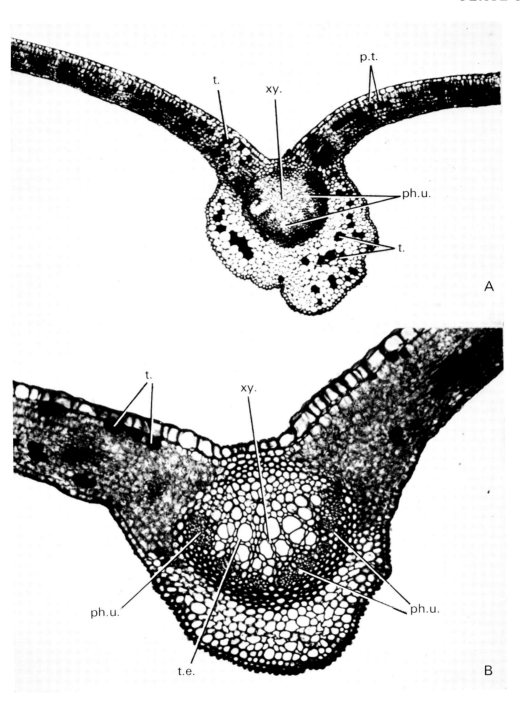

PLATE II. L.S. stem nodal region illustrating the complexity of the xylem- and phloem-glomeruli (after Ayensu 1969) ($\times$ 80).

A, *Dioscorea schimperiana*, exhibiting general orientation of xylem- and phloem-glomeruli. Vessel element (V); phloem-glomerulus cells of the first (PH^1) and second (PH^2) orders.

B, *D. discolor*, interlacing of xylem-glomeruli cells. Arrow points to T.S. of a vessel (V) just entering the node.

C, *D. hirtiflora*, showing an example of the meeting point between the phloem-glomerulus cells (PH^2) of the second order, and a T.S. of a sieve-tube (ST).

PLATE II

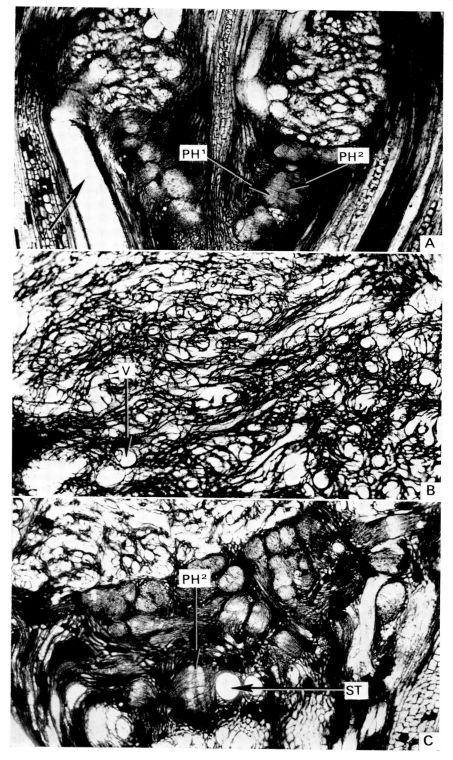

PLATE III. L.S. stem nodal region illustrating the complexity of the xylem- and phloem-glomeruli (after Ayensu 1969) ($\times$ 80).

A, *Dioscorea pentaphylla*, end plates of a vessel-tracheid (VT) and a vessel element (V).

B, *D. dregeana*, end plate of vessel-tracheid (VT) and phloem-glomerulus cells (PHG).

C, *Tamus communis*, exhibiting the presence of xylem- and phloem-glomeruli (PHG).

PLATE III

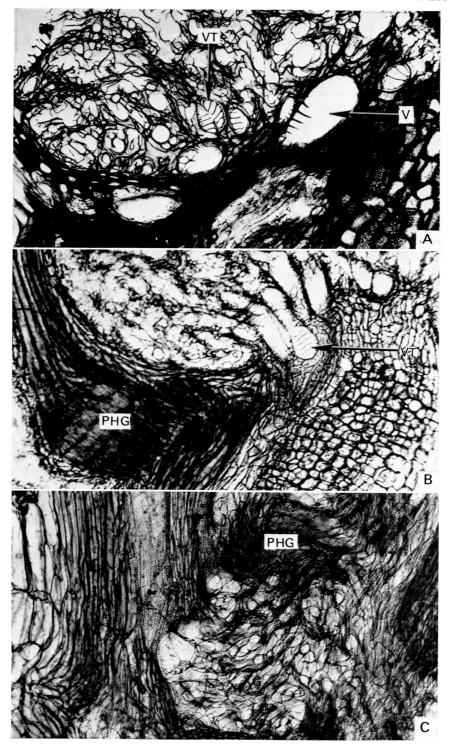

PLATE IV

A, *Dioscorea nipponica*, showing a reticulate perforation plate of a vessel (×270).

B, *D. schimperiana*, showing a complicated compound sieve-plate of the sieve-tube (×650).

C, *D. sansibarensis*, T.S. leaf tip showing two kidney-shaped glands embedded in the mesophyll (×75).

g., kidney-shaped gland; p., pitting on vessel wall; p.v., primary vein; r., ribs of perforation plate; s.a., sieve area; s.v., secondary vein.

PLATE IV

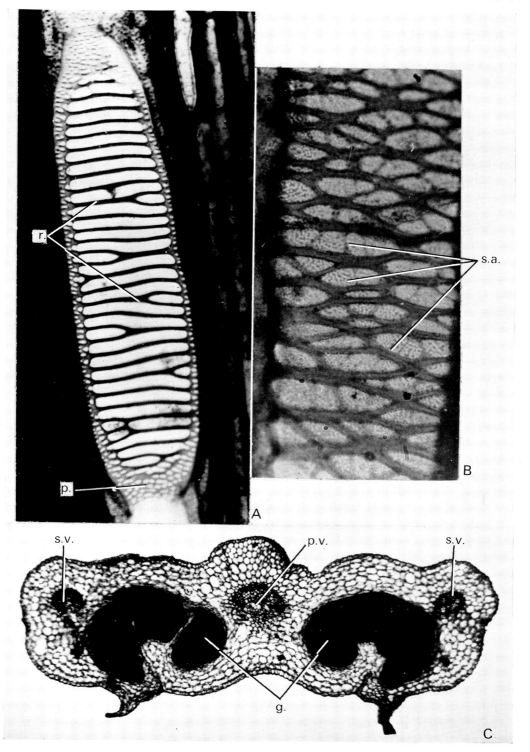

PLATE V. T.S. stems showing the general vascular plan, the V-shaped common bundles and the elliptical cauline bundles, the number and distribution of metaxylem elements, phloem units, and sclerenchyma.

A, *Dioscorea campestris* (×60). B, *D. multiflora* (×35). C, *D. samydea* (×35). D, *D. macroura* (×38). E, *D. sansibarensis* (×38). F, *D. bulbifera* (×35).

cau. vb., cauline vascular bundle; com. vb., common vascular bundle; m.v., metaxylem vessel; ph. u., phloem unit, s.b., sclerenchyma band; s.t., sieve-tube; t., tyloses in metaxylem vessel.

PLATE V

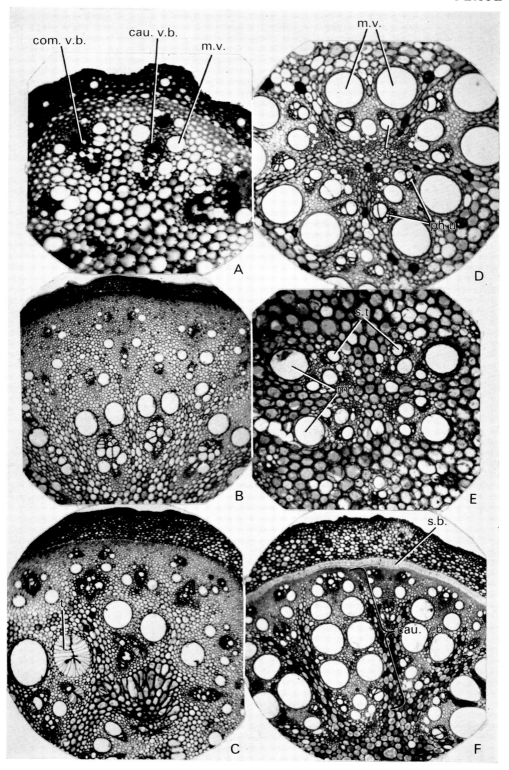

PLATE VI. T.S. stems showing the general vascular plan, the V-shaped common bundles and the elliptical cauline bundles, the number and distribution of metaxylem elements, phloem units, and sclerenchyma.

A, *Dioscorea burchellii* ($\times 70$). B, *D. cotinifolia* ($\times 35$). C, *D. trichantha* ($\times 35$). D, *D. convolvulacea* ($\times 75$). E, *D. galeottiana* ($\times 35$). F, *D. ternata* ($\times 35$).

c., cortex; cau. vb., cauline vascular bundle; com. vb., common vascular bundle; h., hair; m.v., metaxylem vessel; ph.u., phloem unit; p.p., pith parenchyma; s., sclerenchyma surrounding metaxylem vessel; s.t., sieve-tube.

PLATE VI

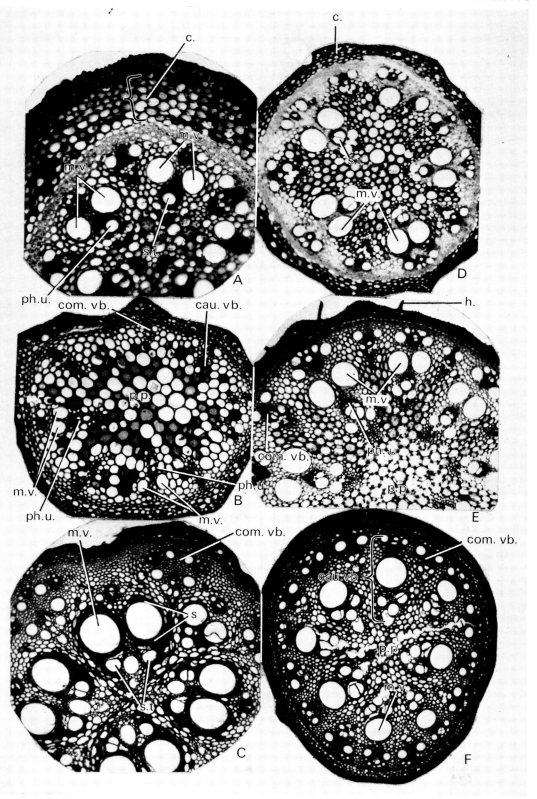

PLATE VII. T.S. stems showing the general vascular plan, the arrangement of common and cauline vascular bundles, the number and distribution of metaxylem elements, phloem units, and sclerenchyma.

A, *Dioscorea dregeana* ($\times 33$). B, *D. dumetorum* ($\times 35$). C, *D. pentaphylla* ($\times 35$). D, *D. cochleari-apiculata* ($\times 25$). E, *D. quartiniana* ($\times 25$). F, *D. retusa* ($\times 54$).

c., cortex; cau. vb., cauline vascular bundles; com. vb., common vascular bundle; m.v., metaxylem vessel; ph.u., phloem unit; p.p., pith parenchyma; s.s., sclerenchyma sheath; s.t., sieve-tube.

PLATE VII

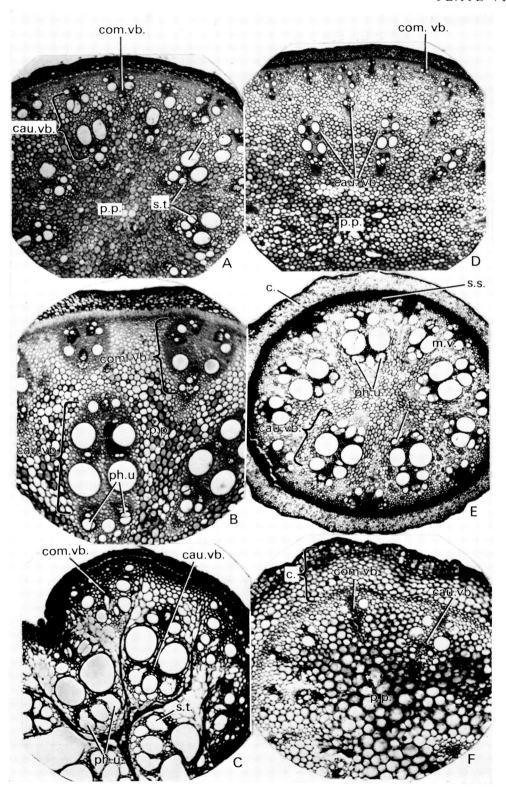

PLATE VIII. T.S. stems showing the general vascular plan, the arrangement of common and cauline vascular bundles, the number and distribution of metaxylem elements, phloem units, and sclerenchyma.

A, *Dioscorea bernoulliana* (×70). B, *D. dugesii* (×35). C, *D. trifida* (×20). D. *D. urophylla* (×40). E, *D. friedrichsthalii* (×40). F, *D. spiculiflora* (×44).

cau. vb., cauline vascular bundle; com. vb., common vascular bundle; m.v., metaxylem vessel; p.o., pith obliteration resulting in gap; p.p., pith parenchyma; s.b., sclerenchyma band; s.s., sclerenchyma sheath surrounding vascular bundles; s.t., sieve-tube; t.e., tracheal element; v.e., vessel element.

PLATE VIII

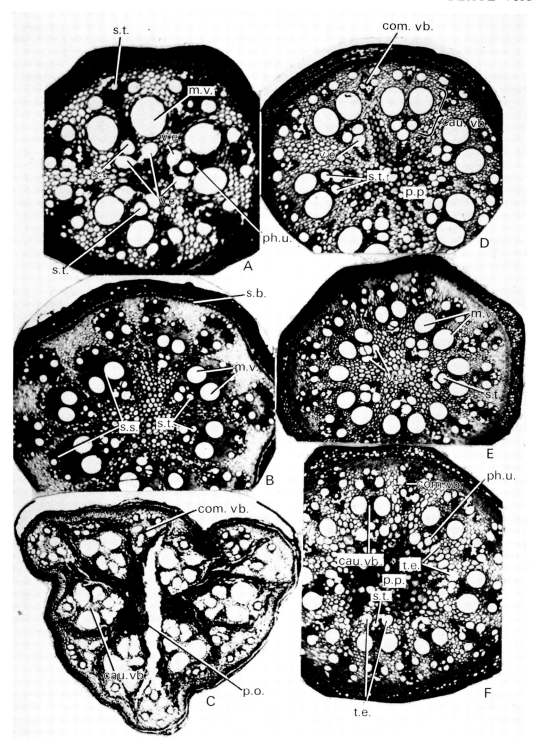

PLATE IX. T.S. stems showing the general vascular plan, the arrangement of common and cauline vascular bundles, the number and distribution of metaxylem elements, phloem units, and sclerenchyma.

A, *Dioscorea balcanica* ($\times$40). B, *D. deltoidea* ($\times$45). C, *D. villosa* ($\times$35). D, *D. zingiberensis* ($\times$45). E, *D. composita* ($\times$35). F, *D. floribunda* ($\times$45).

c., cortex; cau. vb., cauline vascular bundle; com. vb., common vascular bundle; e.l., endodermoid layer; m.v., metaxylem vessel; o.p., obliterated pith; ph.u., phloem unit; p.p., pith parenchyma; v.e., vessel element.

PLATE IX

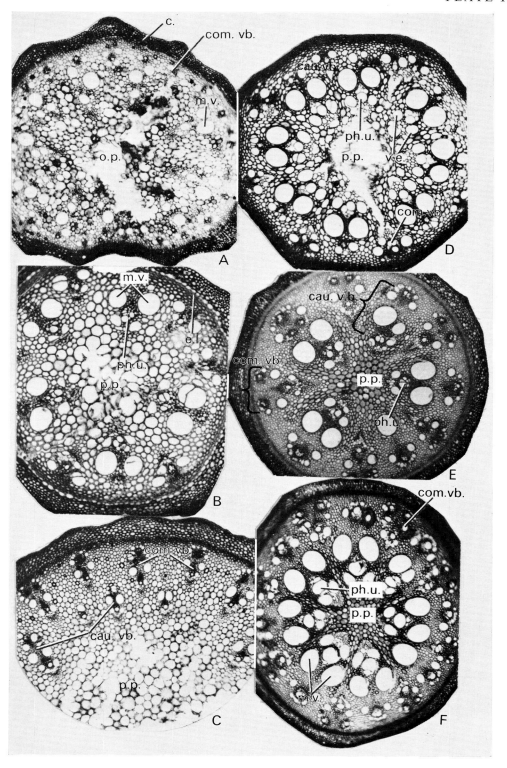

PLATE X. T.S. stems showing the general vascular plan, the arrangement of common and cauline bundles, the number and distribution of metaxylem elements, phloem units, and sclerenchyma.

A, *Dioscorea composita* (*D. tepinapensis*) ($\times$15). B, *D. esculenta* ($\times$45). C, *D. flabellifolia* ($\times$40). D, *D. carionis* ($\times$40). E, *D. densiflora* ($\times$40). F, *D. sinuata* ($\times$40).

cau. vb., cauline vascular bundle; com. vb., common vascular bundle; m.v., metaxylem vessels; ph.u., phloem unit; p.p., pith parenchyma; v.e., vessel element.

PLATE X

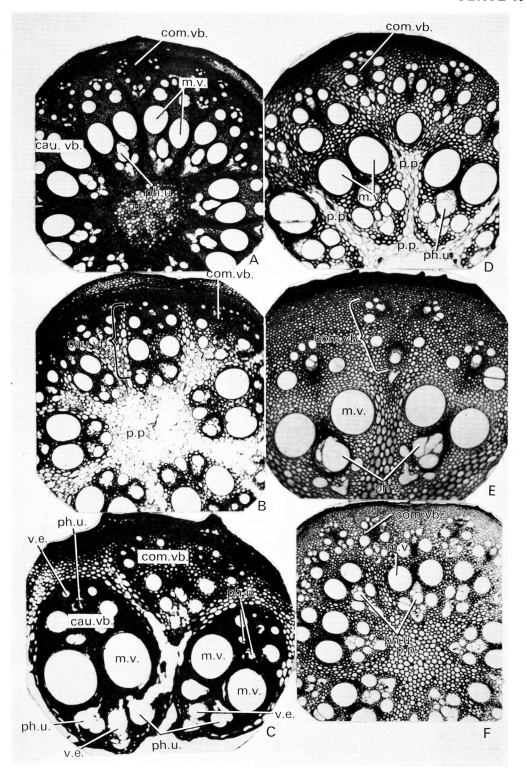

PLATE XI. T.S. stems showing the general vascular plan, the arrangement of common and cauline vascular bundles, the number and distribution of metaxylem elements, phloem units, and sclerenchyma.

A, *Dioscorea polygonoides* (×35). B, *D. preussii* (×45). C, *D. hastata* (×45). D, *D. amazonum* (×40). E, *D. discolor* (×22). F, *D. collettii* (×30).

cau. vb., cauline vascular bundle; com. vb., common vascular bundle; m.v., metaxylem vessel; ph.u., phloem unit; p.p., pith parenchyma; s.t., sieve-tube; t., tyloses in metaxylem vessel.

PLATE XI

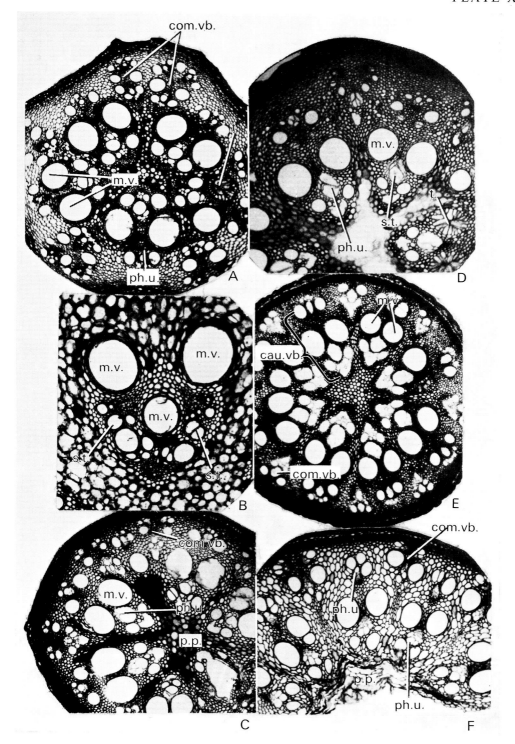

PLATE XII. T.S. stems showing the general vascular plan, the arrangement of common and cauline vascular bundles, the number and distribution of metaxylem elements, phloem units, and sclerenchyma.

A, *Dioscorea gracillima* ($\times 25$). B, *D. schimperiana* ($\times 35$). C, *D. minutiflora* ($\times 40$). D, *D. cayenensis* ($\times 35$). E, *D. luzonensis* ($\times 35$). F, *D. rotundata* ($\times 35$).

c., cortex; cau. vb., cauline vascular bundle; com. vb., common vascular bundle; f.p., fibrous parenchyma; m.v., metaxylem vessel; ph.u., phloem unit; p.p., pith parenchyma; s.b., sclerenchyma band; st.g., starch grain; t., tannin.

PLATE XII

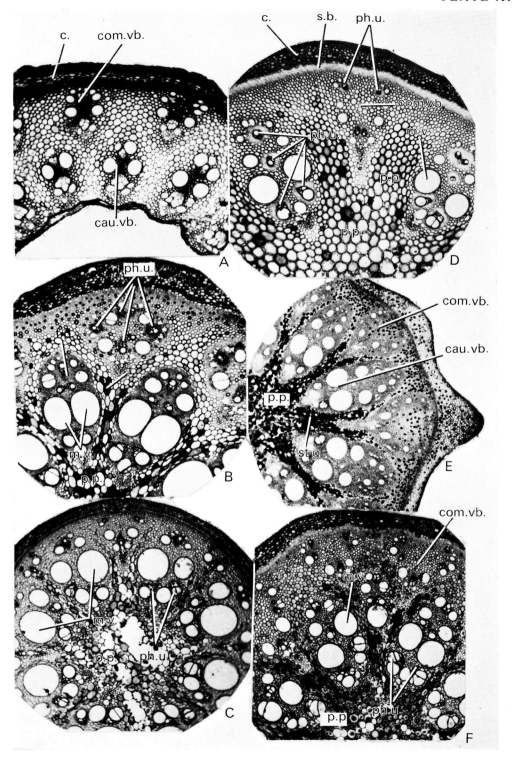

PLATE XIII. T.S. stems showing the general vascular plan, the arrangement of common and cauline vascular bundles, the number and distribution of metaxylem elements, phloem units, and sclerenchyma.

A, *Dioscorea wattii* (×32). B, *D. hirtiflora* (×35). C, *D. stenomeriflora* (×40). D, *D. nipponica* (×40). E, *D. elephantipes* (×40). F, *D. hemicrypta* (×35).

c., cortex; cau. vb., cauline vascular bundle; com. vb., common vascular bundle; m.v., metaxylem vessel; ph.u., phloem unit; p.p. pith parenchyma; t., tannin in cortical cells.

PLATE XIII

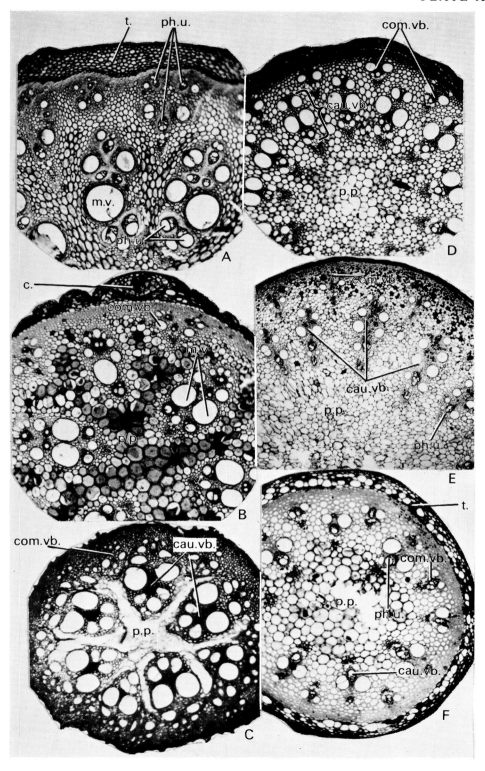

PLATE XIV. T.S. stems showing the general vascular plan, the arrangement of common and cauline vascular bundles, the number and distribution of metaxylem elements, phloem units, and sclerenchyma.

A, *Dioscorea sylvatica* (×38). B, *Rajania cordata* (×65). C, *Stenomeris dioscoreifolia* (×40). D, *Tamus communis* (×24). E, *Tamus edulis* (×40). F, *Trichopus zeylanicus* (×40).

c., cortex; cau. vb., cauline vascular bundle; com. vb., common vascular bundle; f.s., fibrous sheath; m.v., metaxylem vessel; ph.u., phloem unit; p.o., pith parenchyma obliteration; p.p., pith parenchyma; vb., vascular bundle.

PLATE XIV

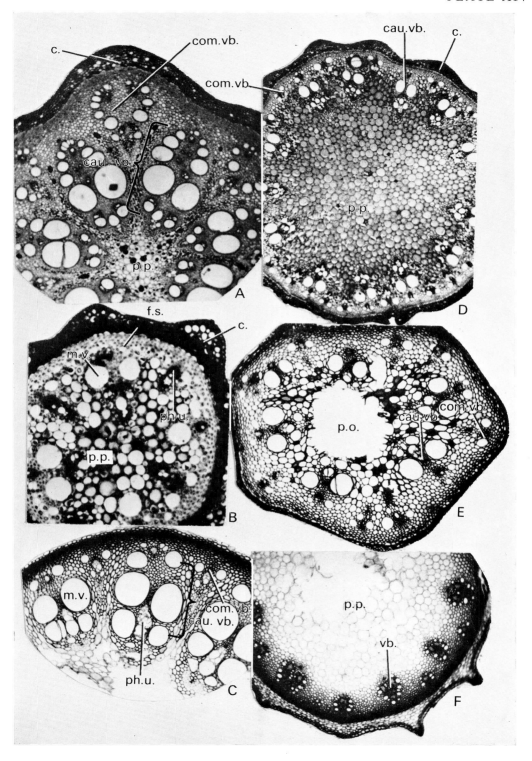

PLATE XV

A, *Avetra sempervirens*, T.S. stem showing general vascular plan
(×34).

B, *Trichopus zeylancius*, T.S. large triangular bundle from stem
showing the distribution of phloem patches (×260).

c., cortex; cau. vb., cauline vascular bundle; com. vb., common
vascular bundle; m.v., metaxylem vessel; ph.p., phloem patches;
ph.u., phloem unit; p.p., pith parenchyma; v.e., vessel element.

PLATE XV

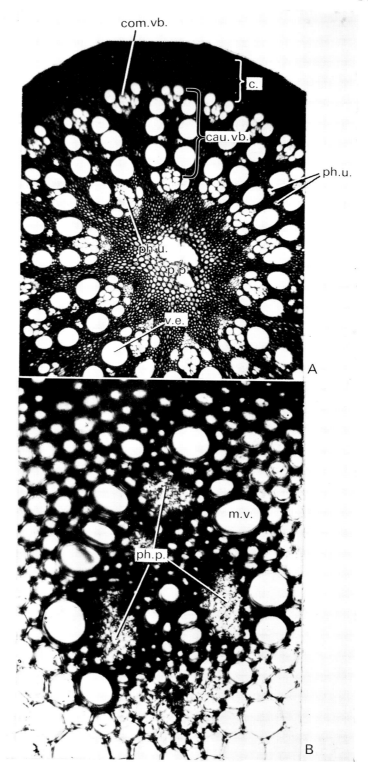

PLATE XVI

A, *Croomia pauciflora*, T.S. portion of stem showing general vascular plan and amphivasal vascular bundles ($\times$45).

B, *Stemona curtisii*, T.S. sector of stem showing common and cauline vascular bundles with metaxylem vessels near periphery of stem ($\times$40).

C, *Stichoneuron caudatum*, T.S. stem showing two rings of amphivasal vascular bundles ($\times$45).

cau. vb., cauline vascular bundle; com. vb., common vascular bundle; p.p., pith parenchyma; p.st., pith cells with starch grains; vb., vascular bundle.

PLATE XVI

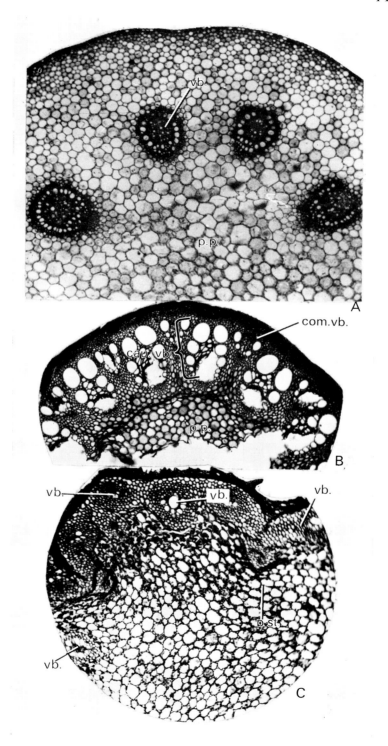